Advances in Computation: Theory and Practice
Volume 14

TECHNOLOGY SUPPORTING BUSINESS SOLUTIONS

ADVANCES IN COMPUTATION: THEORY AND PRACTICE

Volume 14 – Technology Supporting Business Solutions
Rafael Corchuelo, Antonio Ruiz-Cortés and Robert Wrembel
ISBN 1-59033-802-2

Volume 13 – Implementation of Term Rewriting-Based Programming Languages
Nadia Nedjah and Luiza de Macedo Mourelle
ISBN 1-59033-645-3

Volume 12 – Practical Application of Parallel Computing
Laurence Tianruo Yang and Marcin Paprzycki
ISBN 1-59033-532-5

Volume 11 – Numerical Solution of Nonlinear Elliptic Problems via Preconditioning Operators: Theory and Applications
IFaragó and JKarátson
ISBN 1-59033-376-4

Volume 10 - Constructive Methods for Parallel Programming
Sergei Gorlatch and Christian Lengauer
ISBN 1-59033-364-0

Volume 9 - Imaging and Vision Systems: Theory, Assessment and Applications
Jacques Blanc-Talon and Dan CPopescu
ISBN 1-59033-033-1

Volume 8 - Machines that Learn to Play Games
Johannes Furnkranz and Mirsolav Kubat
ISBN 1-59033-021-8

Volume 7 - Scientific Computing and Applications
Peter Minev and Yanping Lin
ISBN 1-59033-027-7

Volume 6 - Weak Intelligence: Through the Principle and Paradox of Multiple Knowledge
Matjaz Gams
ISBN 1-56072-898-1

Volume 5 - Parallel Program Development for Cluster Computing: Methodology, Tools and Integrated Environments
José CCunha, Peter Kacsuk and Stephen CWinter
ISBN 1-56072-865-5

Volume 4 - Structured Matrices: Recent Advances and Applications
Dario Andrea Bini, Eugene Tyrtyshnikov and Plamen Yalamov
ISBN 1-56072-890-6

Volume 3 - Recent Trends in Numerical Analysis
Donato Trigiante
ISBN 1-56072-885-X

Volume 2 - High Performance Algorithms for Structured Matrix Problems
Peter Arbenz, Marcin Paprzycki, Ahmed Sameh and Vivek Sarin
ISBN 1-56072-594-X

Lee Keener, Editor-in-chief
College of Science and Management, University of Northern British Columbia
Prince George, BC V2N 4Z9, CANADA, keener@unbc.edu

Marcin Paprzycki, Editor and Managing Editor
Department of Computer Science, Oklahoma State University
Tulsa, OK 74106, USA, marcin@main.amu.edu.pl

Ilan Bar-On,
baron@cs.technion.ac.il
Graeme Fairweather,
gfairwea@mines.edu
Daniele Funaro,
funaro@unimo.it
Dan Grigoras,
grigd@cs.tuiasi.ro
Michal Karonski,
karonski@math.amu.edu.pl
Andreas Karageorghis,
andreask@trikomo.mas.ucy.ac.cy

Erricos John Kontoghiorghes,
erricos.kontoghiorghes@info.unine.ch
Anna Lawniczak,
alawnicz@opal.mathstat.uoguelph.ca
alawnicz@fields.utoronto.ca
Michael Mascagni,
mascagni@cs.fsu.edu
Nikos EMastorakis,
mastor@softlab.ece.ntua.gr
Lawrence FShampine,
lshampin@post.cis.smu.edu

Jurij Silc,
jurij.silc@ijs.si
Wojciech Szpankowski,
spa@cs.purdue.edu
Gyorgy Turan,
gyt@uic.edu
Jerzy Wasniewski,
jerzy.wasniewski@uni-c.dk
Plamen Yalamov,
yalamov@ami.ru.acad.bg

Advances in Computation: Theory and Practice
Volume 14

TECHNOLOGY SUPPORTING BUSINESS SOLUTIONS

RAFAEL CORCHUELO, ANTONIO RUIZ-CORTÉS
AND ROBERT WREMBEL

Nova Science Publishers, Inc.
New York

Senior Editors: Susan Boriotti and Donna Dennis
Coordinating Editor: Tatiana Shohov
Office Manager: Annette Hellinger
Graphics: Wanda Serrano
Editorial Production: Vladimir Klestov, Matthew Kozlowski, Alexandra Columbus and Maya Columbus
Circulation: Ave Maria Gonzalez, Vera Popovic, Luis Aviles, Raymond Davis, Melissa Diaz, Marlene Nunez and Jeannie Pappas
Communications and Acquisitions: Serge PShohov
Marketing: Cathy DeGregory

Library of Congress Cataloging-in-Publication Data
Available upon request

ISBN 1-59033-802-2

Copyright © 2003 by Nova Science Publishers, Inc.
               400 Oser Ave, Suite 1600
               Hauppauge, New York 11788-3619
               Tele: 631-231-7269 Fax: 631-231-8175
               e-mail: Novascience@earthlink.net
               Web Site: http://www.novapublishers.com

All rights reserved. No part of this book may be reproduced, stored in a retrieval system or transmitted in any form or by any means: electronic, electrostatic, magnetic, tape, mechanical photocopying, recording or otherwise without permission from the publishers.

The publisher has taken reasonable care in the preparation of this book, but makes no expressed or implied warranty of any kind and assumes no responsibility for any errors or omissions. No liability is assumed for incidental or consequential damages in connection with or arising out of information contained in this book.

This publication is designed to provide accurate and authoritative information with regard to the subject matter covered herein. It is sold with the clear understanding that the publisher is not engaged in rendering legal or any other professional services. If legal or any other expert assistance is required, the services of a competent person should be sought. FROM A DECLARATION OF PARTICIPANTS JOINTLY ADOPTED BY A COMMITTEE OF THE AMERICAN BAR ASSOCIATION AND A COMMITTEE OF PUBLISHERS.

Printed in the United States of America

Contents

List of Figures		ix
Contributors		xi
Reviewers		xiii
Preface		xv

I Web Services — 1

1 Electronic Contracts — 3
Heiko Ludwig
- 1.1 Introduction — 3
  - 1.1.1 Electronic contracts in an e-service environment — 3
  - 1.1.2 A case study: SLAs for web services — 5
  - 1.1.3 Goal and structure — 7
- 1.2 Conceptual Model of the Contracting Process — 7
  - 1.2.1 Contracting process phases — 7
  - 1.2.2 Contracting function of a service provider — 9
  - 1.2.3 Contracting function of a service customer — 12
- 1.3 Document Structures and Formats — 13
  - 1.3.1 Information phase documents — 14
  - 1.3.2 Negotiation phase documents and contracts — 15
  - 1.3.3 Setup phase documents — 18
- 1.4 Issues and Approaches to Automate the Contracting Function — 20
- 1.5 Conclusions — 22

2 Web Services Technologies for Outsourcing — 25
Liang-Jie Zhang, Qun Zhou, Hung-Yang Chang, and Jen-Yao Chung
- 2.1 Introduction — 25
- 2.2 Web Services Hub Framework — 26
- 2.3 A Working Prototype — 28
  - 2.3.1 The service outsourcing manager — 30
  - 2.3.2 The central membership portal — 32
  - 2.3.3 The advanced web services discovery engine — 32
  - 2.3.4 The multi-level security model — 34
  - 2.3.5 The purchase order management business process and the intelligent shipping agent — 35

2.4	An E-services Delivery Solution	36
	2.4.1 Registration and provision	37
	2.4.2 Single sign-on	38
	2.4.3 Purchase order creation	38
	2.4.4 Purchase order details	38
	2.4.5 Shipping service providers	39
	2.4.6 Results of invoking the transportation web service	39
	2.4.7 Updated purchase order	40
2.5	Related Work	41
2.6	Conclusions	43

II Database Backends — 47

3 Conceptual Modelling of Business Applications with Dynamic Object Roles — 49
Kazimierz Subieta, Andrzej Jodłowski, Piotr Habela, and Jacek Płodzień

3.1	Introduction	49
3.2	A Business Case Study	50
3.3	Related Work	52
3.4	Prototype of Dynamic Object Roles	54
3.5	The Stack-Based Approach	57
	3.5.1 Objects, classes and stores	57
	3.5.2 Stacks	58
	3.5.3 Binding	59
	3.5.4 Query language	60
	3.5.5 Query evaluation	61
3.6	Object Store Model with Dynamic Roles	61
	3.6.1 Links amongst objects and roles	62
	3.6.2 Dynamic roles and object-oriented models	62
	3.6.3 A formal model of an object store	64
3.7	Specification of Dynamic Roles in Database Schemata	66
	3.7.1 Building an object scheme with dynamic roles	67
	3.7.2 Declarations of data structures	69
3.8	Conclusions	70

4 Temporal Versioning in Data Warehouses — 73
Johann Eder and Christian Koncilia

4.1	Introduction	73
	4.1.1 The problem	75
	4.1.2 Our contribution	75
	4.1.3 Outline	77
4.2	Related Work	77
4.3	A Formal Model for Temporal multi-dimensional Systems	77
	4.3.1 Structure versions	80
	4.3.2 Structural changes	82
	4.3.3 Mappings between structure versions	84
4.4	The *COMET* Metamodel	89
	4.4.1 Goals and features	89
	4.4.2 The elements of *COMET*	90
4.5	Implementation	93
4.6	Conclusions	96

III Data and Applications Integration — 99

5 Identification of Missing Information in Integrated Database Systems — 101
Bogdan D. Czejdo and Kenneth Messa
- 5.1 Introduction — 101
- 5.2 Unavailability Cases and Sample Queries — 102
  - 5.2.1 Incomplete attributes in selection conditions — 102
  - 5.2.2 Incomplete attributes in projections — 104
  - 5.2.3 Combined incompleteness — 104
  - 5.2.4 Temporary unavailability of data sources — 106
- 5.3 LODA Tools for Data Retrieval — 106
  - 5.3.1 Establishing an initial collection — 107
  - 5.3.2 Selection using attributes — 107
  - 5.3.3 Printing the values — 107
  - 5.3.4 Processing relationships — 108
  - 5.3.5 Summary of diagram processing — 108
- 5.4 Processing and Analysing Incomplete Queries — 109
  - 5.4.1 Processing and generating queries — 110
  - 5.4.2 Analysing queries — 111
  - 5.4.3 Generating unavailability queries — 112
  - 5.4.4 Generation of explanations — 112
  - 5.4.5 Creating visual queries in UML-VL — 113
- 5.5 Conclusions — 113

6 Application Integration Patterns — 115
*Matjaž B. Jurič, Ivan Rozman, Tatjana Welzer,
Marjan Heričko, Boštjan Brumen, and Vili Podgorelec*
- 6.1 Introduction — 115
- 6.2 Application Integration Patterns — 116
- 6.3 The Integration Broker Pattern — 117
  - 6.3.1 Context and problem definition — 117
  - 6.3.2 Forces — 118
  - 6.3.3 Solution — 118
  - 6.3.4 Consequences — 120
- 6.4 The Integration Wrapper Pattern — 120
  - 6.4.1 Context and problem definition — 120
  - 6.4.2 Forces — 120
  - 6.4.3 Solution — 121
  - 6.4.4 Consequences — 121
- 6.5 The Integration Mediator Pattern — 122
  - 6.5.1 Context and problem definition — 122
  - 6.5.2 Forces — 122
  - 6.5.3 Solution — 122
  - 6.5.4 Consequences — 123
- 6.6 The Virtual Component Pattern — 124
  - 6.6.1 Context and problem definition — 124
  - 6.6.2 Forces — 124
  - 6.6.3 Solution — 124
  - 6.6.4 Consequences — 126
- 6.7 The Data Mapping Pattern — 127
  - 6.7.1 Context and problem definition — 127
  - 6.7.2 Forces — 127
  - 6.7.3 Solution — 127

		6.7.4	Consequences	127
	6.8	\multicolumn{2}{l	}{The Process Automator Pattern}	128

		6.7.4	Consequences	127
	6.8	The Process Automator Pattern		128
		6.8.1	Context and problem definition	128
		6.8.2	Forces	128
		6.8.3	Solution	129
		6.8.4	Consequences	130
	6.9	A Case Study		131
		6.9.1	Case study description and analysis	131
		6.9.2	Checking authorisation	132
		6.9.3	Checking the balance of an account	133
	6.10	Conclusions		136

IV Data Analysis and Knowledge Discovery — 139

7 Agents, Personalisation, and Intelligent Applications — 141
Giovanni Semeraro, Fabio Abbattista, Marco Degemmis, Oriana Licchelli, Pasquale Lops, and Fabio Zambetta

7.1	Introduction	141
7.2	Adaptive Systems in E-commerce	142
7.3	Intelligent, Personalised Web Services	143
	7.3.1 Virtual dialoguing agents	143
	7.3.2 Personalisation	145
	7.3.3 The architecture of COGITO	145
	7.3.4 Extracting user profiles	147
	7.3.5 Experimental results	151
	7.3.6 The retrieval process in COGITO	153
7.4	An Architectural Framework Hypothesis	155
7.5	Related Work	156
7.6	Conclusions	157

8 Discovering Relationships for Effective Target Marketing — 161
Kok-L. Ong, Wee-K. Ng, and Ee-P. Lim

8.1	Introduction	161
8.2	Warehousing Relationships	163
8.3	Discovering Important Relationships	164
	8.3.1 Problem formulation	164
	8.3.2 Discussion	165
	8.3.3 Algorithm	167
8.4	Visualising the Web of Relationships	168
8.5	Implementation and Deployment	170
8.6	Related Work	172
8.7	Conclusions	173

V Recommended Bibliography — 177

Bibliography — 179

Index — 193

List of Figures

1.1	Overview of the contracting process	4
1.2	WSTK fulfillment system	6
1.3	Phases of a contract life-cycle	8
1.4	Provider functions and flows	9
1.5	Customer functions and flows	12
1.6	Aggregation of metrics	18
1.7	Definition of some service level goals	19
2.1	The web services hub framework	27
2.2	Managed e-Hub solution diagram	29
2.3	Managed e-Hub integration architecture	30
2.4	Registration/provisioning/subscription flow	33
2.5	XML-based UDDI search script	34
2.6	Purchase order management	35
2.7	Business registration	37
2.8	User registration	38
2.9	Service provisioning	39
2.10	Service subscription	40
2.11	Single sign-on interface	40
2.12	Purchase order creation interface	41
2.13	Purchase order creation result	41
2.14	Purchase order details page	42
2.15	Results from the shipping agent	43
2.16	Results of calling a web service	44
2.17	Details of a finished purchase order	44
3.1	Roles played by a person	50
3.2	A part of a UML diagram with subject roles	51
3.3	The ICONS architecture with interfaces to databases	56
3.4	An example state of ES	59
3.5	A state of the object store in the object model with roles	65
3.6	Graphical representation of the object store in Fig. 3.5	66
3.7	Interfaces to database objects with roles	68
3.8	Declarations of data structures stored in the database	70
4.1	An example of a multi-dimensional cube	74

4.2	Structure versions and transformation functions for *Geography*	76
4.3	Computing structure versions	81
4.4	An example of structural changes and transformation functions	83
4.5	Example of a 3-dimensional cube matrix	87
4.6	The *COMET* model (using UML)	91
4.7	Architecture of the indirect approach	94
4.8	A cube built with the administration tool	95
5.1	Schema diagram for dealer A	102
5.2	Schema diagram for dealer B	103
5.3	Global schema diagram	103
5.4	UML-VL query to find the set of red cars	103
5.5	UML-VL query issued for data source B	104
5.6	UML-VL query to find the set of colours of all cars	104
5.7	UML-VL query "list colours of all cars ordered by customers in New Orleans"	105
5.8	UML-VL additional query issued for data source A	105
5.9	UML-VL additional query issued for data source B	105
5.10	Instance attribute selection	107
5.11	Example of query that prints attribute values	108
5.12	Meta-database schema for MDB	110
6.1	The Integration Broker Pattern	119
6.2	The Integration Wrapper Pattern	121
6.3	The Integration Mediator Pattern	123
6.4	The Virtual Component Pattern	125
6.5	The Data Mapping Pattern	128
6.6	The Process Automator Pattern	129
6.7	Relationships amongst integration patterns	130
6.8	Use case diagram for our integration scenario	132
6.9	Relationships to existing applications for the customer virtual component	133
6.10	Application of the patterns to customer virtual component	134
6.11	Relationships to existing applications for checking the balance of an account	134
6.12	Application of the patterns to checking the balance of an account	135
7.1	The architecture of COGITO	146
7.2	The architecture of the Profile Extractor	147
7.3	An example of classification rules for category Kinderbücher	149
7.4	An example of a user profile	150
7.5	(a) PART versus J4.8; (b) PART versus IBK	152
7.6	Susanna offers a list of books written by King	153
7.7	List of books by selected authors and category	154
7.8	A hypothesis for a general framework for e-business applications	156
8.1	The Relationship Wizard	164
8.2	The main screen of CrystalBall	166
8.3	Dialogs to search for potential customers	169
8.4	A detailed report of an active customer	171

Contributors

Fabio Abbattista
Università di Bari
Italy

Boštjan Brumen
University of Maribor
Slovenia

Hung-Yang Chang
IBM T.J. Watson Research Center
USA

Jen-Yao Chung
IBM T.J. Watson Research Center
USA

Bogdan Czejdo
Loyola University
USA

Marco Degemmis
Università di Bari
Italy

Johann Eder
University of Klagenfurt
Austria

Piotr Habela
Polish-Japanese Institute of Information Technology, Polish Academy of Sciences
Poland

Marjan Heričko
University of Maribor
Slovenia

Andrzej Jodłowski
Polish Academy of Sciences
Poland

Matjaž B. Jurič
University of Maribor
Slovenia

Christian Koncilia
University of Klagenfurt
Austria

Oriana Licchelli
Università di Bari
Italy

Heiko Ludwig
IBM T.J. Watson Research Center
USA

Ee-Peng Lim
Nanyang Technological University
Singapore

Pasquale Lops
Università di Bari
Italy

Kenneth Messa
Loyola University
USA

Wee-Keong Ng
Nanyang Technological University
Singapore

Kok-Leong Ong
Nanyang Technological University
Singapore

Jacek Płodzień
Polish Academy of Sciences, Warsaw School of Economics
Poland

Vili Podgorelec
University of Maribor
Slovenia

Ivan Rozman
University of Maribor
Slovenia

Giovanni Semeraro
Università di Bari
Italy

Kazimierz Subieta
Polish-Japanese Institute of Information Technology, Polish Academy of Sciences
Poland

Tatjana Welzer
University of Maribor
Slovenia

Fabio Zambetta
Università di Bari
Italy

Liang-Jie Zhang
IBM T.J. Watson Research Center
USA

Qun Zhou
IBM Software Group
USA

Reviewers

José L. Arjona
University of Seville
Spain

David Benavides
Telvent Interactiva, S.A.
Spain

Amador Durán
Asociación de Técnicos de Informática
Spain

Heinz Frank
Cicero Consulting, GmbH
Austria

Zbyszko Królikowski
Poznań University of Technology
Poland

Jarosław Łagowski
IBM Poland
Poland

José López
Terra Networks, S.A.
Spain

Octavio Martín
University of Seville
Spain

Joaquín Peña
University of Seville
Spain

José A. Pérez
University of Seville
Spain

Valeriano Romero
Latin Mail, S.A.
Spain

David Ruiz
University of Seville
Spain

Preface

The explosive growth of the Internet and the web have created an ever-growing demand for web-based information systems, and ever-growing challenges for Information Systems Engineering. Some of them include the emerging web services technology, database technologies and application integration, as well as data analysis and knowledge discovery.

A web service is a programmable piece of application logic to which one can have access by means of standard Internet protocols. Web services combine the best aspects of component-based development and the web. Like components, web services encapsulate black-box functionality that can be reused without worrying about how the service is implemented. Unlike current component technologies, web services are not accessed via object-model-specific protocols, such as the distributed Component Object Model (DCOM), Remote Method Invocation (RMI), or Internet Inter-ORB Protocol (IIOP). Instead, web services are accessed via ubiquitous web protocols and data formats, such as Hypertext Transfer Protocol (HTTP) and Extensible Markup Language (XML). Consumers of a web service can be implemented on any platform in any programming language, as long as they can create and consume the messages defined for the web service interface. Unfortunately, or fortunately, all that glitters is not gold, and there is a number of hindrances to its widespread adoption. Some of the major obstacles are the discovery and the integration of web services as well as guaranteeing their quality of service.

The second key component of contemporary information systems are database management systems (DBMS), which provide the following functionality: data persistence, efficient access to data by means of various techniques that optimise queries, data integrity ensured by integrity constraints, access control to data by managing users and privileges, concurrency control by means of transaction scheduling protocols and locking mechanisms, database backup and database recovery after hardware or software failures, the SQL *ad hoc* query language, data independence from storage techniques by separating conceptual schemata from implementation schemata, and the management of data dictionaries. Typically, database management systems are designed and optimised for On-Line Transaction Processing (OLTP). Such databases are able to manage dozens of thousand of short-time concurrent transactions that modify or consult small amounts of data. However, the management of a company requires a comprehensive view of all aspects of its activities. Information collected in a company uses often different data formats and has discordant complexity, e.g., relational, object-relational, and object-oriented databases, on-line multimedia data stores, web pages, spreadsheets, flat files, and so on. Even within the same institution, different DBMS and other information management software are often used. Furthermore, different pieces of information are often geographically distributed even within the same company. Heterogeneity and distribution of information make it difficult to have access to it. Therefore, a lot of research efforts were made in order to provide a uniform, integrated, transparent access to heterogeneous and distributed information sources.

There are two basic approaches to data integration: the virtual approach and the data warehousing approach. The former is called virtual as information is stored in native data sources and is retrieved dynamically when a user needs it. In order to have access to these data, an integrated schema must be built and managed in the system. A global user query is decomposed and transformed into queries for each of the data sources. The results of each of the queries are then translated, filtered, and merged to dynamically form a global result. The most common approaches that allow distributed databases and other data sources to be integrated virtually are: federated database systems, and mediated systems.

In the data warehousing approach, data of interest coming from heterogeneous sources are extracted, filtered, merged, and stored in a central repository called data warehouse. The data are also enriched with historical and summary information. Then, queries are issued on this data warehouse. The advantages of the data warehousing approach to data integration are as follows: (i) queries operate on a local, centralised data repository, which reduces access time to data, (ii) queries need not be decomposed into different formats and their results need not be integrated, (iii) a data warehouse is independent of its data sources that may be temporary unavailable. In order to ease the task of systems integration, software engineers have developed so-called integration patterns and templates. That serve as models/guidelines applicable to certain integration scenarios.

Recently, users of data warehousing systems have been paying special attention to the analysis of operational data produced by OLTP applications, in order to discover trends, anomalies, and patterns of behaviour. Different analytical tools enable analysts to reach better decisions. Such applications are called decision support systems (DSS) and data mining. The market analysis of supply and demand is one of the important steps in taking strategic decisions in a company.

Structure of this book

This book is a showcase of recent, significant advances in web-based information systems as well as data integration and analysis. It provides an overview of various technologies used for building innovative information systems applied to real business solutions. It includes eight chapters that are divided into five parts, namely: web services, database technologies, data and application integration, data analysis and knowledge discovery, and recommended bibliography.

Chapter 1, by H. Ludwig, discusses a framework for analysing and designing electronic contracting processes, i.e., a mechanism by means of which an organisation can enter into and manage electronic business relationships. As today's networked economy allows customers to obtain information about products and services from providers around the globe, a customer and a provider of a service must be able to negotiate their contractual relationship over a network efficiently. Furthermore, each party must set up its internal systems to deliver and consume the service that has been promised in the contract. Negotiation and fulfillment of flexible, case-by-case business relationships is predominantly established and fulfilled with significant human involvement. Automating the contracting process is the key to facilitate a company's participation in a dynamic electronic services market, but poses significant challenges. The framework presented in this chapter allows contracting process designers to deal with the trade-off between flexibility and automation. It provides a design guideline for an implementation of electronic contracting systems. It is illustrated by means of a case study that consists of an application for providers of service-level-agreement-based web services.

Chapter 2, by L.J. Zhang, Q. Zhou, H.Y. Chang, and J.Y. Chung, discusses a manageable web services hub framework and enabling technologies for outsourcing. It provides a web-services-based enabling infrastructure for buyers, suppliers, service providers, and trading partners to register business, user and service information as well as to provision and subscribe to services. In addition, the framework enables a business to compose its business processes dynamically, so that they can be easily integrated with other companies according to service requirements solely. The framework leverages an advanced web services discovery mechanism to look up Universal Description Discovery and Interaction (UDDI) registries efficiently. A working system of this framework, Managed e-Hub, provides the infrastructure needed for enabling e-business on demand in a secure, controlled environment.

Chapter 3, by K. Subieta, A. Jodłowski, P. Habela, and J. Płodzień, presents the concept of dynamic object roles both as a facility for conceptual modelling and a data structure to be implemented in object-oriented or object-relational database management systems. The authors discuss the advantages of their proposal and present several approaches to implement it. A new one is also proposed, and it assumes that a role is a distinguished sub-object of an object. A role inherits attribute values and methods from its parent object dynamically. Objects can be accessed by their names, as well as by the names of their roles. Dynamic object roles essentially change the semantics of other notions of object-oriented models, such as classes, inheritance and substitutability. The chapter also contains a discussion on how dynamic roles can be used in the context of an object store, in a query language, and in an object definition language that builds on the spirit of the ODMG standard. The concept has been implemented in a prototype system for intelligent content management, as a canonical database model for integrating heterogeneous web and XML/RDF technologies and applications.

Chapter 4, by J. Eder and C. Koncilia, discusses a promising approach to temporal versioning in data warehouses. The authors propose a formal model of a temporal data warehouse (DW) that supports changes in its schema and, as a consequence, changes to its contents. A DW is modelled as a set of multi-dimensional cubes, with dimensions at axis, and fact data in the intersection. From a user's point of view such a temporal data warehouse is perceived as a set of so-called structure versions, each of which is a view on a DW schema and its data valid for a given time interval. The model supports various operations on a data warehouse structure, i.e., splitting and merging dimension members, changing position of a dimension member in a dimension hierarchy, changing attributes of a dimension member, inserting or deleting a dimension. Every change to a DW structure results in the creation of a new structure version. Users can execute queries for a particular structure version or queries that span over several versions. To answer a query in the latter case, data must be transformed from one version into another, and conversion functions are used to perform this task. Such functions contain information on how to compute data from one structure version to an adjacent structure version, both forward and backward.

Chapter 5, by B. Czejdo and K. Messa, approaches query processing in integrated systems in which data are incomplete. Data incompleteness may result from either missing data in integrated sources or temporary unavailability of those sources. Both cases are supported by a query language. User queries issued for such data sources must return, together with the required data, some additional information explaining the reason of data incompleteness. The cases of data incompleteness are classified, and it is shown how to generate query answers and appropriate additional explanations for each one. The solutions presented are applicable to federated database systems as well as to data warehouses. The chapter also discusses a graphical tool for querying data sources.

Chapter 6, by M.B. Jurič, I. Rozman, T. Welzer, M. Heričko, B. Brumen, and V. Pogorelec, discusses common solutions to integrating information systems and defines six integration patterns: Integration Broker, Integration Wrapper, Integration Mediator, Virtual Component, Data Mapping, and Process Automator. The integration patterns presented provide a sound foundation for the intra-enterprise application integration (EAI), as well as for the inter-EAI problems. They can be used for the component-based approach to EAI problems. The patterns have been validated in more than three large scale integration projects, where they have proven their suitability.

Chapter 7, by G. Semeraro, F. Abbattista, M. Degemmis, O. Licchelli, P. Lops, and F. Zambetta, presents an approach and a working system for developing intelligent and personalised web services for e-commerce. This allows companies to set up and maintain web sites effectively because they can address customers in personalised and pro-active ways. The system, developed within an European project, is mainly based on machine learning techniques that are used to extract permanent features of a given user from the dialogue with an intelligent conversational agent. The proposed strategy represents a very promising solution to overcome the problem of finding information in the growing amount of web resources. The approach was proven to be successful in cases where large data sets were available as it provides tools for retrieving and filtering useful information. Furthermore, it has been applied to the definition of models of users interacting with an information system.

Chapter 8, by K.L. Ong, W.K. Ng, and E.P. Lim, highlights that target marketing may be done by means of data mining techniques. In such cases, the input to data mining is a set of training examples, and the goal is to find out what patterns are likely to be repeated in future. Such a model works well for transactional business like Amazon.com, but fails with non-transactional business such as consultancy, subscription-based services, multi-level marketing, and insurance. These businesses may also have accumulated massive information about their customers by means of on-line systems, for instance. However, their lack of transaction records means the inability to use data mining techniques for effective target marketing. In order to overcome this drawback, a novel data mining algorithm that analyses customer profiles to discover their relationships is proposed in this chapter. By understanding these relationships, a company can pair an existing customer with a potential customer and influence his or her decisions. The system presented in this chapter was implemented using the .NET platform for a practical business case in the field of consultancy.

We think that the material presented in these chapters may help the reader have an overall idea of the research that is being carried out in universities and companies to develop today's innovative business solutions.

Acknowledgements

The editors would like to thank the authors who submitted proposals to this book. The total number of papers submitted was 28, i.e., the acceptance ratio was 28.57%. The authors were from 15 countries around the globe, namely: Arab Emirates, Austria, China, France, Germany, Italy, Mexico, Poland, Singapore, Slovakia, Slovenia, Spain, Turkey, United Kingdom, and USA.

We would also like to thank our referees, who did a tremendous job of reviewing the submissions three times so that the book conformed to NOVA's high-quality standards.

About the editors

Rafael Corchuelo   Antonio Ruiz-Cortés   Robert Wrembel

Rafael Corchuelo is a Reader in Computer Engineering, and he has been with the University of Seville since 1994. He is the head of the Research Group on Distributed Systems of this University, and he has set up several cooperation and exchange programmes with several European universities and research centres. His research activities focus on distributed systems, i.e., quality, fairness, coordination, information extraction, and so forth. Currently, he is a member of the editorial board of Springer-Verlag's Journal of Universal Computer Science, and serves as a reviewer for ACM's Computing Reviews and Wiley's Concurrency and Computation. He is also a member of the Project Evaluation Board of the European Union.

Antonio Ruiz-Cortés is a Doctor of Computer Science, and he is with the Department of Computer Languages and Systems of the University of Seville. Before joining the University, he worked for several companies as an external consultant. His current research interests include requirements engineering and software architecture applied to multi-organisational web-based systems and geographical information systems. He also serves as an expert of the Fifth Framework Programme of the European Commission.

Robert Wrembel works as a Lecturer at the Poznań University of Technology. In 2001, he received his Ph.D. degree in Computer Science. In 1996–2002, he took part of three research projects on databases and four industrial projects in the field of information technology. He has paid a number of research visits to centres such as INRIA Paris-Rocquencourt (France), University Paris Dauphine (France), University of Klagenfurt (Austria), and Loyola University (USA). His research interests encompass object-oriented databases, views, multiversion databases, object-relational data warehouses, and multi-version data warehouses. He also works as a Lecturer at Oracle Poland. He is a member of the executive board of the Polish Oracle Users Group and he was elected to the board of directors of Europe, Middle East, and Africa Oracle Users Group in 2000-2001.

Part I

Web Services

In: Technology Supporting Business Solutions
Editors: R. Corchuelo, A. Ruiz-Cortés and R. Wrembel, pp. 3-23
© 2003 Nova Science Publishers, Inc.

Chapter 1

Electronic Contracts

Heiko Ludwig

1.1 Introduction

The contracting process is the mechanism by which organisations enter into and manage business relationships. Today's networked economy allows customers to obtain information about products and services from providers around the globe. Customers also expect to obtain these goods or services instantaneously, in particular if they are delivered electronically, e.g., application services, or the delivery process can be managed electronically, e.g., logistics services such as parcel delivery. This entails that the customer and the provider of a service must be able to negotiate their contractual relationship over a network in an efficient manner. In addition, each party must set up its internal systems to deliver and consume the service that was promised in the contract. Today, this process is automated for some commodity goods and services only, e.g., in the banking field. Negotiation and fulfillment of flexible, case-by-case business relationships is predominantly established and fulfilled with significant human involvement. Automating the contracting process is the key to facilitate a company's participation in a dynamic electronic services market, but poses a significant challenge. In this chapter, we provide a framework for the design of contracting processes that deal with the trade-off between flexibility and automation. This framework provides a design guideline for the implementation of electronic contracting systems. The guidelines are illustrated by means of an application for providers of SLA-based web services.

1.1.1 Electronic contracts in an e-service environment

When independent parties (organisations or consumers) enter a business relationship, a contract between them is established [13]. The contract defines the mutual rights and obligations of the parties in this relationship, e.g., which services to perform, which goods to deliver, and how much to pay. In many legislations, there are no particular formats prescribed in which a contract has to be expressed, for most matters, anyway. What establishes a legally binding contract as such is the process in which the contracting parties express their will to enter into a concordant agreement [70]. This process involves the steps of offer and acceptance, at least, and the offer contains the content of the proposed contract.

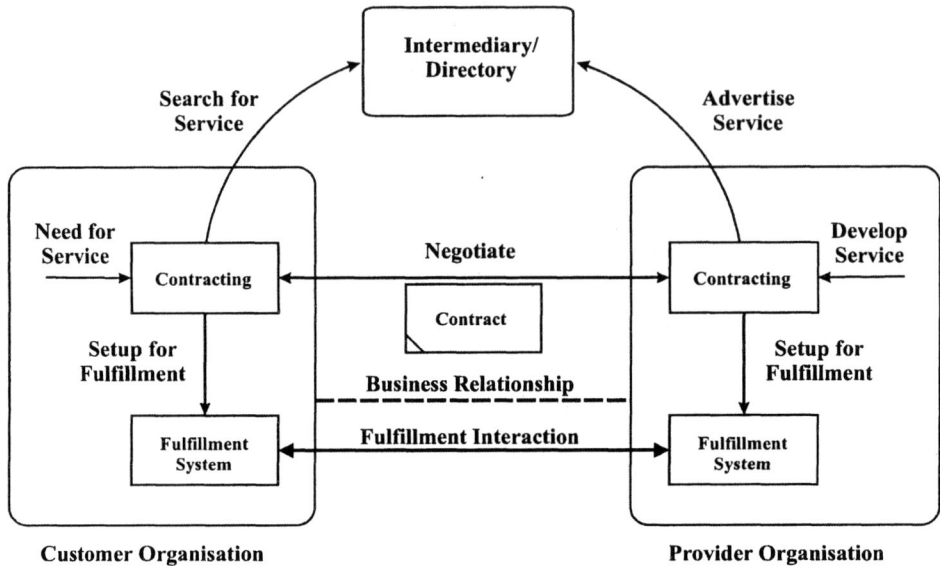

Figure 1.1: Overview of the contracting process.

Contracts can be established verbally, in writing, or in an electronic format. If a contract has an electronic representation, we then call it electronic contract. This term applies to contracts containing natural language only, machine-interpretable (formal) language, or both. In many cases, contracts are between two parties, which we call provider and customer. In some domains, multiple parties enter a contract or are referred in it. This is the case, for instance, in the domain of digital rights, where a rights owner licenses playing rights for some media to a customer and a named set of parties are granted the right to sub-license from the primary licensee. However, we focus on simple bilateral contracts since most conceptual issues are covered by this case.

The (full) contracting process is the process in which contracts are negotiated, established, and the fulfillment is managed. This process includes, for instance, the advertisement of a contract for goods or services by a provider, the search for suitable providers by a customer, the negotiation, the signing procedure, the planning of the fulfillment process by the provider, a service tracking process by a customer, a payment process, and an analysis of a contract post execution. Fig. 1.1 illustrates the contracting process at a high level.

The contracting process in Fig. 1.1 involves two parties, a customer and a provider. Prior to the contracting process, a customer discovers a need for a particular service or a provider develops a service. They learn about the potential for entering a business relationship through an intermediary, e.g., yellow pages or an on-line directory service. Then, the parties negotiate the terms and conditions of their relationship by exchanging offers, which finally results in a contract. It establishes a business relationship between the parties in terms of a set of rights or obligations of those parties; it also governs their further interaction to actually deliver and consume what is promised in the contract at fulfillment time. After signing a contract, both parties have to prepare their fulfillment system accordingly. Depending on the type of service, this might be very different from case to case. If the service consists of sending books by regular mail, it has to be initiated that the book is taken from the shelf, packaged and sent. The customer has to prepare to receive the book, e.g., make sure that somebody is at home when it is delivered. When all obligations have been fulfilled, the business relationship is dissolved.

Conceptually, we distinguish a contracting function that implements the contracting process from the fulfillment function that implements the core service-implementing and service-consuming functions of an organisation. In the sequel of this chapter, we further discuss the structure of the contracting functions of providers and customers, their interaction amongst each other, and the interaction with the fulfillment system and the rest of the environment; the goal is to research how parts of the contracting process can be automated. Apparently, the automation of the contracting function and the concept of electronic contracts is particularly interesting for services whose fulfillment system is automated or can be monitored and managed through a network.

If a contracting process is fully or, more likely, partially executed using a network of computers, we call it an automated contracting process or an electronic contracting process, since it is be based on an electronic contract. Apparently, the property of being automated or manual is not discrete but there is a gradual transition between a fully manual and a fully automated process.

There are several benefits of automating the contracting process:

- Automating the contracting process results in increased speed of negotiation and setup for fulfillment.

- Another important aspect is the reduction of costs associated with employees throughout the contracting process. Key to the (partial) automation is an electronic contract expressed in an machine-readable format to serve as input for the automated parts of the contracting process.

- Once the contracting process is automated, service customers are able to buy services on much shorter notice, thus enjoying the benefit of deferring the buying decision to the point in time when they actually know their current requirements.

- Benefiting from those reduced contracting costs and times, providers and customers can buy services at finer granularity or services that are only available in bundles in an environment of expensive contracting processes can be offered individually.

- Finally, the availability of fine-grained services provides opportunities for service intermediaries to re-bundle services from different providers into new aggregate offerings.

1.1.2 A case study: SLAs for web services

We illustrate the use of the conceptual framework by means of a solution for providers of web services, the Utility Services demonstrator that is part of IBM's Web Services ToolKit (WSTK), version 3.3 [114]. The WSTK Utility Services allow providers to offer services to different customers at different levels of quality, defined by per-customer SLAs, at different rating models. The purpose of this example is to explain how particular design choices were made to meet requirements using the conceptual framework proposed in this chapter. It is not meant to present a role model partially automated contracting process since the suitability of a contracting process implementation depends on the requirements of a particular project.

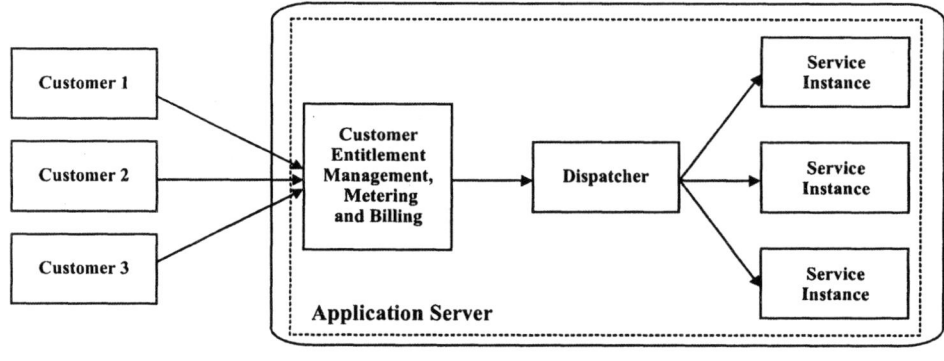

Figure 1.2: WSTK fulfillment system.

Web services are an upcoming technology for cross-organisational services [73]. The interfaces to services are defined in a standardised way using the Web Services Definition Language (WSDL) and the services can be accessed using HTTP as transport mechanism and the Simple Object Access Protocol (SOAP) as encoding format for messages, by default. Other transport mechanisms can be specified in a service's WSDL document. Using loosely coupled, HTTP-based service access, web services are a good basis to provide on-line services such as hosted applications, payment and other transaction banking services across organisational boundaries. A simple example that is often used is a stock quote financial information service.

In a commercial realm, companies do not want to make services freely available to the general public but sell those services to customers and charge customers for using these services depending on various criteria. Those criteria may be time of service access, frequency of use, and quality of service. In addition, service providers want to offer the same service at different levels of quality and price to different customers. Fig. 1.2 describes the high-level architecture of the WSTK Utility Services solution.

The services of a provider run in an application server. When a service invocation from a customer's client comes in, it first meets a component that checks whether the customer is entitled to using the service, determines the class of service according to which to prioritise this invocation, and records its time stamp. The invocation is passed on to a dispatcher that maintains a queue for each class of service into which an invocation is entered accordingly. From this queue, it is submitted to a service instance for processing. The dispatcher prioritises the queues of different service classes relative to each other as described in [104]. For instance, gold class queues could have high priority, silver less priority and best-effort none at all, which means that, under high system load, gold queue invocations are sent often to their services, silver ones less often, and best-effort ones least often. The relationship between these classes is defined by weights. The service instances that process the invocations can be of the same type, e.g., located on different machines of a cluster, or completely different services. Return messages are passed back the reverse way of invocation. The metering functionality can record the time stamp of outgoing messages and thus enable billing according to the response time of an invocation. The dispatcher, entitlement, metering and billing components are implemented as a series of AXIS (Apache eXtensible Interaction System) handlers [60] and services invoked by those handlers run either in a WebSphere or Tomcat servlet engine [61].

A contracting process was implemented so that the system described above would become a fulfillment system for service level agreements (contracts) on web services. Service providers are able to compose offers by associating operations of web services with a level of service. An offer can comprise the interface description of the service, the specification of the quality of service, and a rating model. Offers are advertised on the provider's web site where customers can choose and subscribe to them. On subscription, the setup of the fulfillment system to accommodate the new customer is fully automated. Whereas the dispatcher of the system described above uses classes of service to prioritise invocations relative to each other, this is not a useful model to specify quality of service in a contract with a customer. A customer organisation is not interested in knowing that other customers are addressed better or worse. It wants to have absolute guarantees for its quality of service, e.g., the average response time must be less than two seconds, maybe capped by an invocation rate. One of the challenges of setting up the fulfillment system is to translate those absolute performance guarantees to service classes that the dispatcher can deal with.

The focus of the contracting process of this solution is not to make sure that a contract is legally enforceable, but to automate the subscription and the setup process whilst maintaining sufficient flexibility to deal with a variety of quality of service levels. In the sequel of this chapter, we further discuss how this solution relates to the conceptual model of the contracting process and the design choices were made.

1.1.3 Goal and structure

The goal of this chapter is to provide a conceptual model of the contracting process to enable its analysis, analyse the potential to automate parts of the contracting function, and design automated functions of the contracting process.

The rest of the chapter is organised as follows: In Section 1.2, we introduce our conceptual model of the contracting process, decomposing the function and interactions on the service provider and customer side; in Section 1.3, we address the information associated with interactions with respect to their contents and format; in particular, this also includes the contract document itself; in Section 1.4, based on our understanding of the contracting process, we analyse issues of automating the contracting functions and propose some strategies. At the end of each section, we discuss how the issues discussed in the respective section were addressed in the WSTK Utility Services case. In Section 1.5, we summarise and conclude the chapter. The chapter presents many examples of how parts of the contracting process have been approached by various projects. However, it is not a survey.

1.2 Conceptual Model of the Contracting Process

We need a good model of the contracting process to understand the potential for automation of its parts, i.e., the conceptual functions involved and the interactions amongst those functions.

1.2.1 Contracting process phases

The contracting process has several phases. There are multiple models of phases of business relationships, such as the one used in the context of the SeCo project [69, 70] and a similar

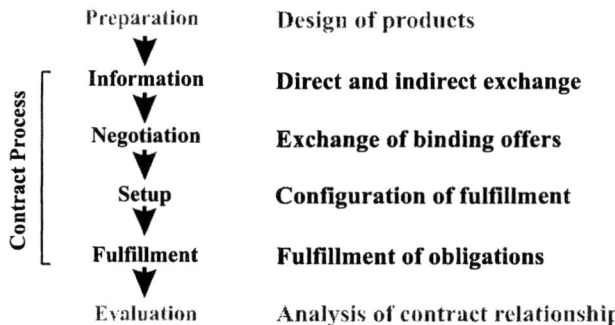

Figure 1.3: Phases of a contract life-cycle.

one proposed by Angelov and Grefen [13]. For the purposes of this book, we structure the contracting process as outlined in Fig. 1.3.

The term contracting process relates to dealing with a single contract. The preparation phase precedes this contracting process. In this phase, a provider designs the service it wants to offer and takes all preparatory steps to actually provide it to customers. On the customer's side, this step entails the evaluation of the needs that lead to entering the contracting process.

In the information phase, both parties can identify potential business partners, gather information about their counterparts and the services in question. This phase can be either conducted by directly requesting and sending information between the parties or by using an intermediary, e.g., yellow pages or a public web site.

During the negotiation phase parties exchange offers, counter-offers, acceptance, and rejection messages. This can be either conducted in a direct interaction or mediated by an intermediary. Depending on the negotiation protocol in use, this phase can lead to different interaction patterns. The negotiation phase is completed once both parties have accepted an offer.

Once a contract is signed, both parties have to prepare for the fulfillment of the contract in the setup phase. This comprises potentially the technical setup of the fulfillment-system, e.g., in the case of the application hosting service the system must be installed and applications started. In the context of network and application services, this step is often referred to as provisioning. In the case of the logistics system, warehouse space must be assigned or even be built. On the administrative side, current and future financial flows have to be accounted.

In the fulfillment phase, both parties manage their obligations and monitor the compliance of the other party. In general, the management of a party's obligations means providing service or a payment to fulfill the contractual obligations. However, in some cases, a party may decide not to live up to its obligations and cause a dispute. therefore, dispute resolutions are also part of this phase. When the service is completed and there is agreement that all contractual obligations have been fulfilled by all parties, the fulfillment system for this particular contract can be dismantled. In the case of the application hosting service, this may comprise disconnecting the application-hosting servers from the network so that they cannot be accessed again by the customer and re-assigning them to the pool of servers for

Electronic Contracts

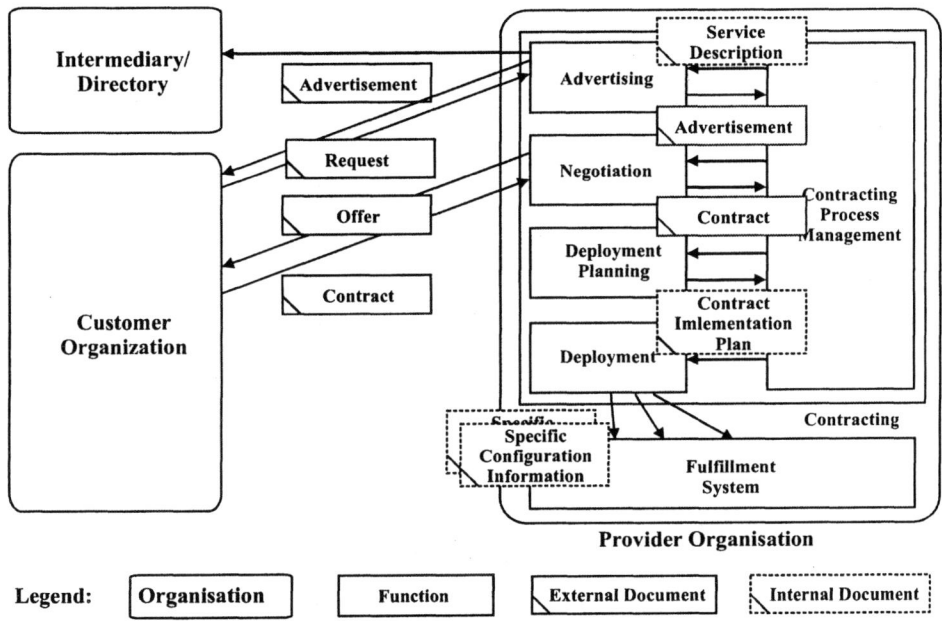

Figure 1.4: Provider functions and flows.

new contracts.

After the fulfillment phase, the contracting process is completed. Still, parties may want to analyse the performance of their contractual relationships. This is done in an evaluation phase, which conceptually is performed after the contracting process. Since the evaluation is not necessarily done each time a contracting process is completed but may be decoupled from it for a whole set of contracts at a time, it is not considered part of the core contracting process.

The WSTK case: In the WSTK Utility Service solution, the implementation of the services and the definition of the offers are activities of the preparation phase. The information phase begins as soon as an offer is put on the web site. The negotiation phase corresponds to the subscription of a customer to a particular offer because the system does not support sophisticated negotiation. The setup phase consists of setting up the entitlement, metering and billing component to admit invocations from the new customer and to bill to the new contract's account. The fulfillment phase is the time span in which the service is used. There is no support in the system for evaluation.

1.2.2 Contracting function of a service provider

With the understanding of the phases of the contracting process, we now analyse further the role of the contracting function. Providers and customers have different requirements, so they are discussed separately. A decomposition of the contracting function for a provider, the flows between its components and external partners, as well as the information associated with these flows are shown in Fig. 1.4.

We decompose the contracting function of a service provider into five elements:

The role of the advertising function is to deal with the information phase of contract life-cycle. It decides how to advertise a service and to whom. It also answers requests from potential customers. These advertisements are based on a description of the service to be advertised, which has been developed prior to the contracting process in the preparation phase and are input to this function. The contracting function segments the market for a particular type of service and creates advertisements that correspond to different types of customers. In the context of the application hosting example, the same application hosting service would be advertised as a service with pre-configured applications to small- and medium-sized businesses and as a bring-your-own-application service to enterprise customers. The advertising function sends the advertisement directly to potential customers and to intermediaries such as directories or on-line marketplaces.

The negotiation function negotiates contracts with potential customers; it thus corresponds to the negotiation phase of the contract life-cycle. It receives the set of current advertisements as input. The negotiation function comprises two parts:

Interaction The negotiation is conducted by exchanging offers and counter-offers with potential customers. If an offer is accepted a contract is established. The negotiation process can be initiated either by a potential customer reacting to an advertisement or by the provider responding to a call for bids.

Decision-making Offers are made or evaluated based on the resource situation at the time the customer requires a service, his or her status, e.g., he or she is very loyal and does much business with the provider, and the general market situation. It may be that because of generally low demand the provider is prepared to accept a lower offer and vice versa. Negotiations can be conducted with multiple potential customers at the same time. This function can be very complex, if the parties are very flexible with respect to what can be negotiated, or relatively simple, if the advertisements, which form the basis of the negotiation, are very specific already, e.g., a specific services bundle at a fixed price.

The decision-making problem in negotiation has been analysed in many disciplines, e.g., operations research, economics, business administration, and psychology. The reader can consult Bichler's [23] or Ströbel's [154] articles for further information.

Once an agreement on a contract has been reached, or signed, a provider organisation must plan which resources to assign to fulfill the obligations arising from the contract, the deployment planning function. In the case of the application hosting service, this comprises the assignment of server machines, the choice of install images and the choice of network service providers. In the case of the logistics service, warehouse space must be assigned, the delivery workflow must be defined, and the provisioning of the web interface has to be prepared. The result of this planning function is the contract implementation plan. In a classic production environment, this function corresponds to a new entry to the master production schedule.

The deployment function executes the contract implementation plan. It creates specific configuration information for the involved automated components of the fulfillment system and executes the respective provisioning processes. For instance, if the contract implementation plan foresees to provide an application service on a Linux server, it would install a Linux image and perform Linux-specific configuration steps, which are different from, e.g., the provisioning process of a Windows 2000 server. If the service involves elements performed by employees, the service process is started and the employees are informed about their task assignments.

The contracting process management function manages the execution of the contracting functions. The contracting functions are not necessarily executed in a strict order. Advertisement is done in many cases far prior to negotiation. Also, deployment planning and the deployment itself can be separated if services are purchased in advance. In addition, the contracting process management maintains the state of the contracting processes and stores the corresponding documents.

The contracting function deals with several documents (conceptually, not necessarily in the form of document files). Advertisements, requests, offers, and contracts are external documents that are exchanged with customers and intermediaries (see Fig. 1.4). The contract implementation plan and the specific configuration information is internal to the service provider.

The WSTK case: The contracting function in the WSTK Utility Services is implemented to a large extent by its Contract Service. The WSTK Contract Service provides a user interface for administrators to specify offers on the basis of service instances registered with it. Offers are stored in the WSTK contract service. In addition, it exposes offers on a web interface for customers, which represents the implementation of the advertising function.

It also implements a subscription interface for customers, thus implementing a simple negotiation function. The customer can choose the desired pairs of response time and invocation per minute cap (throughput) from a pull down menu. The customer can then choose a rating package, and can view a detailed formal description of the metric specification of response time and throughput and the specification of the service level goals represented in the Web Service Level Agreement language (WSLA) [90, 111]. However, negotiation of the metrics, i.e., the way the average response time and the throughput are measured is not offered since the available instrumentation of the WSTK Utility Services solution is limited to response time and invocation count measured through the AXIS handlers.

The external documents advertisement, request, and offer are represented as web pages. The details of document contents are discussed later in the chapter. However, there is no explicit contract document since no signature mechanism was needed in this case. The contract content corresponds to the offer content viewed by a customer through the web interface.

The most important step of deployment planning in the WSTK case is the mapping of absolute quality of service guarantees as part of offers to service classes used by the dispatcher (cf. Fig. 1.2). This association is done at system setup time. For each combination of response time and throughput, a corresponding class of service is defined. For each offer and also for each instance, internal class of service to which it relates is stored in the contract. This represents the central part of the contract implementation plan. Other subjects of a contract implementation plan such as the choice of components are irrelevant since the services are set up beforehand. A more sophisticated solution, however, would have to specify which services must be started on which computers and when.

To discuss the deployment function, we need to discuss further the entitlement, billing and metering function. A contract handler checks the entitlement of a customer invocation by mapping the customer ID to a contract ID. For this purpose, it looks the contract up in the Contract Service. therefore the contract handler does not need any further specific

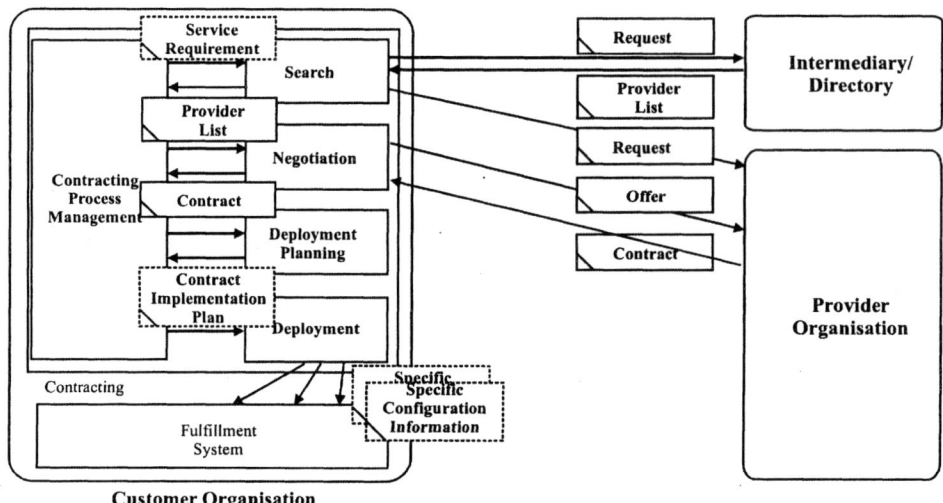

Figure 1.5: Customer functions and flows.

configuration information. The contract handler also provides the mapping from a contract ID to a specific internal class of service, which is also looked up from the Contract Service. The metering handler writes time stamps of incoming and outgoing messages to a log, which is later interpreted by an accounting service for producing the bill. The metering handler does not require further configuration information.

Reading from the meter log, the WSLA Compliance Monitor (CM) checks whether the provider lived up to the service level goals given in the contract. Using the metering entries, the CM computes individual response times and from them aggregates them to average response times and throughput rates, which are the metrics on which the service level goals are defined. If a violation occurs, it sends a notification that can be processed, e.g., displayed on a console. The CM requires no specific configuration information; however, it receives the quality of service specification in WSLA format as input. therefore, on activation of the contract, the primary deployment activity is to submit the WSLA part of the contract to the WSLA Compliance Monitor.

1.2.3 Contracting function of a service customer

The contracting function of a service customer can be decomposed similarly to the service provider's, but the individual sub-functions are partially different. Functions and interactions are outlined in Fig. 1.5.

In the information phase, the search function identifies provider organisations that can potentially address a customer organisation's service requirements. It sends requests to intermediaries, e.g., directory services, which yields a list of service providers that meet the criteria specified in the request. In addition, as discussed in last sub-section, a request can be sent to a service provider directly to receive an advertisement. The result of the search is a list of suitable providers for a particular service requirement (provider list). This function can be designed in different ways. It can rely entirely on a particular single directory service for finding its partners or inquire many different sources. In addition, the search function can reach out to intermediaries and providers for each individual service requirement or it can store request results locally within the search function and serve service requirement request from this local data.

The negotiation function receives a list of suitable providers and the service requirements. Its goal is to negotiate a contract with a provider; therefore, it corresponds to the negotiation phase of the contract life-cycle and organisationally to the purchasing department within an organisation. The customer's negotiation function is the counterpart of the provider's and interacts with it through offers that establish a contract on acceptance.

A customer's negotiation function also comprises an interaction element and a decision-making element. The latter takes into account the service requirements and the constraints of providers to fulfill these requirements. Requirements and constraints relate to different attributes such as service time, quantity, e.g., application service accommodating 500 transactions per hour, quality, e.g., average response time less than 2 seconds, and price. These attributes have to be taken into account when evaluating an offer and submitting a counter-offer.

The customer's deployment planning function is different from the provider's in that it deals with the setup of the service consumption fulfillment system, rather than the service-providing one. In the case of an application service, configuration information for service clients has to be prepared and roll-out procedures have to be designed. In the case of the logistics service, a warehouse customer has to list the suppliers that need to be informed to deliver to the service supplier's warehouse. In addition, e.g., in case of a customer being a mobile phone service company, internal business processes must be changed so that delivery requests are routed to the service provider. For this purpose, e.g., a mobile phone company's CRM application may have to be reconfigured to trigger a service invocation to a provider. On the administrative side, the customer has to plan for the payments due in the course of the service. The result of the planning is the contract implementation plan.

Like in the case of a service provider, a customer's deployment function executes the contract implementation plan. For this purpose, it executes a process that configures the elements of the fulfillment system with specific configuration information. It also encompasses the administrative measures foreseen in the contract implementation plan, e.g., opening an account-payable position in the creditor accounting system.

The contracting process management function facilitates the interaction amongst these functions and implements the contract life-cycle by involving them. Similar to the provider's case, the contracting process management functions maintains the state of contract life-cycles.

The WSTK case: The WSTK Utility Services are a solution for a service provider. The only customer functions supported are search and negotiation. The browser interface allows prospective customers to view offers and subscribe to them. However, customers are not supported to find other providers or in any deployment function on their side. For search, deployment planning and deployment, customers must use a different means.

1.3 Document Structures and Formats

Having outlined a model of the contracting functions of a service provider and the service customer, we can discuss in more detail the artifacts involved in the contracting function, in particular the contract itself.

The internal information, service description, service requirement, contract implementation plan, and the specific configuration information for the fulfillment system carry the information needed to fulfill their purpose and, since they are internal to an organisation, do not need to adhere to an agreed format. In most cases, these internal information items are not literally one document but are available from many different sources. However, looking towards the automation of contracting functions, formats that can be shared amongst applications implementing (parts of) contracting functions are beneficial. The formats of the external documents, however, must be well-understood by all involved parties, including intermediaries.

1.3.1 Information phase documents

The service description is the internal representation of what type of service can be offered to customers and allows the advertising function to combine it with market knowledge and create advertisements. This encompasses the information that would be shared with customers, e.g., in the case of application hosting service, the type of application or the network connections it requires, but also internal details of the service, e.g., Linux is used as server OS, which types of computers are deployed, and the costs associated with resources used in a service.

On the customer side, the service requirement information must contain the information about the type of service needed, when, how much, in which price range, and other criteria.

The advertisement is the document type by which a provider publishes information about a service to potential customers, either directly or through an intermediary. The items published in the service are those that a service provider deems relevant for the decision of a potential customer to start negotiating. This may include properties of the provider organisation and its service as well as constraints on the customer, e.g., the type of customers for which this particular service is suited [58]. The difference between the content of an advertisement and an offer is twofold: (a) not all details of an offer may be in the advertisement if they are not considered decision-relevant for negotiation, e.g., the small-print of an offer; (b) a provider may include information that is not part of an offer but may be relevant for the decision to start negotiating. Examples are credit ratings of a provider or reference customers. Whereas offers are legally binding, advertisements are invitations to treat and therefore not directly binding [70]. They can entail some weaker liability in some legislations.

Since the advertisement is the first point of contact between a provider and a customer, it must be in a format that can be interpreted by the customer without further agreement. What makes a format suitable depends largely on the context in which it is used. If advertisements are scanned by people, HTML web pages, potentially indexed by search engines, may be good. If the matching process should be automated, a more formal representation of the advertisement content is necessary. For instance, if providers of web services advertise to UDDI [73], they have to describe their *businessEntity*, which is the entry describing a provider, and the *businessService*, which is the service itself. To interpret these parameters, their semantics, the ontology of this domain needs to be generally known, either imposed by an intermediary such as marketplace provider or by a domain-specific standards body. The virtual marketplace system ViMP is an example for a technology for intermediary-managed ontologies [58]. Standards for classifying goods and services are, for instance, the ECCMA Universal Standard Products and Services Classification scheme (UNSPSC) [15].

Like the advertisement depends on the target of advertising, the content and format of a request depend on the system that is requested. It can be as simple as a key word search to Google and an email to a sales representative of a provider or as complex as a query to a virtual marketplace or a directory service. The request process can extend multiple phases, e.g., for step-wise refinement of search criteria and revelation of information.

The result of a search for service providers is a provider list. The provider list could be ordered, e.g., by the extent to which provider advertisements fulfill the search criteria.

Advertising and search functions of providers and customers may want to support a multitude of formats to be able to use multiple intermediaries and potential business partners. This requires not only to observe different syntaxes but also dealing with different ontologies.

The WSTK case: The information phase documents of the WSTK Utility Services solution were designed to be simple. The service description that is input to the offer creation process is the WSDL description of a service. Since the customer is not expected to use tools beyond a web browser, the advertisement consist of web page that displays the set of offers comprising particular web services. No formal representation of offers is foreseen.

1.3.2 Negotiation phase documents and contracts

The documents of the negotiation phase are offers and contracts. An offer is a binding proposal for a contract. Its content corresponds to the content of a contract. However, a part of its content can still be kept flexible, to be chosen, or filled in, by the other party within the limits specified. Also, offers usually have an expiration date. Acceptance of an offer, which may entail deciding on the options of the offer, establishes a contract. The acceptance notice is not shown in the figures of the previous section because it usually corresponds to the contract. Although, as mentioned in the introduction, the intent to enter into a contract can be expressed in many ways, e.g., verbally, it is common practice on many occasions to sign written contracts, which is easier to use in court in the case of dispute. Since electronic signatures are currently accepted in legal processes in many countries, e.g., in the United States of America and the members of the European Union, there is little obstacle for expressing offers, and thus contracts, in an electronic format. An interesting example of a system to exchange offers and sign contracts electronically is the Secure Contract Container (SeCo), which was developed in a project involving the Universities of St. Gallen and Zürich and the Zürich Chamber of Commerce [75, 138]. A similar approach was chosen by the COSMOS system [118].

Given the lack of formal requirements for the actual contract content and format, the content can contain the required information in a format suitable for those interpreting the contract. Since the contract is used to set up the fulfillment system, it must be understood by the deployment planning function and, possibly later, the part of the fulfillment system dealing with a dispute.

The content of the contract defines the rights and obligations of the contracting parties [69, 70]. Conceptually, on an abstract level, the contract comprises three types of information elements:

Description of the parties. This comprises all relevant properties of parties, e.g., name and address, but also technical properties such as interfaces, if applicable. This comprises primarily the parties signing the contract but can also extend to third parties that are just mentioned, e.g., a public directory service to be used.

Description of the rights and obligations. This is core of the contract. It describes which party must perform an action (deliver a parcel), achieve a particular state (average response time is less than 5 seconds), or allow another party to do something (use intellectual property, e.g., play a piece of music), which is a right of the benefiting party.

Definitions to establish a shared ontology. It is beneficial if all parties to the contract interpret the rights and obligations in the same way. This reduces dispute handling effort at fulfillment time. Specifying the rights and obligations unambiguously requires a common ontology between the contracting parties. In many cases, this common ontology cannot be assumed and thus has to be defined within the scope of the contract. In our application hosting example, the term average response time of a request over a network may be ambiguous. Is it the time that the service provider's application server needs to process the request? Is it measured from the customer's infrastructure point-of-view, including network delays? These issues must be clarified. The definitions section can comprise a large section of the contract.

If the deployment planning and deployment functions are fully performed by people, natural language is apparently the most convenient way to expressing the contact content. However, we also want to automate deployment planning and deployment to some extent. What are the options to formalise contact content?

The simplest approach to formalisation is to apply structural markup to a natural language document. One can sub-divide the contract into sections, clauses and so on. This markup can be enriched to carry some specific semantics in labels such as preamble and termination clause.

Name-value tuples are a simple and convenient way to express formal content. In the application hosting scenario, quality of service guarantees can be expressed as

```
average_response_time = 1.5
availability = 0.98
```

but also could carry more complex content such as

```
customer_address = "235 W 2nd Street, New York, NY 10025, USA"
```

as is potentially required in the logistics example. The contract-interpreting functions need to understand the semantics of the field names and be able to interpret the content. As such, the name-value tuple approach is an extension to the structural markup by detailed semantics of fine-grained fields, as opposed to rough structuring of content. Name-value tuples can be used for every aspect of a contract, party description, ontology, and obligations.

Beyond name-value tuples, contractual content can be defined using a more complex format or formal language. We can separate the issues of defining the obligations and defining the common ontology, the shared definitions of the parties. In the definition part of a contract, we have a wealth of formal languages to support the definition of those terms to be used in specification of the rights and obligations. A very general approach to defining terms are models and languages to describe ontologies, e.g., DAML and OIL [41], which are based on the Resource Description Framework [42] used by W3C to markup resources on the web semantically. Using these approaches, one can define classes, properties and sub-class and instance relationships. Beyond this general approach, we can use specialised description languages. For instance, to describe an interface of a web service, e.g., in the application hosting scenario, we can use WSDL [73] or CORBA IDL. For common process descriptions, the Business Process Execution Language for web Services (BPEL) can be used [44]. Early approaches based on Petri Nets to inter-organisational process descriptions were presented in [101] and [48]. Some formal agreement languages for particular domains provide a means to describe a contract ontology: the Web Services Agreement Level (WSLA) language contains a model and syntax to define how quality of service parameters should be measured or computed from low-level metrics [111]. The Open Digital Rights Language (ODRL) has a model to describe assets, e.g., a music file, to which rights expressions refer [84]. The CrossFlow contract language provides syntax to describe an outsourced business process and its transactional behaviour [93].

There are several models and formal languages for rights and obligations. Several general purpose models and languages of rights and obligations are based on Dynamic Deontic Logic [169]. In the Open Distributed Processing (ODP) environment, work from multiple groups [40] led to ODP Enterprise Language, standardised as ITU-T Recommendation X.911 [165]. Despite its name, X.911 defines a model of enterprise policies for a community that can be obligations, permissions, prohibitions, and authorisations. In [148], the authors proposed a syntax for X.911 . Obligations can also be expressed in some domain-specific or subject-specific agreement languages. This is particularly the case in the aforementioned ODRL, which provides the concept of right-to-an-asset, and in the CrossFlow contract language, which has rich means of expressing the rights of an outsourcing customer to intervene into a business process. WSLA also has a model and a language to define service level goals, which define the assertion of a performance level for a service, and action guarantees, which are promises to perform an action if a particular condition holds, e.g., to send a notification if a service level goal is violated.

Apparently, it is difficult to formalise the entire contract content. However, this is not necessary. There are always aspects of a contract that are to be interpreted and assessed by people. Therefore, in future, electronic contracts are likely to be documents containing both natural language parts and formalised elements on all levels of sophisticated formal expression. Likewise, it appears difficult to envision a single formal language that suits all formalisation needs. Coexisting and possibly interrelated special-purpose languages seems to be a good approach.

The WSTK case: In the WSTK case, offers and contracts are expressed in a mixed form. A part of an offer is written in English, but another may reside on a set of web pages. This comprises the description of the content of the services. Natural language is appropriate since it is not processed automatically. The rating model is offered as a pull-down menu, which results in a name-value pair. It is stored in the contracting service and later used for accounting. In addition, the quality of service specification is expressed in the formal, XML-based WSLA language because the WSLA Compliance Monitor is used to supervise the quality-of-service aspects of the contract.

The WSLA language is used to define the common ontology of the parties in terms of the metrics that are subject of the service level goals. It also provides a means to express service level goals, i.e., contractual guarantees. The WSLA language uses a constructive approach to define the parts of a contract. Resource metrics are described using measurement directives, which are supposed to be known and understood prior to the contracting process, e.g., access this counter of the application server. On the basis of resource metrics, composite metrics are defined by defining functions over resource metrics and other composite metrics. On this basis, metrics used in the service level goals can be defined, e.g., the average response time.

```
<wsla:Metric name="AverageResponseTimeMetric"
            type="float" unit="seconds">
    <wsla:Function xsi:type="wsla:Divide" resultType="float">
        <wsla:Operand>
            <wsla:Metric>SumResponseTime</wsla:Metric>
        </wsla:Operand>
        <wsla:Operand>
            <wsla:Metric>Transactions</wsla:Metric>
        </wsla:Operand>
    </wsla:Function>
</wsla:Metric>
```

Figure 1.6: Aggregation of metrics.

The WSLA snippet in Fig. 1.6 illustrates how to aggregate metrics. This example describes metric *AverageResponseTimeMetric*; it is computed by dividing the total amount of time spent on all operations, defined in *SumResponseTime*, by the number of invocations, defined in metric *Transactions*. Those metrics are defined similarly.

Based on the metrics of the definitions part, the service level goals can be defined as illustrated in Fig. 1.7. The guarantee corresponds to the mathematical formula ($TransactionRate < 25$) $\Rightarrow$ ($AverageResponseTime < 500$), valid in the year 2003. These statements can be processed automatically by the WSTK CM.

1.3.3 Setup phase documents

The contract implementation plan contains the following information: (a) Which components of the fulfillment system will be involved to either fulfill contractual obligations, to consume contractual rights, or to supervise the activities of the other contract party? (b) how to configure them? (c) how are elements of the contract mapped onto configuration parameters of the fulfillment system?

The contract implementation plan can be defined in many different ways, depending on the particular components involved and the implementation of the deployment function. If the fulfillment system is non-technical and the deployment function is performed by an employee, natural language seems to be the most convenient representation. Since we are interested in electronically-accessible services, we assume that a subset of the components of the fulfillment system is automated and thus can benefit from an automated deployment system, requiring a formal description of (a part of) the contract implementation plan. Currently, there are very few representations that were explicitly designed to contain the information of a contract implementation plan. An example is the internal enactment specification of the CrossFlow system, which describes the set of components to be instantiated and how to map contract elements into their configuration information [82, 110]. This language is not too complex because all components share a way to be instantiated and configured [109].

More generic approaches to describe how to set up or provision a system are scripts, workflow specifications, and policies. In scripts, configuration operations are defined as invocations of configuration programs. A workflow specification could contain a configuration activity for each component, which performs the individual configuration invocations within

```xml
<wsla:ServiceLevelGoal name="AverageResponseTime">
    <wsla:Obliged>Provider</wsla:Obliged>
    <wsla:Validity>
        <wsla:Start>2003-01-31T14:00:00.000-05:00</wsla:Start>
        <wsla:End>2003-12-31T14:00:00.000-05:00</wsla:End>
    </wsla:Validity>
    <wsla:Expression>
    <wsla:Implies>
        <wsla:Expression>
        <wsla:Predicate xsi:type="wsla:Less">
            <wsla:SLAParameter>
                TransactionRate
            </wsla:SLAParameter>
            <wsla:Value>25</wsla:Value>
        </wsla:Predicate>
        </wsla:Expression>
        <wsla:Expression>
        <wsla:Predicate xsi:type="wsla:Less">
            <wsla:SLAParameter>
                AverageResponseTime
            </wsla:SLAParameter>
            <wsla:Value>500</wsla:Value>
        </wsla:Predicate>
        </wsla:Expression>
    </wsla:Implies>
    </wsla:Expression>
    <wsla:EvaluationEvent>NewValue</wsla:EvaluationEvent>
</wsla:ServiceLevelGoal>
```

Figure 1.7: Definition of some service level goals.

this activity. Thus, workflows provide a higher level of abstraction. Policies describe behaviour, e.g., to prioritise network traffic. An information model for policies is defined in the IETF RFC 3060 [123]. In many cases, policies are put in a central repository where they can be retrieved by components behaving according to policies. As opposed to the script and workflow case where configuration information is pushed to components, components pull their configuration information in this case.

The specific configuration information is the aspect of the contract implementation plan that contains the information specifically needed for a component in a format that this component understands. If the contract implementation plan already contains the configuration information in a suitable format, the specific configuration information is just a part of the contract implementation plan. Otherwise, we need a translation step as part of the deployment function.

As mentioned above, the WSTK Utility Services solution is not meant to be very flexible and therefore the contract implementation plan is mostly hard-coded, with the exception of the WSLA part of the contract. Since it is directly interpretable by the WSLA Compliance Monitor, no further specific configuration information is needed. In different systems, other monitoring systems can be used, but would require the WSLA document to be translated into their formats.

1.4 Issues and Approaches to Automate the Contracting Function

In previous sections, we provide some insight into the contracting process and realise its complexity. As discussed in the introduction, speed and cost are important parameters of the process. Improving those parameters is the primary target of automating the contracting function. Other parameters, which are dealt with well in many manual contracting processes, are flexibility, i.e., the ability to deal with a wide spectrum of contracts, and the quality of decision-making and execution in each function. Improving cost and speed whilst maintaining flexibility and quality is not easy for several reasons:

Maybe surprisingly, an important issue in discussing the automation of contracting functions is the complexity of the fulfillment system. Sometimes, it is very difficult for service providers to understand what their fulfillment system is capable of doing. In our application service provider example, we can assume that the provider has several servers and networking components available to fulfill customer contracts. It is not trivial to decide how many servers of a particular type and which network bandwidth is needed to achieve a particular quality of service, for instance, sub-second response time up to 1000 invocations per minute. The performance of storage, network, memory, and CPU are interdependent. This is particularly true if customers bring their own application. This is of course a general problem, not only occurring when automating the advertising and negotiation function. However, a person can try to solve it using his or her skills.

In the introduction, we discussed that advertising or search, as well as negotiation functions, potentially interact with a large number of partners, intermediaries or potential business partners. People are usually good at dealing with a heterogeneity of interaction formats, in particular because they can establish common understanding (shared ontology) in the course of a conversation. This requires complex behaviours.

The most difficult issue of automating contracting functions is the inherent complexity of the decision-making. When advertising a service, people take many inputs, including cultural knowledge and understanding of market behaviour, to design advertisements and choose the right channels. While negotiating, people draw information from many sources and sometimes decide intuitively, which is difficult to formalise. However, there are also shortcomings in human ways of decision-making, in particular to process vast amounts of data. The discipline of decision support systems addresses this issue.

Considering the above issues, the approaches can consider to automate a subset of contracting functions include the following:

The first approach is to keep people assigned to functions involving decision-making and focus on improving interaction between functions and between organisations. To connect people executing contracting functions within an organisation by integrating them into a business process and letting them share information is low-hanging fruit and can be done in a standard business process re-engineering and automation project. For the above-mentioned reasons of establishing common ontology and using a common format, automating inter-organisational interaction is more difficult. However, interaction for which a common ontology exists and all parties share the same format can be automated. To advertise and search for services, organisations can use the format UDDI provides [125] and use, e.g., the standard UNSPSC to categorise their service. In the negotiation phase, parties can use the aforementioned SeCo or COSMOS systems. They only rely on very few, domain-independent concepts such as offer, accept, signature and thus do not pose an ontology problem. In [153], the author goes beyond this static, simple semantics and proposes a new negotiation protocol in the context of the SilkRoad project; it first phase is the design of negotiation media or offers, assuming a name-value tuple level of formalisation of the negotiated parts of the offer. This includes the clarification of the semantics of the fields to be negotiated. Subsequently, the actual negotiation starts. This protocol is facilitated by a negotiation intermediary.

The second approach aims at improving people's decisions-making quality. As we mentioned above, people have problems making goal decision in a complex product space in which each product has many interrelated attributes. Besides general decision-support systems, there have been several approaches to support buyers of services to evaluate and compare multiple offers. In [151], for instance, the author proposes a system that enables soft navigation in product catalogs by assigning scores to the relevance of attributes. Another approach facilitates an interviewing process that aims at helping a customer clarify his or her preferences and reach a decision [152].

The third approach is based on early decision-making and later execution based on templates. In some scenarios, decisions can be stored in templates that can be used later by simpler, automated functions. Such scenarios include those in which either a mass market demands relatively homogeneous services or a fulfillment system can only create a limited number of different services. To store decisions, advertisements are associated to a contract template. The contract template of a service provider contains several open fields to be negotiated, e.g., using the above-mentioned SilkRoad system, or simply to be filled in on a web site. These contract templates can be associated with constraints that limit the contracts that customers can create. For these contract templates, providers also define a contract implementation plan template (CIPT) that lists components of fulfillment systems to be instantiated. In addition, the CIPT describes how to map elements of a contract to configuration parameters of the components involved. This can include both negotiated and pre-set parts of the contract. If the contract implementation plan created from the CIPT already corresponds to the specific configuration formats and no manual translation is required, the deployment function can also be fully automated. Therefore, the whole contracting function for a particular contract instance can be automated by working hard on template design. However, this comes at the price of reduced flexibility. This approach has been implemented in the CrossFlow project in the context of business process outsourcing [82]. Templates can be used by both service providers and service customers if they procure similar services very often.

Regarding the issues raised above, the WSTK Utility Services solution is not much concerned with heterogeneity because it does not exchange formal interaction with other systems, which limits its applicability to scenarios in which customers have their own implementation of contracting functionality. However, the issues of complexity of the behaviour of the underlying fulfillment system and the corresponding decision-making by the service provider do apply to this case. It is primarily addressed by the approach of early decision-making. The primary concern of the solution is the automation of subscription and setup, traded off against limited flexibility of negotiating specific contracts with customers. For this reason response time-throughput pairs are fixed at system setup and offers little choices for a subscribing customers. The advantage is that it is know that only viable configuration are sold and the quality of service guarantees can always be monitored by the WSLA Compliance Monitor.

1.5 Conclusions

In this chapter, we introduced a conceptual model of the contracting process to facilitate the discussion of automating some parts. The discussion is motivated by the demand of businesses to buy and sell services through a network fast and at low cost, thus requiring a (partially) automated contracting process. Since many legislations do not require a specific form or format for contracts in many areas, we can include formal specifications in a contract. The formal elements can comprise known specification languages such as WSDL or specifically made languages such as ODRL and the WSLA language, as illustrated in the case study. The conceptual model decomposes the contracting function in sub-functions and interaction between them. Beyond advertisement, search, offer and contract, the contract implementation plan is an information item in the contracting process that is very important for the automation of the setup phase of the life-cycle.

We have identified the complexity of the fulfillment system, heterogeneity of interaction formats, and the complexity of decision-making functions as major issues that must be addressed when automating parts of the contracting function. This requires the designer of a contracting process to trade off flexibility of contracts that can be created and automation. Three approaches that help automating the contracting process were proposed: process automation, improved decision-making, and the use of templates, which capture decisions so that they can be reused. Based on the conceptual model and the proposed approaches, contracting processes for specific scenarios can be designed, as shown in the case study of this chapter, the WSTK Utility Services solution.

We can already find partial or domain-specific solutions for many issues that are addressed; they usually rely on formal contract content and support functions such as advertising, search, and negotiation. However, other issues are not yet addressed sufficiently, in particular the representation of contracts across specific domains, representation and processing of contract implementation plans, and the interoperability of different automated functions in the contracting process.

About the author

Heiko Ludwig

Heiko Ludwig studied Computer Science and Business Administration (Information Systems/Wirtschaftsinformatik) at the Otto-Friedrich University in Bamberg, Germany. He holds a Master degree (Diplom) and a Ph.D. (Dr.rer.pol.) in Computer Science and Business Administration. He joined IBM's Zurich Research Laboratory in September 1996, and mostly worked on cross-organisational process management, mainly in the context of the Virtual Enterprise Coordinator and the CrossFlow projects. In June 2001, he crossed the Atlantic to visit IBM's T.J. Watson Research Center. Currently, he is a member of the Distributed Systems and Services Department, and he is working on electronic contracts, in particular SLAs for electronic services. He is interested in both languages and the related deployment and enactment infrastructure.

Chapter 2

Web Services Technologies for Outsourcing

Liang-Jie Zhang, Qun Zhou, Hung-Yang Chang, and Jen-Yao Chung

2.1 Introduction

One of the fastest growing industries in the United States of America is the outsourcing of information systems, with large and small companies employing contractors to manage information networks [137]. Outsourcing is a direct, effective way so that an organisation can keep costs under control, improve profits, and enhance the overall responsiveness to changing market conditions.

However, today's traditional software-based outsourcing solutions need to be installed at the edge and behind the firewall. Not only are they expensive and use incompatible communication protocols, which are inhibitors to interoperability, but also offer little control and security. Proprietary interfaces and lack of standards prevent the integration of different solutions from vendors, so partners must maintain multiple software packages. Therefore, it is expensive to add new and maintain existing partners, which restricts business expansion and increases operating costs. Every partner must be individually connected to every system, incurring high costs for each. Subsequently, it is hard to manage and deliver messages across multiple business processes reliably. Furthermore, when an Internet transaction across multiple applications is needed, its delivery is not guaranteed or traceable, and, usually, the security mechanism is not consistent across the applications. Thus, the challenges are to find a way to quickly and easily integrate systems with external business processes or services provided by partners using a secure, low-cost, manageable solution.

Web services are the next step in e-business capabilities; they enable a dynamic e-business model, fosters collaboration with layered services, and opens the doors to new business opportunities [115]. Web services [142] are supported by new technologies such as the Simple Object Access Protocol (SOAP), the Web Services Definition Language (WSDL), the Web Services Flow Language (WSFL), the Web Services Inspection Language (WSIL), and the Universal Description, Discovery, and Integration engine (UDDI) [43]. These technologies consist of a model for exchanging XML information, a language for describing services, a language for describing workflow between business partners, and a directory for finding new business partners, respectively. Together, they enable web services and turn them into a powerful, new paradigm for creating e-business applications by integrating reusable software modules available through the web.

However, several problems and issues arise when using web services for outsourcing and enterprise integration, namely:

P1 Limited or no control over other enterprise business logic;

P2 No service provisioning and subscription capability;

P3 Inefficient UDDI search for e-business integration;

P4 Insecure message delivery;

P5 No dynamic web services invocation mechanism;

P6 Limited or no support for B2B integration;

P7 No tracking of messages.

In this chapter, a web services hub framework for outsourcing is proposed. It provides a wide range of services to address the above-mentioned problems. The framework is an integrated environment, which provides buyers, suppliers, service providers and trading partners with the following capabilities: (a) Register businesses, users and services; (b) provision services and subscribe to services; (c) perform advanced UDDI searches to discover web services at run time; (d) configure service providers' business processes to be easily integrated with other partners based on service requirements; (e) a multi-level security mechanism that ensures that communications are secure; and (f) monitor and control the business processes that are composed using this proposal.

The rest of the chapter is organised as follows: Section 2.2 describes the web services Hub framework for outsourcing; Section 2.3 introduces the Managed e-Hub, which is the major component of a working system based on this framework because it provides the infrastructure necessary to enable the next generation e-utilities in a secure, controlled environment; Section 2.4 presents a working B2B based e-services delivery solution called the KEPEX Trading Network that shows the following elements at work: rapid on-boarding of businesses, users, and services, purchase order management process, dynamic business process composition, service access control, and mechanisms for advanced search, discovery, and invocation of web services published in UDDI via an intelligent shipping agent that connects to a live UPS server to obtain shipping quotes; related work is discussed in Section 2.5; finally, some conclusions and future research directions are presented in Section 2.6.

2.2 Web Services Hub Framework

Fig. 2.1 shows an interacted hub framework, which comprises multiple connected hubs for outsourcing. Each hub may have buyers, suppliers, service providers, and trading partners, and may be viewed as a multi-level model consisting of core infrastructure services, system management services, horizontal business services, vertical industry applications, a service outsourcing manager, and value-added services. The outsourcing framework can have multiple virtual hubs, which share the same information infrastructure and interact with each other.

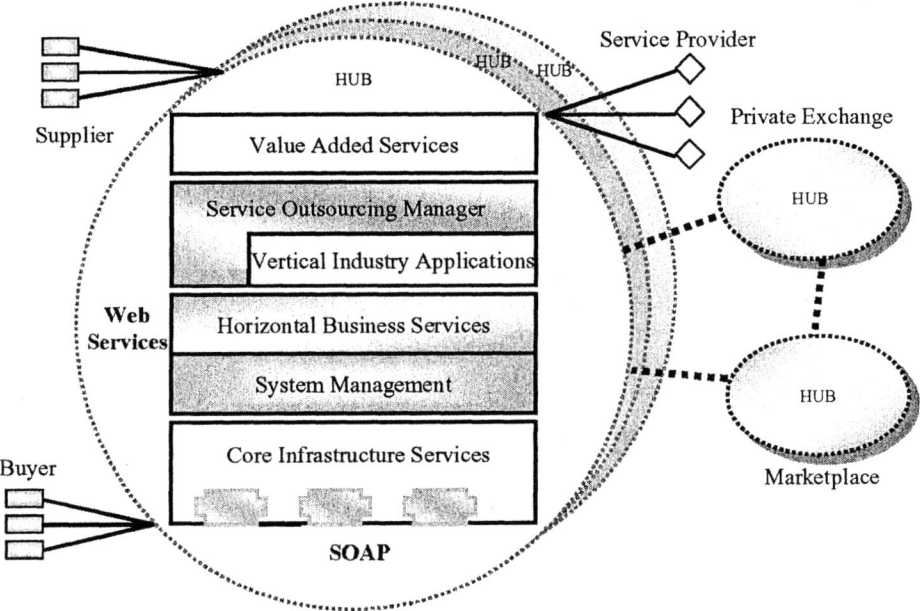

Figure 2.1: The web services hub framework.

Our framework is an enhanced version of a basic outsourcing model [112] that consists of four layers: core infrastructure services, system management services, horizontal business services and industry application services. The additional layers introduced by our framework on top of the basic model are the following: the service outsourcing manager, which enables the dynamic configuration of new business processes, as well as the value-added services. The business processes we can configure may include many related services hosted by the framework or by registered service providers.

As for the core infrastructure services, a membership portal is provided to rapidly onboard business entities and users, as well as to provision services and subscribe services. In order to monitor the transaction and trace communications across web services hubs, a business process level solution manager, which we describe later, is required.

Business process on demand can help you acquire e-business applications (even entire business processes) over the network as a service [112]. With business process on demand, your organisation does not waste time or money on unproven services or personnel. Horizontal business services or vertical industry applications may belong to business process on demand.

The horizontal business services refer to services that can be used by many other vertical industry applications or hub applications. These services are required by businesses from all sorts of industries: human resources applications, e-commerce, or e-procurement, for instance. Vertical industry applications refer to applications that can be used to implement a specific business process or solution for a specific industry. Some sample vertical services may be web services for the transportation industry and another for the insurance industry.

The service outsourcing manager is a featured module within a hub. It enables a customer to configure a business process dynamically, based on incoming requirements and precious solution expertise. Furthermore, it can be used by the internal applications to build a new value-added service using the existing services hosted by a hub or other community hubs. In fact, our framework is a typical hub-style grid computing system. That is, every service can be deployed as a web service so that it can be used and accessed by other applications using standard communication protocols such as SOAP.

2.3 A Working Prototype

A working system based on this framework provides a business process outsourcing infrastructure, which consists of a central membership portal, a service outsourcing manager, a connection and control centre to control the access to services, and a web services enabling and management suite. The membership portal allows trading partners to register and remove business entities, users and services with the e-Hub. In addition, the e-Hub enables trading partners and their users to subscribe and unsubscribe to the services provisioned by service providers.

The goal of the managed e-Hub is to provide an infrastructure for enabling next generation e-utilities in a secure, controlled environment. We propose the following enabling technologies or solutions to address the problems mentioned in Section 2.1:

A service outsourcing manager to solve problem P1;

A membership portal to address problem P2;

An advanced web services discovery engine to solve problem P3;

A multi-level security mechanism to solve problem P4;

A generic web service invoker to solve problem P5;

A web services relationships language to address problem P6;

A solution manager for monitoring and controlling business processes so that we can solve problem P7.

As shown in Fig. 2.2, the e-Hub cloud connects the services hosted by the e-Hub itself or registered service providers. Application clients can use the protocol of their choice, e.g., XML, SOAP over HTTP, SMTP, FTP or MQ, to connect to it. The e-Hub communicates with external legacy applications, web services providers, customer's supply chain management systems (SCM), supplier's enterprise resource planning systems (ERP) or partner's customer relationship management system (CRM). The e-Hub cares of interoperability concerns when connecting to multiple parties using different transport protocols, data formats and business protocols; it offers a membership management service, a data format translation service, a business protocol translation service, a advanced discovery service, and a business flow management service.

Therefore, the only software a user needs to use the services provided by the managed e-Hub is a web browser or a lightweight connection adaptor to handle SOAP communication. For instance, the customer can use a web browser to register itself and its users on the e-Hub. The roles a user can play are the following: regular user, business administrator, service provisioning manager, and service subscription manager.

Fig. 2.3 illustrates a concrete integration architecture. There are a few major users and components, namely:

Enterprise application: KEPEX;

Businesses and users within businesses;

Web Services Technologies for Outsourcing

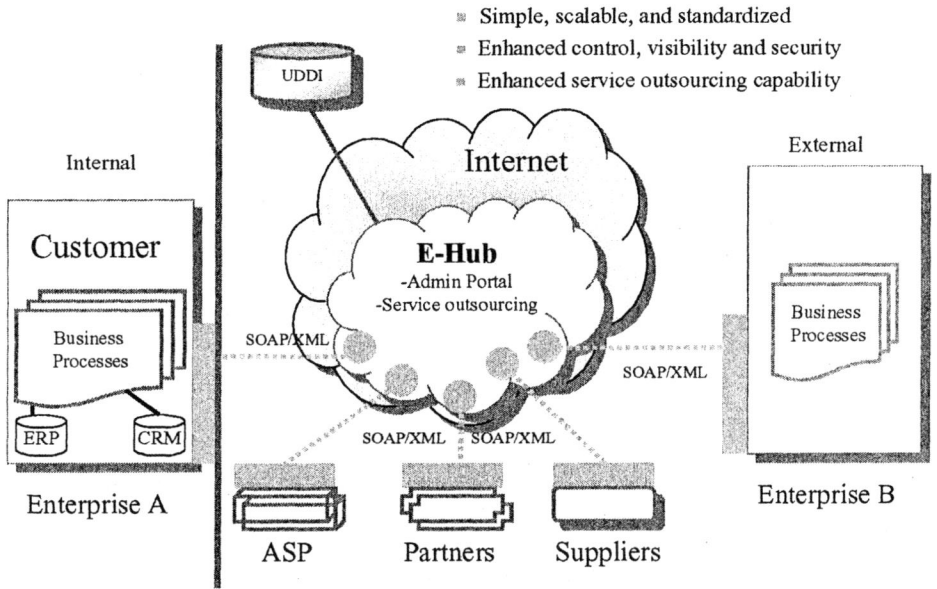

Figure 2.2: Managed e-Hub solution diagram.

Service providers: USearch, UPS, KEP, and so on.

Not only provides the e-Hub an administration/membership portal to manage the profile of businesses and users, but also supports a variety of core services for registered businesses and users. The service outsourcing manager is able to construct a customised business process automatically, according to a customer's requirements that may include preferences, flow rules and some additional constraints.

In Fig. 2.3, we present a centralised web services invoker; it can be used to construct SOAP calls using the Remote Procedure Call protocol (RPC) and the Web Services Invocation Framework (WSIF) [142]. Any application can use this generic web services invocation broker to invoke any web service in a simple way. The only input parameters are the location of the WSDL specification that describes the web service under consideration, the method name, and the input parameters to this method.

The e-Hub hosts several horizontal business services, namely:

E-Procurement services or purchase order (PO) web services: they are used to create purchase orders, update them, and get their details;

Advanced web services discovery: it enables e-Hub applications to look up one or more UDDI registries efficiently by constructing an XML script;

Web service invoker/syndicator: it enables e-Hub applications to easily invoke web services as well as to syndicate or enable an enterprise business process as a web service.

In addition, there is a value-added service that illustrates the collaboration and knowledge sharing capability of our proposal. We refer to it as the Intelligent shipping agent. It looks up the e-Hub UDDI registry and constructs dynamically an appropriate shipping service provider list based on the information of the selected purchase order, e.g., dispatch country, shipping address, price, and so on.

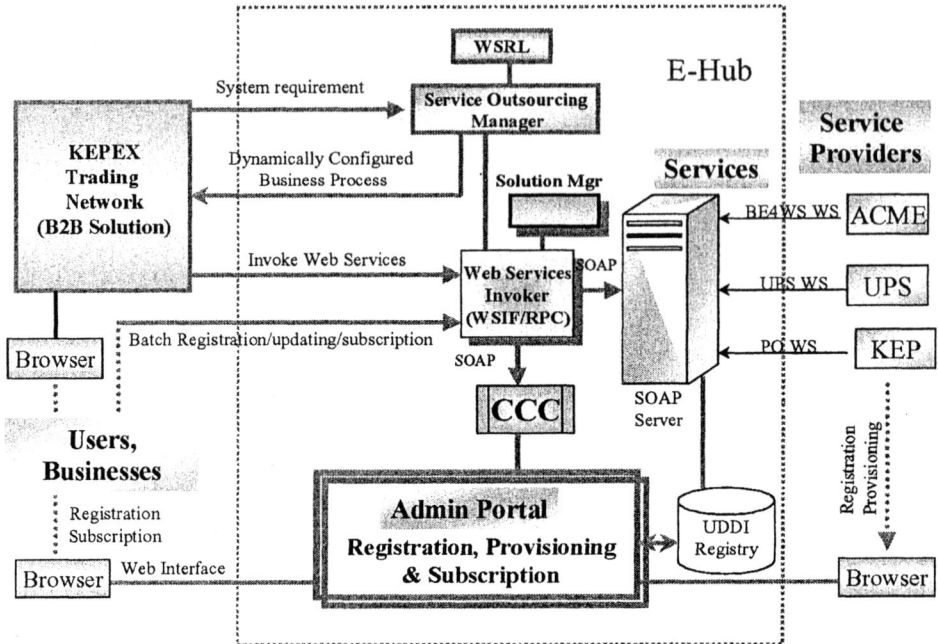

Figure 2.3: Managed e-Hub integration architecture.

To monitor the transaction and trace communications across the e-Hub, a business process level solution manager is needed because any interaction amongst business entities, users, and services should be traceable. In addition, the behaviours of the running business processes need to be monitored and controlled based on the service level agreements (SLA) [21, 111] or other performance indicators. The controlled actions could be either stopping a business process that is running, starting a new business process, or changing a property file to dynamically affect the execution flow. The SLA can be created to monitor the interaction between a business entity (buyer, supplier, or other trading partner) and the e-Hub. It can also be created to monitor the interaction between a business and a service as well as the interaction between two services.

Other major components of e-Hub are the following:

The services outsourcing manager;

The membership portal for service provisioning;

The advanced web services discovery engine;

The multi-level security model.

2.3.1 The service outsourcing manager

The service outsourcing manager enables customers to configure a new business process dynamically, based on incoming requirements. It can also be used to build new value-added services using the existing services hosted by the hub, such as the purchase order management business process described in Fig. 2.6.

However, composing individual web services into a business process is not a trivial task, and the current technology does not support many important aspects. Therefore, it requires many manual steps, which is complex and time-consuming. Typical tasks include: (a) Gather requirements, which are subjective; (b) translate the requirements into UDDI search criteria; (c) perform the search to obtain a list of web services that meet the criteria; (d) filter and select the one that best fits customer preferences; (e) compose the end-to-end process by repeating steps (c) and (d) to collect a set of web services that can perform the functions required in the business process; (e) select the optimal combination of web services in the end-to-end process; (f) monitor and tune the service composition at run time.

Currently, web services and UDDI specifications lack the definitions and descriptions of the generic relationships amongst business entities, business services and operations. Although the binding template in a UDDI registry provides the mapping between business services and service types, there is no information on the relationships amongst services, service types and business entities. Those kinds of relationships binding information are very important for the next level of integration. For instance, two business entities or service providers may have a partnership programme so that the prices are discounted if both services are selected. Therefore, it is essential to take the relationship into consideration when selecting services to compose a business process so as to yield the optimal result. Therefore, relationships are keys to composing and executing dynamic business processes integration, which implies that the business-level relationships supported by UDDI v2 [125] may not be enough. In [178], multi-level web services relationships are described between businesses, services, business-operations, service-operations, and so on. They are captured in an XML-based language called Web Services Relationships Language (WSRL) to facilitate the composition of business processes.

Next, we use a concrete example to illustrate how the service outsourcing manager can compose a business process using existing web services, thus automating the set of manual steps described previously. In this example, we compose a business process whose goal is to produce moving plans for a customer who wants to move from San Francisco to New York. The customer specifies certain tasks and requirements that need to be carried out in a given order, namely:

Open a checking account in New York City;

Select a moving company to move within a month for less than $2000;

Select a local phone company in New York with a monthly fee less than $25;

Preferred bank location is in Midtown.

The customer first enters these requirements on price, time frame, type of services needed, and the sequence of tasks to be performed by means of a menu-driven graphical user interface; the requirements are captured as XML-based specifications. In addition, preferences, process flow rules, constraints, and business logic can also be captured.

Based on those specifications, the service outsourcing manager creates automatically search scripts to look up the private UDDI registry for the available web services required, i.e., bank services, moving companies, and phone services. The discovery of such web services is performed by the advanced web services discovery engine (cf. Section 2.3.3). Next, based on the customer preferences as well as the relationships between service providers, the outsourcing manager selects the best services that meet the combined requirements for a composed business process; it also generates the process specification according to the sequence of tasks to be performed.

Another example is the purchase order management process shown in Fig. 2.6; it is based on requirements for transportation planning for a selected purchase order. This composed business process comprises three web services for managing purchase orders: PO Creation, PO Details and PO Listing as well as a value-added service to which we refer to as the intelligent shipping agent (cf. Section 2.3.5).

2.3.2 The central membership portal

At the core infrastructure services layer, we introduce a membership portal to manage business entities and users as well as to provision and subscribe to services. The central membership portal offers two major functions, namely: membership management and rapid on-boarding.

Membership management provides functions to register several types of membership information. For each business entity, it captures the information about the business, the users of the business, a business administrator, a provision manager if provisioning services are needed, and a subscription manager if subscription to services is needed.

A business entity that provides services needs to register or provision its services with the e-Hub. A business entity that consumes services, however, needs to register a subscription manager to subscribe to services.

In Fig. 2.4, we present some details about the registration process, provisioning and subscription flows. The left hand side of the diagram illustrates the provisioning process to register a business, and how to provision one of its services. Once the provision manager registers a service, the e-Hub administrator has to approve it. The provision manager can then enable this service. On the right, we illustrate the subscription process to register a business and then subscribe to the service that has been previously provisioned and enabled. Notice that a service can be provisioned but not enabled. However, a service needs to be enabled so that others can subscribe to it. Furthermore, subscription to services can be necessary at both the business entity level and the user level, or only at one level. However, in order for a user to subscribe to a service, the business entity must have already subscribed to the same service. A user subscription request must be approved by the subscription manager.

The rapid on-boarding suite is a set of web services to register and update membership information, thus enabling rapid on-boarding of business entities and users, as well as provisioning and subscription to services. An XML configuration file is used to update business registry information incrementally, and it can be customised for individual business entities.

Furthermore, e-Hub allows to synchronise the information in its business registries with UDDI registries for the corresponding businesses and services information. That is, after a business entity has registered with the e-Hub, the information can be published automatically to the UDDI registry by the e-Hub. On the other hand, e-Hub can also fetch the information about this business entity if it already existed in the UDDI registry and store it in a local business registry.

2.3.3 The advanced web services discovery engine

Exploring an appropriate business application that is published as a web service in the UDDI registry is a critical issue. The search for such an application should be effective in terms of time and uniform in terms of interfaces. The UDDI project is a cross-industry initiative that aims at creating a platform-independent, open framework for describing services, discovering

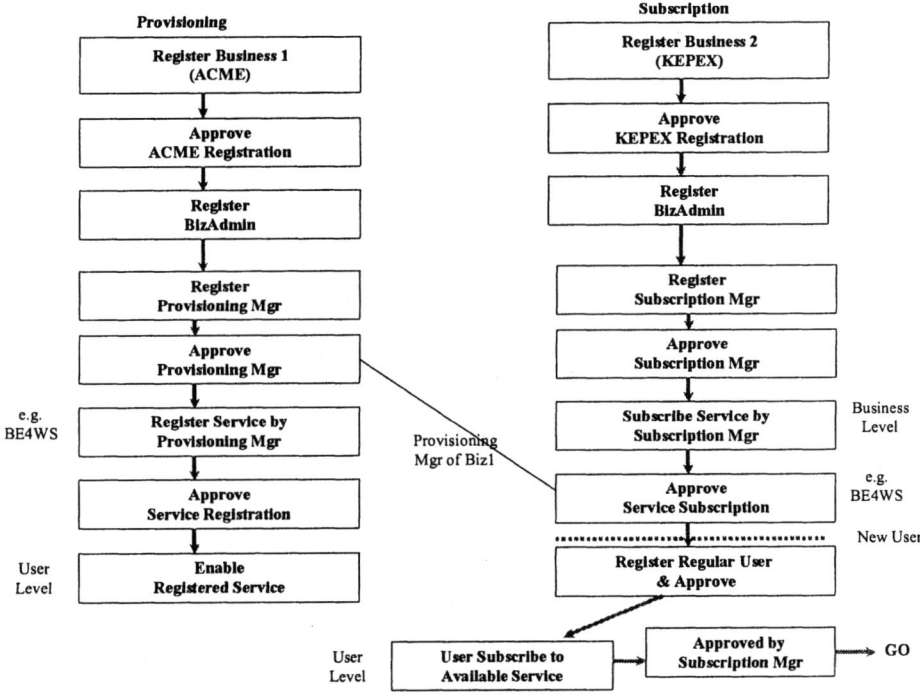

Figure 2.4: Registration/provisioning/subscription flow.

businesses, integrating business services using the Internet, and sharing information with operational registries [142]. However, current search technologies have several limitations.

In general, current search technologies provide two ways to search UDDI registries: *ad hoc* programme clients or browser-based search tools such as the one provided by UDDI registry operators or web sites such as soapclient.com. Searching using programme clients requires the developer to write a piece of code to obtain information by means of APIs such as UDDI for Java (UDDI4J). Searching with browser-based tools may be difficult if there are too many or no results, which is likely to happen unless one has some information about the businesses or services, e.g., partial business names, service types, categories in which data are registered, and so on.

In either case, both types of search technologies are limited because only one registry can be specified per request, i.e., multiple sequential searches must be performed if multiple registries are involved, and no advanced search capabilities to perform result aggregation exists, i.e., to union or intersect multiple search results returned by several UDDI registries. However, it cannot be accomplished by using a browser-based search tool. Thus, there is a need for advanced search capabilities, such as those provided by the advanced web services discovery engine called Business Explorer for Web Services [179]. This explorer provides an XML-based UDDI "exploring engine" that provides developers with a standard set of interfaces to perform complex searches in multiple UDDI directories with a single request. It gathers results from several UDDI queries and then processes the resulting intersecting information. The benefits are the following:

```xml
<?xml version="1.0"?>
<Search>
  <Query>
    <Source>Private UDDI Registry 1</Source>
    <SourceURL>http://USearch.com/services/uddi/inquiryAPI</SourceURL>
    <BusinessName>Video</BusinessName>
    <FindBy>Business</FindBy>
  </Query>
  <Query>
    <Source>Private UDDI Registry 2</Source>
    <SourceURL>http://TSearch.com/services/uddi/servlet/uddi</SourceURL>
    <BusinessName>%Processing</BusinessName>
    <FindBy>Business</FindBy>
  </Query>
  <AggOperator>OR</AggOperator>
</Search>
```

Figure 2.5: XML-based UDDI search script.

Script-based search simplifies developer's work because it does not rely on complex Java programming skills using UDDI4J;

Support all search criteria specified by the UDDI v2 specifications;

Multiple search requests can be specified in one script, so that all the results can be returned at the same time;

Complex searches involving searching business, services, and service types can be performed via script-based searches. Aggregating the results is done by the Business Explorer for Web Services instead of the requesters individually, which saves programming efforts. If we take into account how often these complex searches are necessary, the saving can be considerable.

In Fig. 2.5, a sample XML-based search script with two search queries is shown. Each query is specified between the tags `<Query>` and `</Query>`. The first query is for searching Private UDDI Registry #1 with the URL value specified between tags `<SourceURL>` and `</SourceURL>`. The value between tags `<BusinessName>` and `</BusinessName>` specifies the search criteria of business names, i.e., starting with "Video". The value we write between tags `<FindBy>` and `</FindBy>` specifies a data type, which is for business entity. There are similar construct for the second query, which searches a different UDDI for business names including the word "Processing".

2.3.4 The multi-level security model

A multi-level security mechanism is used to ensure that communications are secure. It consists of the following levels:

Level 1 Secured Infrastructure (HTTPS, SSL);

Level 2 Authentication and authorisation checks by means of directory services. Web services based access is processed by the connection and control centre, whereas web browser based access is processed in the membership portal.

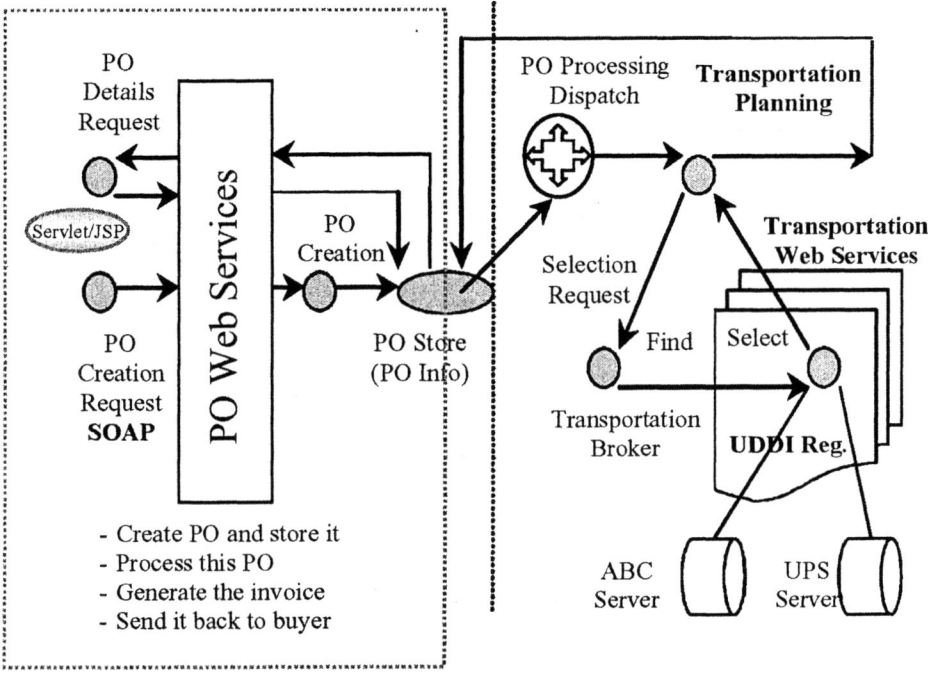

Figure 2.6: Purchase order management.

The connection and control centre (CCC) shown in Fig. 2.3 provides the foundations for the web services access layer of e-Hub's multi-level security model. It is the central access point for the web services based authentication and authorisation methods. In addition, the connection and control centre also handles requests such as obtaining quotes on available services and generates responses.

The multi-level security mechanism addresses the security issues related to a virtual private e-Hub where the hub supports virtual communities of businesses that share private collaborative business processes via the hub. The connection and control centre of e-Hub is the centre where business applications that are willing to perform business transactions get authenticated and authorised.

2.3.5 The purchase order management business process and the intelligent shipping agent

This section provides a discussion on the purchase order management business process composed by the service outsourcing manager. The composed process also includes the intelligent shipping agent, a value-added service that provides intelligent selection of transportation providers.

Fig. 2.6 illustrates the details of the purchase order management business process, which consists of several tasks: (a) Create a purchase order; (b) look up details of a purchase order; (c) plan for purchase order shipping; (d) search for qualified transportation providers. The left side of this figure illustrates how to create and look up details of a purchase order. Once a purchase order is created, it shall be processed further by downstream components. The right side presents the processing regarding transportation planning, which is important and involves factors such as lowest shipping cost, provider's location and availability, and so on. The intelligent shipping agent can filter the available transportation services obtained by searching the UDDI registry dynamically, and it can produce a narrowed list of service providers that best meets the criteria on cost or location, for instance. Notice that the transportation services providers that participate in the e-Hub would already have their web services published in the UDDI registry so that they can be discovered dynamically.

UPS web services, ABC web services and other warehouse management services are good examples of transportation web services. The detailed integration architecture of UPS web services shown in Fig. 2.6 was presented in [14]. It interacts with the UPS XML on-line tools. When a web service is invoked by a SOAP call, it binds data such as country of dispatch, source, and weight to the XML request template. It is then sent to the Adaptation Layer, which works both as a service dispatching broker and a service aggregation broker. Once it receives an XML request, which might be the aggregation of multiple requests, it sends them to the UPS Server. The responses received shall be aggregated by an adaptation layer. After mapping the live data received to the response XML template, the adaptation layer shall send the aggregated result back to the requester. Several sample screens that show further details are provided in Section 2.4.

From the above description, we can see that the managed e-Hub is a new paradigm for information technology: e-business on demand. It has flexible usage and flexible pricing features, i.e., what you need, when you need it. This instant access capability provides a way so that a company can connect and take advantage of outsourced applications when they need them. Companies themselves do not have to install and set up the application; they pay for what they use. This is the pay-as-you-go pricing model. Furthermore, our managed e-Hub is a shared, standardised, scalable infrastructure so that a virtual or private e-Hub can be built based on the managed e-Hub infrastructure foundation. These virtual hubs can share the horizontal services and vertical industry application, and even value-added services hosted by the e-Hub.

2.4 An E-services Delivery Solution

In this section, we present a working B2B-based e-services delivery solution to which we refer to as the KEPEX Trading Network. It allows us to show the following elements at work:

Rapid on-boarding of businesses, users and services;

Purchase order management;

Dynamic business process composition;

Advanced search, discovery and invocation of web services published in UDDI;

Service access control;

Intelligent shipping agent connecting to a live UPS server to obtain shipping quotes.

The KEPEX Trading Network acts as a trading exchange. A buyer can log in to the exchange to create purchase orders and track their status. Similarly, a supplier can log in to check the purchase order details that he or she owns, as well as to manage the transportation planning for the orders, as described in Section 2.3.5.

In this prototype system, the following core web services are used by the e-Hub:

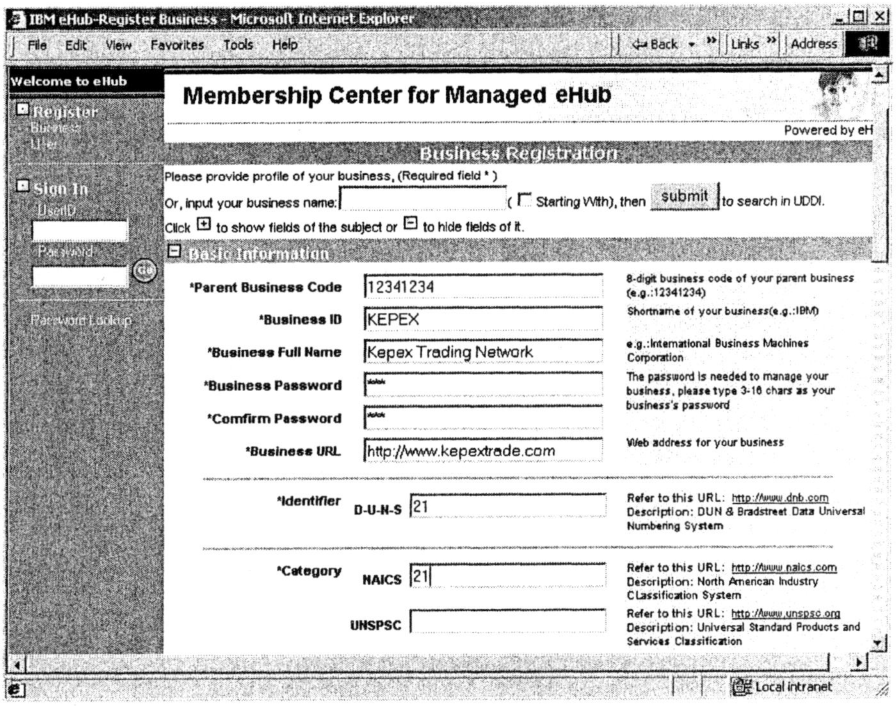

Figure 2.7: Business registration.

Purchase order web services;

Advanced search, discovery and invocation services;

Authentication and authorisation services;

Shipping web services.

2.4.1 Registration and provision

In this section, a web-based membership portal for a working e-service delivery solution hosted by the e-Hub is shown. Using the business registration function shown in Fig. 2.7 and the user register function shown in Fig. 2.8, business entities and their users can register with e-Hub.

For the sake of simplicity, several business entities and their corresponding users are assumed to have registered previously, namely:

Service providers (a business administrator and a provisioning manager for each): USearch Corporation, KEP, UPS;

Service subscribers (a business administrator and a subscription manager): KEPEX.

Using the service provisioning function shown in Fig. 2.9, USearch Corporation registered an advanced search service called BE4WS; UPS registered the UPS RFQ web service; KEP registered the PO web services. Next, KEPEX uses the service subscription function shown in Fig. 2.10 to subscribe to several services.

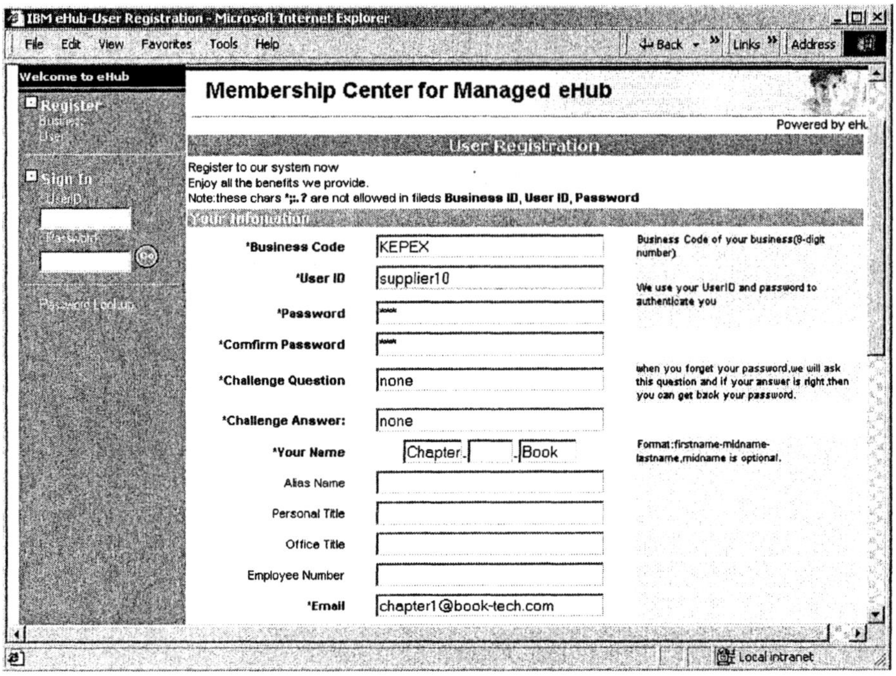

Figure 2.8: User registration.

2.4.2 Single sign-on

Fig. 2.11 illustrates the single sign-on interface. After a user has entered his identifier and password and gets authenticated, the user credential information shall be passed on to the subsequent processes.

2.4.3 Purchase order creation

In the managed e-Hub system, service provider KEP has provisioned its PO web service. Since the KEPEX Trading Network application has also been registered with the e-Hub and subscribed to the PO web services, KEPEX can use this outsourced service to create a purchase order, view the details and perform transportation planning by using another outsourced valued-added service, the intelligent shipping agent.

A sample web-based purchase order tool provided is shown in Fig. 2.13, and the confirmation number it returns is shown in Fig. 2.14.

2.4.4 Purchase order details

As shown in Fig. 2.14, the details of a purchase order are displayed. Notice that field *Dispatch Country* is "USA", which shall be used by the shipping agent to locate shipping service providers to be further explained in the following sections.

After a buyer creates a PO, it is stored in the database and processed later. Transportation planning is a typical purchase order processing procedure. It entails several flow

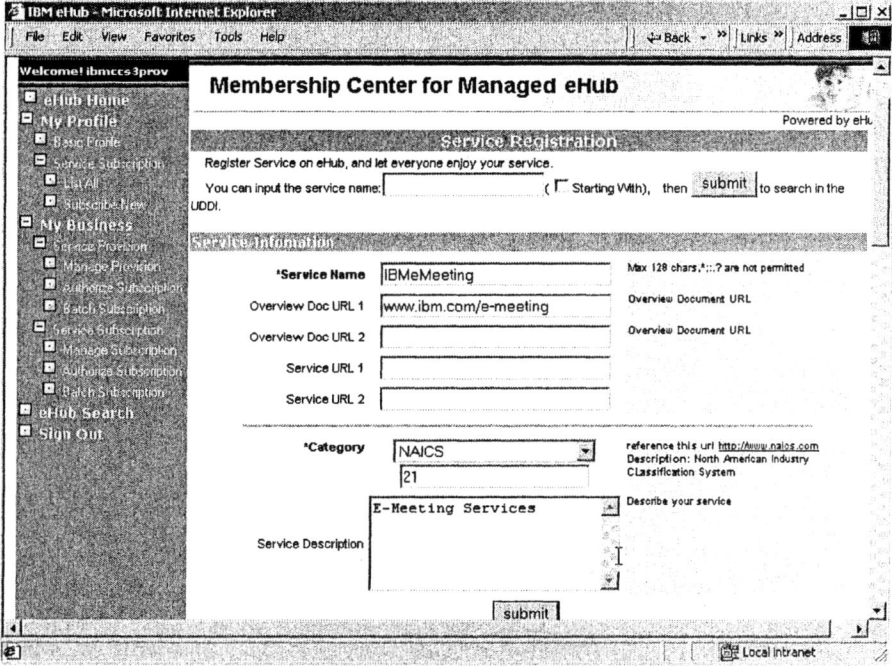

Figure 2.9: Service provisioning.

definitions, control flows and data flows, and the business rules that orchestrate the process. The supplier selects a shipping service provider for this specific PO using a shipping agent, which is designed to search the UDDI registry using the advanced web services discovery engine and filter the results using the country of dispatch.

The subsequent web pages attach automatically the user's credential information, which serves to authenticate the user to the transportation planning process. This, in turn, invokes a command to search an UDDI server using the discovery engine; however, it can also invoke a web service based on the business context.

2.4.5 Shipping service providers

The intelligent shipping agent uses the advanced web services discovery engine to look up a private UDDI registry and construct a list of transporters from the *Dispatch Country* field in a PO. In the example in Fig. 2.16, for instance, only transporters from the United States of America are returned.

2.4.6 Results of invoking the transportation web service

A supplier can select one or more service providers from the list in Fig. 2.15 by checking the boxes in column "Select". Later, he or she can hit button "Get Transporter Quotes" to invoke the service(s) to get quotes. In the example in Fig. 2.15, the three transportation providers are selected to obtain quotes. In Fig. 2.16, there are quotes returned by

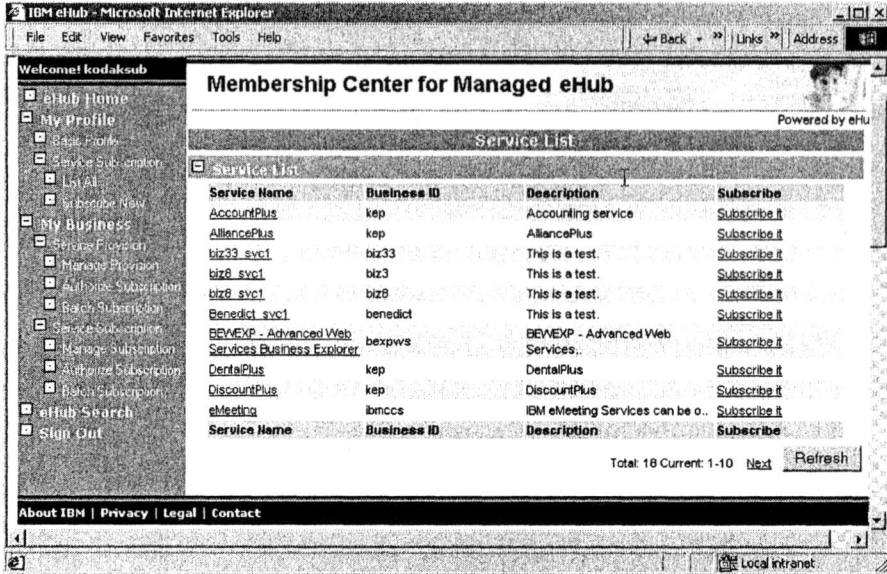

Figure 2.10: Service subscription.

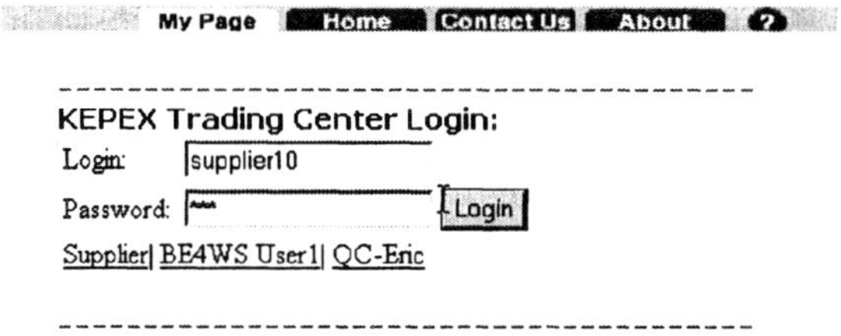

Figure 2.11: Single sign-on interface.

seven services provided by UPS, one service provided by ABC, and one service provided by Sunshine.

After the supplier reviews the quotes, he or she can select the one that best fits his or her needs by clicking on the radio button in column "Select". In this example, service UPS Second Day Air was selected.

2.4.7 Updated purchase order

The updated purchase order with "UPS" as "Transport Service Provider" is shown in Fig. 2.17. The notification shall be sent to the buyer, supplier, and shipping company at the same time. The PO identifier was mapped onto the real tracking identifier generated by the shipping carrier so that it can be used for tracking.

The lessons learned in this B2B prototype is that web services are emerging e-business applications that can connect and interact with one another on the web more easily and more efficiently because they avoid time-consuming custom code integration. Furthermore, using our advanced UDDI search mechanism reduces the development time of B2B applications

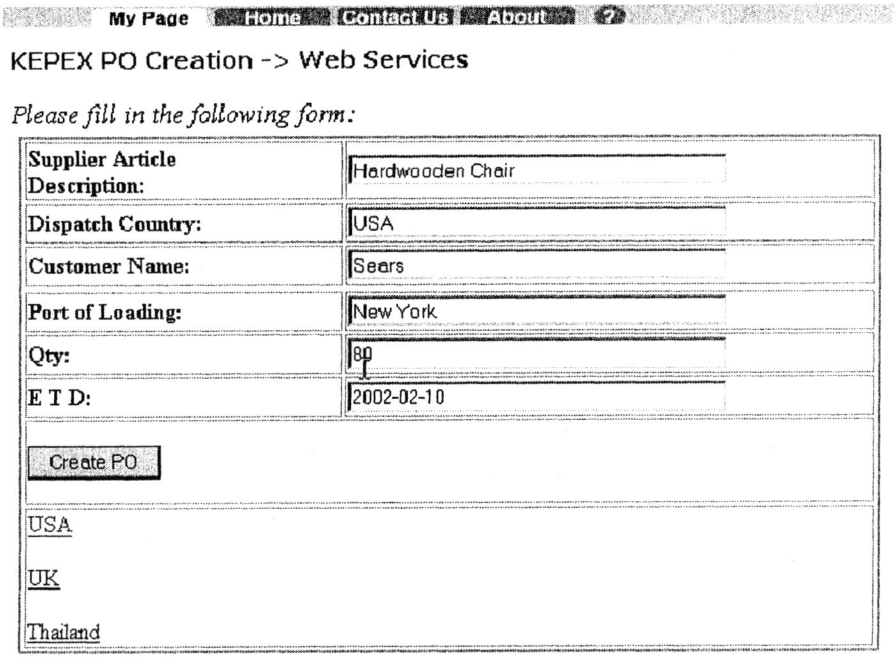

Web Services Technologies for Outsourcing

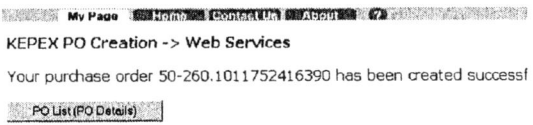

Figure 2.12: Purchase order creation interface.

Figure 2.13: Purchase order creation result.

supporting dynamic and collaborative B2B activities powered by the UDDI registry; it also facilitates dynamic business process brokering and intelligent agents with open and real-time business services.

As a result, KEPEX does not need to develop and create all the services they need because most of them are outsourced from the e-Hub or from registered service providers.

2.5 Related Work

The Internet provides a revolutionary way to doing business, and offers tremendous opportunities for business to thrive. Furthermore, it represents a market that amounts to potentially hundreds of billions of dollars.

E-marketplaces and private exchanges are two major B2B transaction models. The B2B e-commerce was blooming with huge commercial potentials. Different aspects of the B2B integration have been addressed in the literature, namely: integration architecture [30, 31, 145], workflow composition [18], management systems [141], federated accounting services [22], web services solutions [7] and security issues [143]. The business climate

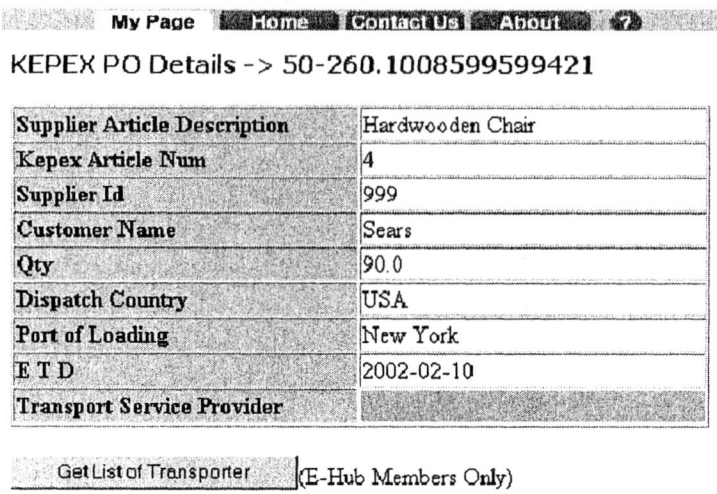

Figure 2.14: Purchase order details page.

changed quite dramatically with the demise of many dot coms, and there was a consolidation of several public e-markets.

In [7], the authors proposed the Process Coordination Framework (PCF) and presented the building blocks required for web services-enabled e-business automation. PCF helps understand the roles of the various proposed standards with respect to these building blocks; it also helps identify overlapping areas and gaps. PCF groups the features that e-business automation requires into a multi-layered stack. This is a conceptual framework rather than a real integration framework for web services based B2B integration.

As for the B2B marketplace, the concept of e-Union is discussed in [31]; it integrates the services provided by different e-trading sites to provide an open e-trading service. The authors focus on the design of a mobile agent enabled framework for building such an open e-trading marketplace environment. In [79], the authors presented a system that matches buyers and suppliers in B2B marketplaces. In [159], the authors described a method for planning and managing IORs based on Shalliamson's transaction cost theory, to guide managers when negotiating B2B alliances, and procurement of IT support for them. But their systems cannot handle the growing set of web services in a B2B integration environment.

In [21], the authors proposed an architecture that uses contracts based on service level agreements (SLAs) to share selective management information across administrative boundaries. In [111], it was introduced an XML-based SLA language that allows parties to define quality guarantees for electronic services, the processes for monitoring them, and show to which extent this language meets the requirements. These mechanisms could be used to enhance the solution manager in our framework.

Our proposal is a practical B2B integration framework and platform that is powered by industry standards such as SOAP and XML. The security, accessibility, configurability and solution management are powered by our enhanced enabling technologies such as the advanced web services discovery mechanism, the service outsourcing manager, the multi-level security mechanism, and rapid on-boarding, service provisioning, and subscription.

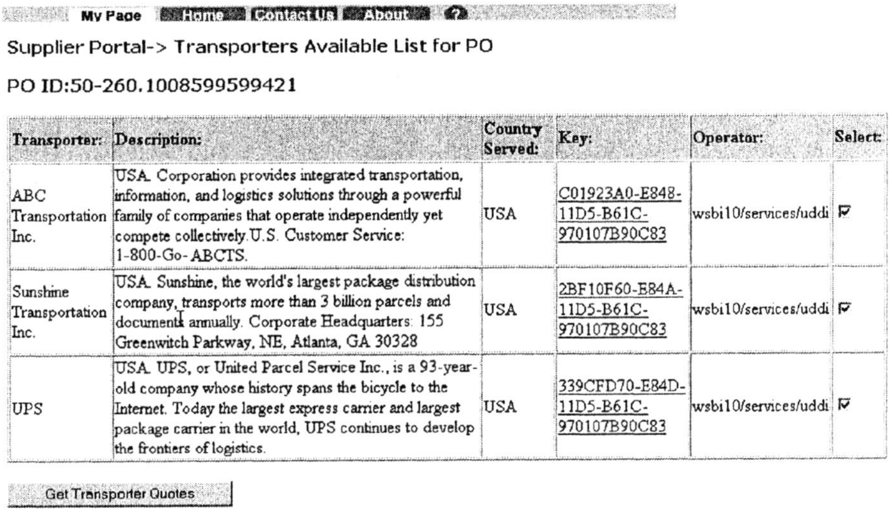
My Page | Home | Contact Us | About | ?

Supplier Portal-> Transporters Available List for PO

PO ID:50-260.1008599599421

Transporter:	Description:	Country Served:	Key:	Operator:	Select:
ABC Transportation Inc.	USA Corporation provides integrated transportation, information, and logistics solutions through a powerful family of companies that operate independently yet compete collectively.U.S. Customer Service: 1-800-Go-ABCTS.	USA	C01923A0-E848-11D5-B61C-970107B90C83	wsbi10/services/uddi	☑
Sunshine Transportation Inc.	USA Sunshine, the world's largest package distribution company, transports more than 3 billion parcels and documents annually. Corporate Headquarters: 155 Greenwitch Parkway, NE, Atlanta, GA 30328	USA	2BF10F60-E84A-11D5-B61C-970107B90C83	wsbi10/services/uddi	☑
UPS	USA UPS, or United Parcel Service Inc., is a 93-year-old company whose history spans the bicycle to the Internet. Today the largest express carrier and largest package carrier in the world, UPS continues to develop the frontiers of logistics.	USA	339CFD70-E84D-11D5-B61C-970107B90C83	wsbi10/services/uddi	☑

Get Transporter Quotes

Figure 2.15: Results from the shipping agent.

2.6 Conclusions

In this chapter, we have introduced a web services hub framework for business-to-business integration. It consists of a centralised membership portal with UDDI synchronisation for rapid registration, subscription, and provisioning of web services, and a control security model so that all businesses and users can have secure access to the services. Furthermore, as an outsourcing platform, it enables users to configure a business process dynamically, based on incoming requirements using the hub-hosted services or registered services provided by other application service providers. We have also created some example web services for advanced UDDI search, shipping (UPS web services), purchase order creation and a web service for authentication and authorisation.

Building on our experience, we think that we still need to work on the following issues: (a) when multiple SOAP request are sent to a hub, it should be able to aggregate and analyse them so that it can invoke one or multiple web services; (b) intelligent data transformation and protocol translation within a hub; (c) resource management on a grid computing environment; (d) dynamic web services routing; (e) adaptive method signature adaptation for dynamic web services invocation; (f) billing outsourced services.

In the meanwhile, e-marketplaces can be viewed as the next generation B2B initiatives, which look beyond traditional companies and marketplaces through collaborative interactions and dynamic e-business solution binding [37]. It is an evolution in the field of e-business solutions that integrates all kinds of applications and processes located at different companies or marketplaces within a uniform solution. Web services provide a new way for such an integration. Meanwhile, grid and autonomic computing are very important enabling technologies leveraging web services for creating next-generation e-business solutions.

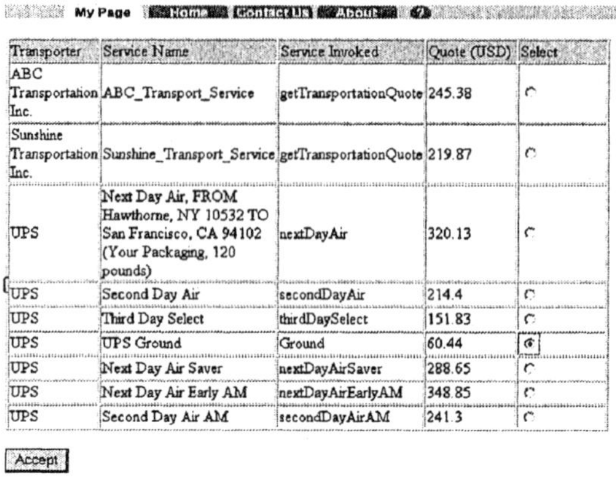

Transporter	Service Name	Service Invoked	Quote (USD)	Select
ABC Transportation Inc.	ABC_Transport_Service	getTransportationQuote	245.38	
Sunshine Transportation Inc.	Sunshine_Transport_Service	getTransportationQuote	219.87	
UPS	Next Day Air, FROM Hawthorne, NY 10532 TO San Francisco, CA 94102 (Your Packaging, 120 pounds)	nextDayAir	320.13	
UPS	Second Day Air	secondDayAir	214.4	
UPS	Third Day Select	thirdDaySelect	151.83	
UPS	UPS Ground	Ground	60.44	
UPS	Next Day Air Saver	nextDayAirSaver	288.65	
UPS	Next Day Air Early AM	nextDayAirEarlyAM	348.85	
UPS	Second Day Air AM	secondDayAirAM	241.3	

Figure 2.16: Results of calling a web service.

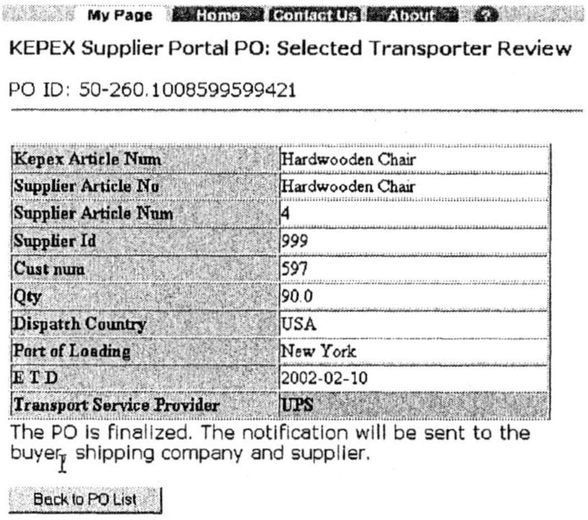

Kepex Article Num	Hardwooden Chair
Supplier Article No	Hardwooden Chair
Supplier Article Num	4
Supplier Id	999
Cust num	597
Qty	90.0
Dispatch Country	USA
Port of Loading	New York
E T D	2002-02-10
Transport Service Provider	UPS

Figure 2.17: Details of a finished purchase order.

Acknowledgements

The authors would like to thank Jingmin Xu, Shunxiang Yang, Yingnan Zuo and Zhong Tian for their design and implementation of the membership portal. We would not like to forget Tian Chao for her contributions to the enhancements of the web services discovery technology used in this framework.

About the authors

Liang-Jie Zhang   Qun Zhou   Hung-Yang Chang   Jen-Yao Chung

Liang-Jie Zhang is a research staff member at the IBM T.J. Watson Research Centre. He is part of the e-business solutions and autonomic computing research team with a focus on collaborative business process integration and management innovations. Dr. Zhang has over 12 years experience in creating novel technologies and products for e-business integration, streaming media, and intelligent information appliances. He is actively leading the research on web services and grid computing technologies for business process integration and design collaboration. He is the general co-chair of the First International Conference on Web Services (ICWS'03) and a program co-chair of IEEE Conference on E-Commerce (CEC'03). Dr. Zhang is the vice chair of communications for IEEE Task Force on E-Commerce.

Qun Zhou is a software engineer at the IBM Software Group, where she has been working on media search and catalog. She researches on web services and enterprise application integration. Prior to this position, she has been involved in lots of cutting-edge projects such as IPO2U e-commerce voice solution, Morgan Stanley Dean Witter web usage reporting system, and IBM HotMedia e-card solution. Her experience spans interactive web programming, e-commerce, web services, Internet telecommunication, database programming, collaborative workspace, bank communication and networking systems, and wavelet signal processing.

Henry (Hung-Yang) Chang is the manager of B2B Service Infrastructure in the e-Commerce research department at the IBM T.J. Watson Research Centre. He is involved in various B2B infrastructure engagements, and he was the lead architect of the IBM enterprise extranet for large enterprise customers. His recent research focus includes business process performance monitoring, dynamic composition of web services, design collaboration and virtual process integration. Before the Internet arrived, he conducted research in mobile application infrastructure, data replication, web database transaction management, and parallel operating systems. Henry received a Ph.D. and a M.S. degree in Computer Science from the University of Wisconsin-Madison in 1987, and a B.S. in Electric Engineering from the National Taiwan University. Currently, he is a member of ACM.

Jen-Yao Chung received a M.S. and a Ph.D. degree in Computer Science from the University of Illinois at Urbana-Champaign. Since 1989, he has been with the T.J. Watson Research Centre as a research staff member. Currently, he is the senior manager of the electronic commerce and supply chain department, and a programme director for the IBM Institute for Advanced Commerce Technology office. He has been involved in research, development, and customer engagements in electronic commerce, electronic marketplaces, and web application systems. Dr. Chung's current research focus on e-marketplaces, XML, EDI, integrating existing business with the World Wide Web, and business process integration and management. He is a co-chair for the IEEE task force on e-Commerce, and he shall serve as a programme co-chair of the IEEE Conference on e-Commerce (CEC'03). Recently, he served as a programme co-chair for the IEEE Workshop on e-Commerce and Web-based Information Systems. He has authored or co-authored over 70 technical papers published in journals or conference proceedings. He is a senior member of the IEEE and a member of ACM.

Part II

Database Backends

In: Technology Supporting Business Solutions
Editors: R. Corchuelo, A. Ruiz-Cortés and R. Wrembel, pp. 49-71
ISBN 1-59033-802-2
© 2003 Nova Science Publishers, Inc.

Chapter 3

Conceptual Modelling of Business Applications with Dynamic Object Roles

Kazimierz Subieta, Andrzej Jodłowski, Piotr Habela, and Jacek Płodzień

3.1 Introduction

For several years, dynamic object roles have had the reputation of a notion on the brink of acceptance. There are many articles advocating the concept [10, 16, 20, 62, 72, 89, 94, 95, 106, 107, 128, 131, 134, 170, 172, 173], but many researchers do not consider its applications sufficiently broad to justify the extra complexity of conceptual modelling facilities. Furthermore, the concept is neglected on the implementation side. As far as we know, no popular object-oriented programming language or database system supports it explicitly. Some authors assume a tradeoff, where the role concept is the subject of special design patterns [19, 62, 66, 136], applied both on the conceptual modelling and the implementation sides.

In our opinion, this view should be revised. In this chapter, we show that dynamic object roles are useful both for conceptual modelling and implementation. The concept could much facilitate modelling tools such as UML [77] and could be an important paradigm for object databases that build on the spirit of ODMG [32]. The notion has already been adopted by the SQL:1999 standard [117], although the name is different, it has specific semantics, and some limitations.

The idea of dynamic object roles assumes that a real or abstract entity can acquire and get rid of some roles during its lifetime without changing its identity. The roles appear during the life of a given object, they can exist simultaneously or disappear at any moment. For instance, a person can be a student, a worker, a patient, or a member of a club at the same time, as depicted in Fig. 3.1. Similarly, a building can be an office, a house, a magazine headquarters, and so on.

The concept relies on the idea that an object is associated with other objects (subobjects) that model its roles. Object-roles cannot exist without their parent object. Deleting

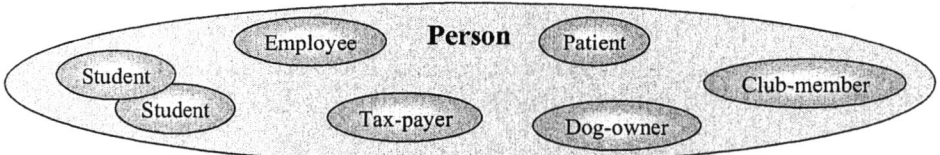

Figure 3.1: Roles played by a person.

an object causes deleting all of its roles. Roles can exist simultaneously and independently. A role can have its own additional attributes and methods. Two roles can contain attributes and methods with the same names, and this does not lead to conflict. This is a fundamental difference with the concept of multiple inheritance. Relationships (associations) between objects can connect objects with objects, as well as objects with roles and roles with roles. For instance, a relationship *works_in* connects an *Employee* role with a *Company* object. This makes the referential semantics clearer if we compare it to traditional object models. Roles can be further specialised as subroles, sub-subroles, and so on. For instance, *Club_Member* can be specialised by role *Club_President*.

The role concept requires introducing composite objects with special structure, semantics and generic operations. In this chapter, we describe the structure formally and present a sketch of a query/programming language supporting generic operations to process such structures. Our idea to deal with dynamic roles in a query language [86] is based on the *stack-based approach* (SBA) [85, 132, 156], which is the only formalism able to accommodate this concept naturally. A version [157] was implemented in the prototype system Loqis [155]. Currently, we are working on a prototype of an object-oriented DBMS aiming at intelligent content management for web applications; our goal is to implement the ideas presented in this chapter.

The rest of the chapter is organised as follows: Section 3.2 describes a real business case study in which the dynamic role concept was built in a UML class diagram; Section 3.3 shortly presents the state-of-the-art concerning dynamic object roles; Section 3.4 outlines general assumptions concerning the implementation of a prototype based on dynamic object roles; Section 3.5 presents the SBA, and Section 3.6 introduces our object model with roles and discusses its differences with traditional object models introduced in programming languages and database management systems; Section 3.7 presents changes to popular design notations and object definition languages that allow them to use roles; finally, Section 3.8 reports on our conclusion and future research plans.

3.2 A Business Case Study

In October 2001, we started a project for a Polish governmental institution dealing with regulations and investigations of the capital market. The investigations concern various forms of data mining, making summary reports and checking legality of investors' operations on the market. The main requirement of the system is that it should record all past and present information that could be relevant for the investigations. Typical entities identified in the business domain were the following: person, broker, investment advisor, organisational unit, company, stock instrument, share, stock session, stock transaction, stock order, brokering house, document, legal regulation, and so on.

Conceptual Modelling of Business Applications with Dynamic Object Roles

Trying to develop a class model in UML, we faced three main difficulties:

Some objects have many specialisations at the same time. For instance, a person can be an employee and a broker simultaneously. This leads to multiple inheritance.

Some objects have many specialisations of the same type. For instance, a person can be a member of many boards of directors at the same time.

Some objects have specialisations that depend on time. For instance, a person was a broker a year ago, but he or she can be the director of a company currently. Furthermore, a person can be a broker several times, at different times and brokering houses.

Similar problems, mostly related to recording historical information, have occurred with other entities such as institutions, companies and documents. We concluded that the classical inheritance concept, as presented in UML, for instance, is not fully adequate for data environments dependent on historical data. The design that we developed is illustrated in Fig. 3.2.

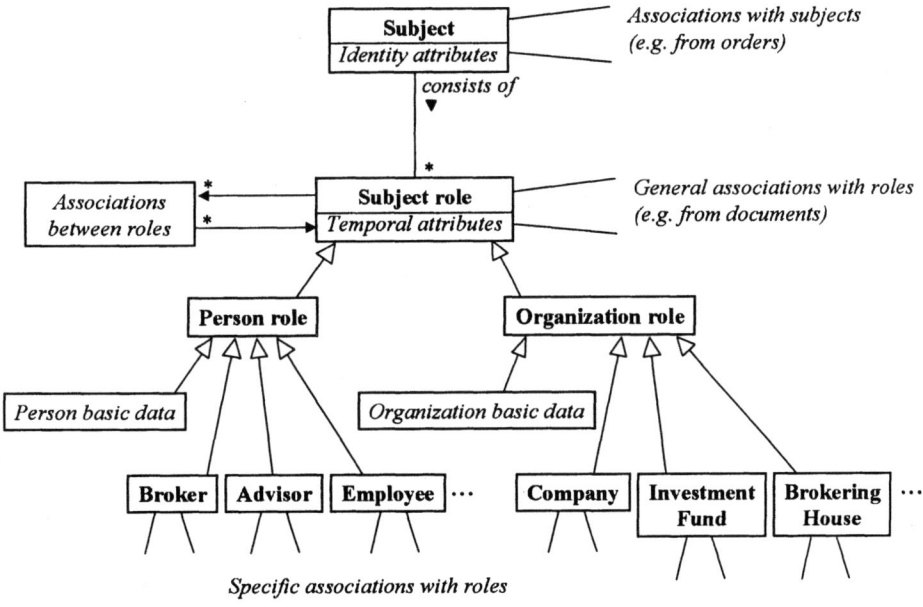

Figure 3.2: A part of a UML diagram with subject roles.

During the design we have assumed that each subject (person or organisation) is described by some attributes that are unique and invariant during the subject's entire lifetime. All other pieces of information about a subject can be changed. A change means recording a new piece of information rather then overwriting an old piece of information. We thus introduce a class called *Subject role* that has temporal attributes. A subject consists of many subject roles. A subject role is described by attributes such as "beginning date", "terminating date", or "is historical?" Subject roles can be associated through a special class to record that a person is/was an employee of an organisation. Subject roles are then specialised into *Person role* and *Organisation role*. Then, the *Person role* is further specialised into *Broker*, *Advisor*, *Employee*, and so on. (The process is similar for the *Organisation role*.) This way, we are able to record any current and historical information; for instance, the information that somebody is currently a *Broker* and an *Employee*, but previously was an *Advisor*, then a *Broker*, then an *Advisor* again, and so on.

As usual, subject specialisations such as *Broker* and *Advisor*, should inherit basic attributes of a person. However, *Person basic data* and *Organisation basic data* can change unexpectedly; for instance, a person can change his or her address, and a company can change their name. As a firm requirement, we must record information on all such changes. A simple solution is to consider *Person basic data* and *Organisation basic data* as regular roles. If something changes in these roles, they are then "frozen" (with proper temporal data written to the *Subject role*); then a copy is created and modified accordingly to the new subject's state.

Notice that classical inheritance is non-applicable in this case. We cannot record that an *Employee* is a *Person*. Instead, we have implicit inheritance through temporal attributes: an *Employee* "inherits" from a *Person* if their associated time periods overlap. Unfortunately, this could be inconvenient in cases when temporal data are unknown or imprecise. For instance, we know that Smith was a broker but we do not know when. Therefore, *Broker* should inherit from *Person basic data*, but we are unable to record this information (or must record it artificially). Another disadvantage of the design is complexity, chiefly after mapping it to a relational DBMS. Very complex relational structures imply very complex SQL queries. We have concluded that such cases are poorly dealt with in UML and cause difficulties during implementation. The only radical cure is to introduce dynamic object roles both at the level of UML class diagrams and at the level of data structures implemented in object-oriented or object-relational DBMS.

3.3 Related Work

The idea of changing object roles dynamically was proposed for the network database model by Bachman and Daya [16]. During the era of relational models and systems, the concept was not considered in the context of databases because it did not fit well with the relational model. The interest in dynamic object roles increased when computer professionals began realising the meaning of conceptual modelling in software construction. In fact, object-orientedness has been popularised in various domains of information technology. Together with object-orientedness, dynamic roles are considered more frequently.

The concept often appears in articles devoted to object design, programming languages and databases, sometimes with other names, in different contexts and with various semantics. The classical object-oriented model assumes that each object is associated with its most specific class. A deviation from this rule can be treated as a certain variation of the role concept. In particular, the Iris system [59] supports many types for a single object. A similar proposal can be found in [20]. The dynamic role notion appears in papers related to modelling office information systems [131], computer aided manufacturing [173], workflow management [89], multimedia [172], semantic modelling [134, 146, 150], and object modelling [128]. These articles propose to take advantage of dynamic roles for various dynamic properties, such as object migration, schema evolution, conceptual object clustering, creation of several views for one object, and so on.

In a popular approach, roles are represented informally by means of design patterns that build on existing notions in the field of conceptual modelling [19, 62, 66, 95, 136]. The design pattern *decorator* [66] is considered in [62] as a good mapping of dynamic roles. The pattern allows one to insert additional functionality into a class without subclassing. In a more general setting, roles correspond (to some extent) to Aspect-Oriented Programming [91], the separation of concerns principle [50] and the Subject-Oriented Programming [80]. There are features that show that AOP and SOP have conceptual similarities with dynamic roles. Another approach introduces the role concept as an explicit notion of conceptual modelling and a database feature that is orthogonal to other features. Such an approach was implemented in Aspects [134] and Fibonacci [9, 10, 11]. A feature called "subtable" has some correspondence to a dynamic role in the emerging SQL:1999 standard [117] (formerly known as SQL3).

In Fibonacci, it is assumed that a role does not have its own behaviour. The support for contextual object behaviour was first introduced in the Clovers system [149], in the proposal presented in [170], in Multiple View in the Smalltalk context [72], in the ORM model [144], and in Aspects [134]. In these approaches, however, the roles do not have their own classes and they do not support inheritance amongst roles. Neither can a role be moved from an object to another. The proposals do not define operators that allow a programmer to switch from one object role to another one.

The proposals can be classified according to the way they deal with strong static typing, and depending on whether the classes introduced are first-class or second-class citizens. In [146], classes are first-class citizens and they are referred to as *prototypes*. ORM [144] is a similar proposal, but classes are second-class citizens. Strong static typing requires the second-class citizenship of role types.

Articles such as [170] pay attention to the fact that a unique object identifier becomes problematic in the case of dynamic roles. Indeed, for consistent referential semantics, e.g., for implementing relationships amongst object and roles, each object role should have its own unique identifier. Therefore, an object has a unique *identity*, but it can have many *identifiers*. This is an essential semantic novelty in comparison to the classical object model.

Multiple interfaces, which are a feature available in Sun's Java and Microsoft's COM/DCOM, have some similarities with dynamic object roles. The programmer is able to define interfaces so that a single interface represents a single object role. However, multiple interfaces do not support all dynamic role features, in particular, they do not deal with addition or deletion of roles at run time.

In comparison to the state of the art in dynamic object roles, our approach is original in that it combines the following features:

At the conceptual level, we define an object store model that deals with dynamic object roles. The model is a *sine qua non* prerequisite for defining the semantics of all database and programming constructs: typing, classes and inheritance, query language, meta-model, imperative constructs, and so on.

We use the classic notions of classes and static inheritance as well as a new notion of dynamic inheritance amongst roles.

Each role has a unique identifier, which is important for building consistent semantics of references to roles. In particular, this feature allows us to express precisely the semantics of name bindings, the semantics of relationships (associations) amongst roles, and so on.

Roles may have their own behaviour, in particular methods, virtual attributes, constraints, and so on. The behaviour is the subject of static and dynamic inheritance.

Objects may have several roles of different types (or even the same type). This feature allows us to model flexible overlapping heterogeneous collections of objects. This feature, which is very useful, is not available in any current object-oriented programming language or system.

Roles are properties of a database. We define an object-oriented query language dealing with roles. As far as we know, this is the first such query language. Semantics of the query uses the stack-based approach, which offers many advantages over other formal approaches to query languages. In particular, simple and precise formal semantics, universality and robustness, and very powerful query optimisation methods.

3.4 Prototype of Dynamic Object Roles

The 5-th Framework EU ICONS project (IST-2001-32429) aims at building a content management system prototype to support uniform, knowledge-based access to information resources available on the web. It should be able to integrate pre-existing heterogeneous databases, e.g., formatted, text, and multimedia ones, as well as legacy systems. One of the main problems addressed in the project is dealing with the inherent variety of data and knowledge modelling paradigms. Our approach relies on developing a special canonical data model that is powerful enough to cover all the paradigms and to integrate them transparently by means of wrappers, as in a CORBA-like context.

The ICONS project architecture involves (potentially) the following data models:

an object database model;

a relational and an object-relational database models;

the XML and RDF models;

the Datalog knowledge representation and processing model;

semantic networks as a structure for searching knowledge bases;

temporal models for storing and processing the time category associated with facts, e.g., to record and process historical information on business entities;

process models such as the workflow model developed by WfMC.

Further models may appear during the project. An inherent part of the ICONS prototype will be the Rodan Portal, a commercial tool for developing web applications. The Rodan Portal has its own database management system based on a specific variation of an object database model. These models are defined on different abstraction and genericity levels, and they use specific terminology, often incompatible. They are also associated with different kinds of meta-information. Some models introduce explicitly a schema or ontology specification language, whereas others neglect this issue; some of the models are in common use currently, and others are not. Dealing with so many models is difficult, and we must take into account that this implies (more or less explicitly and precisely) specific constraints on data, e.g., the XML model is based on hierarchical, "schema-shy" structures; the Datalog model is based on the pure relational model; object models include several kinds of relationships, and so on. Furthermore, some models are closely related to particular processing capabilities, e.g., the Datalog model is associated with an inference engine, semantic networks (with navigation within a network, object models) with access and processing by means of methods, and so on.

It is a challenging goal for the ICONS project to integrate all of these paradigms within a single framework. Therefore, we decided to apply a special kind of data model, to which we refer to as *canonical*, that is universal enough to express the specific structures and operations of all the models involved in the project.

Regarding the canonical model, a key question is whether we should apply an existing model or develop a new one. From the existing models, the first choice seems to be the XML model, but it has some disadvantages. In particular, it is still unstable and does not cover useful features such as object identity, inheritance, methods, associations, and so on. The relational and the object-relational models are not viewed as a satisfactory solution either. The relational model offers only simple data structures (tables) and does not support directly higher-level abstractions such as object identity, complex objects, inheritance, associations, behaviour, and so on. According to many professionals, the era of the relational model is over, at least regarding research. Concerning object-relational models, they are too complex due to historical legacy, bottom-up commercial development (with little care about homogeneity and minimality) and eclecticism. The consequences are dramatically disadvantageous. In particular, the emerging ANSI/ISO SQL:1999 standard does not seem to be fully implementable according to many professionals' opinions (its specification is over 2000 pages). In fact, it is turning to be a loose guideline rather than a strong standard.

We concluded that the only viable alternative for the canonical model is some variation of the object model, which does not have many of the flaws of its competitors. An example is the ODMG standard, but it needs to improve some of its elements, e.g., refining its concepts, cleaning up its semantics, improving its ODL and OQL languages, and so on [8]. Therefore, we have developed a universal, versatile object data model, the object model with dynamic object roles. Through combining static and dynamic inheritance, the model does not entail the anomalies of the classical object models with regard to multiple, multi-aspect, repeating inheritance, and so on. Furthermore, it also allows to express easily many conceptual modelling notions that are difficult to map directly in other models, namely: overlapping heterogeneous collections of objects (impossible in ODMG), object migration, representing historical objects, aspect-oriented programming, representing meta-data, and so on.

A key component of the model is SBQL, a query/programming language based on SBA. SBQL can be viewed as a theoretical framework that builds on the spirit of object algebras, but without disadvantages such as conceptual and mathematical flaws and a limited scope. Due to its universal, sound and powerful theory, SBQL is syntactically and semantically simpler than the existing proposals for object-relational databases, e.g., SQL:1999. SBQL is integrated with imperative constructs (creating, inserting, altering, deleting, and so on), and database and programming abstractions such as views, (stored) procedures and functions. An inherent ability of SBQL concerns querying semi-structured data. This feature is especially important for XML-based web sources, which frequently introduce irregularities into data, namely: missing or repeating fields, heterogeneous records such as variants or unions, and different types or representation of values within the same field in different objects.

The general architecture of the ICONS prototype is presented in Fig. 3.3:

An application programme can use many APIs, namely: a graphical API, an API to a database, and an API to other facilities of the ICONS architecture.

The API to a database is based on SBQL, because all the data models included in the ICONS prototype are mapped onto the canonical data model processed by SBQL.

The SBQL processor is a kind of wrapper that transforms SBQL queries into lower-level CRUD (Create, Retrieve, Update, Delete) requests. It uses organisational information, such as the meta-base repository, views built on top of SBQL queries, and so on. This organisational information is stored in a special database (SBQL DB).

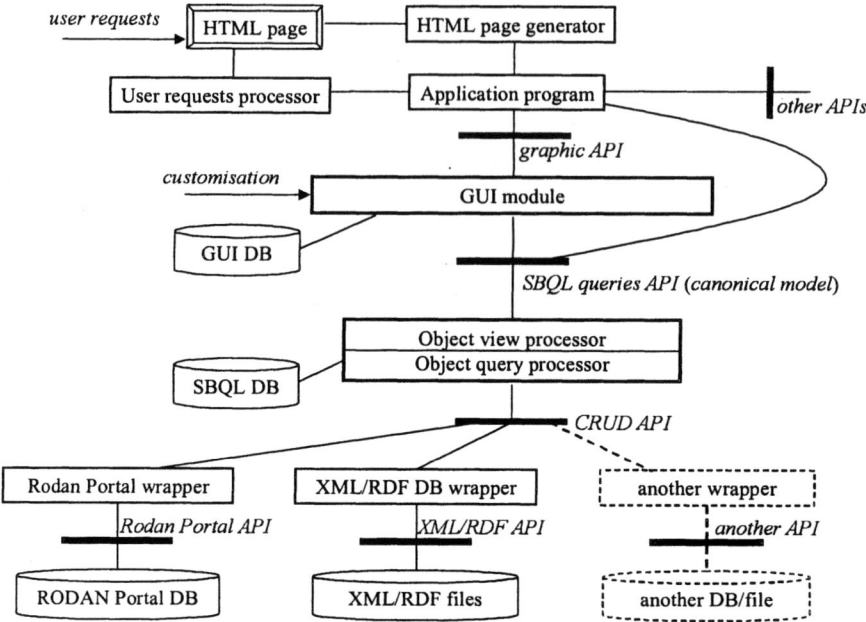

Figure 3.3: The ICONS architecture with interfaces to databases.

In this architecture, any specific data or knowledge base can be adapted as a single (complex) object with proprietary methods, e.g., deductive rules for a Datalog knowledge base.

CRUD level requests are input for wrappers that have to be written for any particular database, knowledge base, repository, and file. Those wrappers, which map one-to-one a CRUD command into a sequence of commands of the API for a particular data source, are important architectural components that allow us to isolate the external application developer interface from the particular solutions concerning data/knowledge management systems, e.g., the Rodan Portal. The wrappers do not change the conceptual model of a source data structure whilst mapping it onto the canonical model; e.g., an XML object is represented in the canonical model as a hierarchical object. The wrappers can be generic (for particular types of data source) or proprietary (for particular applications).

More sophisticated mapping of source data structures into canonical objects will be possible through virtual object-oriented views built on top of SBQL queries. We assume that views are stateless, i.e., they are pure functions on source data, and they are processed in the query modification mode, that is, by macro-substitution [158]. Such views can be used for retrieval. Updateable virtual SBQL views will be the subject of a separate research.

The CRUD API to a database is of a lower "physical level" than SQL. This implies that optimisers developed for particular SQL-based systems are hard to use. Furthermore, our experience shows that automated translation of other languages (in particular SBQL) into SQL is a too challenging task and may fail. Therefore we propose that queries should be optimised by an SBQL query processor and our optimisation methods by rewriting [85, 132]. Using indices or other structures to have access to a particular source data may be problematic, and thus requires further research.

Concerning distribution of data sources, a natural solution is to write a wrapper for each remote database. This approach does not determine how to deal with transparency of vertical and horizontal fragmentation of distributed data. This will also be the subject of separate research.

Currently, SBQL is fully implemented for an XML-based model DOM, including read-only XML views on this model. This implementation is now being generalised for the object model with roles. Independently, we have developed the CRUD interface, and we have also designed and implemented our own database system with roles, which will be used as a test-bed for designing wrappers to other databases.

3.5 The Stack-Based Approach

The SBA assumes that query languages are a special case of programming languages; it is an attempt to build a uniform semantic foundation for integrated query and programming languages. The approach is abstract and universal, which makes it relevant to a general object model. SBA makes it possible to precisely determine the semantics of a query language, their relationships with object-oriented concepts, with imperative programming constructs, and with programming abstractions, including procedures, functional procedures, views, modules, and so on. Its main features are the following:

The *naming-scoping-binding* principle is assumed, which means that each name occurring in a query is bound to the appropriate run-time entity (an object, attribute, method parameter, and so on) according to the scope of this name.

One of its basic mechanisms is an *environment stack* (ES), which is responsible for scope control and for binding names. In contrast to classical stacks, it does not store objects, but some structures built on object identifiers, names, and values.

The principle of *orthogonal persistence* is assumed, which means that there are no differences in defining queries accessing persistent and volatile data.

Results of functional procedures and methods belong to the same semantic category as the results of queries. As a result, functions and methods can be invoked in queries. Furthermore, those results can be augmented with "virtual names", like in SQL.

In contrast to relational languages and OQL, the *relativity* principle is assumed, i.e., the syntax, semantics, and pragmatics are identical at an arbitrary level of data the hierarchy. In particular, an attribute is an object.

Types are a mechanism to determine whether objects are built properly, i.e., in accordance with the database schema.

The principle of *internal identification* for objects is assumed, i.e., each run-time entity has a unique internal identifier.

3.5.1 Objects, classes and stores

In SBA each object has the following features:

Internal identifier (OID); identifiers cannot be directly written in queries and are not printable;

External name, which is provided by the programmer or the database designer; it is used to have access to an object from within a programme;

Content, which can be a value, a link, or a set of objects.

Therefore, the following three sets are used to define objects: I, the set of unique internal identifiers, N, the set of external data names, V, the set of atomic values, e.g., integers, strings, pointers, blobs and so on. Atomic values can also be procedures, functions, methods, views, and other procedural entities.

Formally, let $i, i_1, i_2 \in I$, $n \in N$, $v \in V$. Objects are modelled as the following triples (we distinguish four kinds of objects):

Atomic objects as <i, n, v>;

Link objects as <i_1, n, i_2>;

Inheritance link objects as <i_1, *inheritsFrom*, i_2>, where *inheritsFrom* is a distinguished name;

Complex objects as <i, n, S>, where S denotes a set of objects.

This definition is recursive and makes it possible to create complex objects with an arbitrary number of hierarchy levels. Relationships, e.g., associations, are modelled through link objects. In order to model collections, SBA does not assume the uniqueness of external names at any level of data hierarchy. The unification of records, tuples, arrays and all bulk structures is assumed; SBA abstracts from their differences. In the model, the names of objects, attributes, relationships, and the like are shifted on to the first-class citizenship.

In SBA, classes are used as prototypes, which means that they are objects and have the features normal objects have, although their task is different. A class object stores invariants, e.g., methods, of the objects that are instances of that class; a special relationship (*instantiation*) between a class and its instances is introduced. Furthermore, the inheritance relationship between objects is assumed; this relationship makes it possible to apply the *substitutability principle*.

In SBA, objects populate an *object store*, which is composed of the following elements:

The structure of objects, subobjects, and so on;

OIDs of *root objects*, which are accessible from the outside, i.e., they are starting points for querying;

Constraints, e.g., uniqueness of OIDs, referential integrity, and so on.

The term object is associated exclusively with elements of the object store; in our model, there are not any other objects. Queries in this approach never return objects, but some structures built on object identifiers, values and names. As a result, the *closure property* is not understood as a closure over objects, but as a closure over such structures [158].

3.5.2 Stacks

An environment stack (ES) is one of the most basic auxiliary data structures in most programming languages. It accomplishes the *abstraction principle*, which allows a programmer to abstract a piece of code from the contexts in which it can be used. The stack makes it possible to associate parameters and local variables to a particular procedure (function, method and so on) invocation. Thus safe nested calls to procedures from other procedures are possible, including recursive calls. The stack is also used to accomplish strong typing, encapsulation, inheritance, and overriding.

In SBA, the stack has a new function: processing queries that work on the object store. It makes it possible to control scopes of all names occurring in a query uniformly. It also makes it easier to understand the precise semantics of queries.

There are some differences between building the SBA ES, and a classical stack in a programming languages. Whilst they usually assume that objects *live* on the stack, i.e., they are allocated dynamically in proper stack sections, in SBA the object store and the stack are separate data structures; the stack contains only references to objects. The main reason for this assumption is the fact that the same object can be referred to from different stack sections.

The stack consists of *sections* that are sets of so-called *binders*. A binder is a pair (n, x), where n is an external name $(n \in N)$, and x is a reference to an object $(x \in I)$; such a pair is written as $n(x)$. We refer to n as the *name* of the binder, and x as its *value*. The concept of binder can be generalised; in particular, x can be an atomic value or a complex structure. Furthermore, if a binder models a procedural entity, its value is then the address of that subprogramme.

3.5.3 Binding

The mechanism which makes it possible to determine the meaning of each name is called *binding*. Binding follows the "search from the top" rule: to bind name n, the binding mechanism looks for the ES section (closest to the top of the stack) containing a binder $n(x)$ storing some value x. The result of the binding is x. To cover bulk data structures of the store model, the SBA assumes that binding can be multi-valued, i.e., if the relevant section contains several binders whose names are n, e.g., $n(x_1)$, $n(x_2)$, ..., $n(x_k)$, then all of them contribute to the result of the binding. In such a case, the binding of n returns the collection x_1, x_2, ..., x_k. Some modification of the binding rules is necessary to take inheritance and the substitutability principle into account.

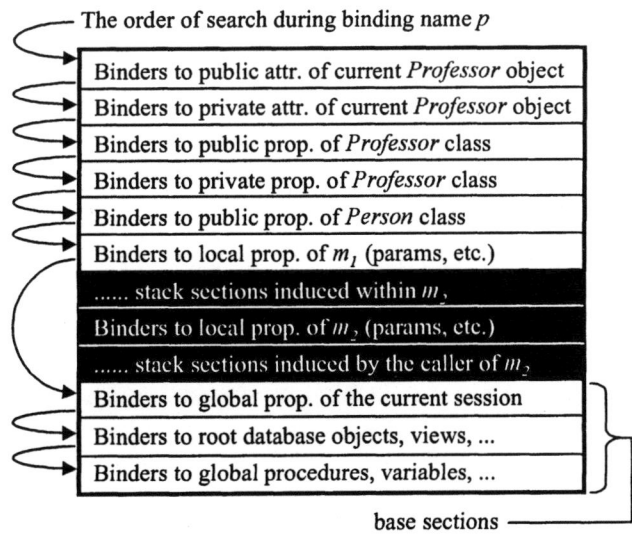

Figure 3.4: An example state of ES.

In SBA, ES consists of several so-called *base sections* at the beginning of a user session. They contain binders to the global properties of the current session, root database objects, views, global procedures, variables, and so on. During query evaluation the stack grows in size and shrinks according to query nesting. Assuming no side effects in queries, i.e., no calls to updating methods, the final ES state is exactly the same as the initial state. In Fig. 3.4, we present a sample state of ES during the evaluation of the following SBQL query:

Professor **where** (predicate having name p)

The above state concerns the binding of the name p occurring in the **where** clause of the query that is invoked in the body of method m_1 called by method m_2 (assume that method m_1 is defined in the *Professor* class). The name p can be the name of a *Professor* object attribute, the name of a method from the *Professor* class, the name of a method from the *Person* class, the name of a root database object, the name of a view, and so on. The system is trying to bind p to the proper entity of the environment following the order presented by the arrows. Lexical scoping is assumed; for instance, the environments of method m_2 and of its potential caller are invisible within the body of method m_1.

3.5.4 Query language

SBQL is based on an abstract syntax and the principle of compositionality: syntactic sugar is avoided and query operators are syntactically separated as far as possible. All basic constructs of OQL have direct counterparts in SBQL. However, the use of "iteration variables", i.e., auxiliary names is not mandatory in SBQL, which makes it closer to SQL.

The syntax of SBQL is as follows:

A single name or a single literal is a query. For instance, *Student*, *name*, *year*, *x*, *y*, "Smith", 2, or 2500 are (atomic) queries.

If q is a query, and σ is a unary operator, e.g., *sum*, *count*, *distinct*, *sin*, *sqrt*, then $\sigma(q)$ is a query. The operator defining an auxiliary name is a unary operator, too. We denote it by means of the typical syntax q **as** n (where $n \in N$).

If q_1 and q_2 are queries, and θ is a binary operator then $q_1 \; \theta \; q_2$ is a query.

With the exception of typing constraints, we assume the orthogonality of operators. For instance, *Professor*, *name*, *age*, "White" are atomic queries, and we can use them to build complex queries, namely:

(*Professor* **where** (*name* = "White")).*age*

The query has the following equivalent in SQL:

select *age* **from** *Professor* **where** *name* = "White"

Which, in turn, is equivalent to the following OQL query:

select *age* **from** *Professor* **as** *p* **where** *p.name* = "White"

In contrast to SQL and OQL, SBQL queries have a very useful property: they can be decomposed into subqueries, down to atomic ones, connected by unary or binary operators. In particular, *name* and *age* are queries on their own because all queries in SBQL are evaluated *relatively* to the current state of ES.

Each SBQL (sub)query returns a table, which is understood as a bag of rows. Such a table can be empty, can contain a single row, or can contain an arbitrary number of rows. A row is a sequence of elements; all rows in a table have the same type. A row can contain the following elements: atomic values $v \in V$; identifiers $i \in I$; binders $n(x)$, where $n \in N$ and x is a table.

3.5.5 Query evaluation

The result of a (sub)query is pushed on top of an auxiliary stack called QRES (*Query RESults*), which stores all temporary and final results of (sub)queries. Its elements are tables, as defined in the previous subsection. At the beginning of the evaluation process, the stack is empty. In general, queries are evaluated as follows:

For query l, where l is a literal denoting an atomic value $v \in V$, a table containing v is pushed onto the top of QRES. For instance, query "2" pushes a table containing value 2.

For query n, where $n \in N$, ES is inspected from top to bottom, and the result of binding n is pushed onto the top of QRES as a single-column table of the values of all the binders named n occurring in the first section containing one or more such binders.

Queries (and their results) are combined by operators, which in SBA are subdivided into algebraic, e.g., numerical operators, string comparisons, aggregate functions, the Cartesian product, and so on, and non-algebraic, e.g., selection, navigation, quantifiers. The main difference between algebraic and non-algebraic operators is whether they modify the state of ES during evaluation or not.

3.6 Object Store Model with Dynamic Roles

We assume that an object can contain many subobjects called roles. These subobjects can be added and removed at run time [10, 134]. Roles cannot exist without their parent objects. Deletion of an object causes deletion of all its roles. Roles can have different types and can exist simultaneously and independently. A role can have its own attributes and behaviour, i.e., methods, rules, or event processing. Identical names in two or more roles of different types do not imply any semantic dependency between the corresponding properties. For instance, a person can play simultaneously the role of an employee of a research institute with the attribute *Salary*, and the role of an employee of a service company with the attribute *Salary*, too. These two attributes may not share any other feature, including values, types, semantics and business ontologies. A role dynamically imports attributes (values) and behaviour from its super-roles, in particular, from its parent object.

Basic features of the store model with dynamic roles are the following:

An object has one main role *Person* and any number of specialised roles, e.g., *Employee* and *Student*.

Each role has its own name, which is used to bind the role from a programme or a query. For instance, objects can be bound through name *Person*, *Employee* or *Student*. Each binding returns the identifier of a proper role (or the identifiers of proper roles in the case of multi-valued bindings).

Each role is encapsulated: its properties cannot be viewed from other roles unless it is explicitly stated through a dynamic inheritance link. For instance, role *Employee* imports all properties of its parent role *Person*, thus the properties of a *Person* object, e.g., Name="Brown", BirthYear=1975, are available from the *Employee* role. However, properties of role *Student* are not directly available from the role *Employee*.

Each role is connected to its own class. Classes contain invariant properties of corresponding roles, in particular, names, attributes and their types and methods.

3.6.1 Links amongst objects and roles

Given that each object has a single main role, links join object roles rather than objects. For instance, a link *works_in* joins main role *Company* with role *Employee*. A similar link *studies_at* joins role *Student* with main role *School*. If such a link leads to *Employee*, it indirectly leads to *Person*, because the role *Employee* imports the properties of its parent object *Person*. After accessing the object via such a link, the properties of the role *Student* remain invisible.

The ability to create links between roles is an important feature for analysis and design methodologies and notations, e.g., OMT and UML. Links must lead to parts of objects, not to entire objects. To model this issue, current methodologies recommend to use the notion of aggregation/composition. Such an approach implicitly assumes that an *Employee*, for instance, is a part of a *Person*. Although the approach achieves the goal because we can connect the relationship *works_in* directly to the *Employee* subobject of *Person*, it obviously misuses the concept of aggregation, which is normally provided for modelling "whole-part" situations. Design patterns that have been proposed to deal with dynamic roles [19, 62, 66, 95, 136] offer a limited solution. They map the conceptual structures with roles onto structures without roles, but the resulting data structures must be processed by classical programming constructs, which usually need not (and are not) structured so that they show the initial design concept. Thus, the initial idea of the designer is distorted, which may result in various anomalies during software maintenance, for instance. (The reverse mapping from the code into conceptual structures with roles may become problematic.) In our opinion, the only radical cure for these drawbacks are dynamic roles introduced explicitly within design methodologies and within implementation environments.

3.6.2 Dynamic roles and object-oriented models

Below, we list several features, which make the concept of dynamic roles different in comparison to the classical object-oriented concepts.

Multiple inheritance: Because roles are encapsulated, there is no name conflict even if the super classes have different properties with the same name. There is no need for *EmployeeStudentClass*, which inherits both from *EmployeeClass* and *StudentClass*.

Repeating inheritance: An object can have two or more roles with the same name; for instance, *Brown* can be an employee in two companies, with different *Salary* and *Job*. Such a feature cannot be expressed by the traditional inheritance or multi-inheritance concepts.

Multiple-aspect inheritance: A class can be specialised according to many aspects. For instance, a vehicle can be specialised according to the environment in which it works (ground, water, air), and/or according to its power source (horse, motor, jet, and so on). Modelling tools such as UML take this feature into account, but it is neglected in object-oriented programming and database models. One-aspect inheritance leads to some problems with conceptual modelling and usually requires multiple inheritance. Roles avoid problems with this feature.

Variants (unions): This feature, provided by C++, CORBA and ODMG object models, for instance, leads to many semantic and implementation problems. Some professionals argue that it is unnecessary because it could be substituted by specialised classes. However, if a given class can have many properties with variants, then modelling this situation by specialised classes leads to combinatorial explosions, e.g., 32 specialised classes for 5 properties with binary variants. Dynamic object roles avoid this problem. Each branch of a variant can be considered as a role of an object.

Object migration: Roles may appear and disappear at run time without changing identifiers of other roles. In terms of classical object models, it means that an object can change its classes without changing its identity. This feature can hardly be available in classical object models, chiefly in models where binding objects is static.

Referential consistency: In our model, relationships are connected to roles, not to the entire objects; thus, it is impossible to refer to *Salary* and *Job* of *Smith* when one navigates to its object from the object *School*. In classical object-oriented models, this consistency is enforced by strong typing, but it is problematic if the typing is weak.

Overriding: Properties of a super-role can be overridden by properties of a subrole. The ability of overriding is extended in comparison to the classical object models: not only methods but also attributes (with values) can be overridden.

Binding: An object can be bound by the name of any of its roles, but the binding returns the identifier of a role rather than the identifier of the object. By definition, the binding is dynamic, because, in general, it is impossible to decide that a particular object has a role with a given name during compilation.

Typing: A role must be associated with a name, because this is the only feature that allows the programmer to distinguish a role from another one. Therefore, the role name is a property of its type (unlike classical programming languages, where a type usually does not determine the name of a corresponding object/variable). Because an object is seen through the names of its roles, it has as many types as different names for roles.

Subtyping: It can be defined as usual; for instance, the definition of type *Employee* relies on type *Person*. However, it does not make sense to introduce type *StudentEmployee*. Due to encapsulated roles, properties of a *Student* object and properties of an *Employee* object are not merged within a single structure.

Substitutability: Since names of roles are determined within types, it makes little sense to say that type *Employee* can be used everywhere type *Person* can be used. Thus the substitutability principle must be re-formulated, at least.

Temporal properties: As shown in Section 3.2, dynamic object roles are very useful for temporal databases since roles can represent any past facts concerning objects, e.g., the employment history through many *Employee* roles within one *Person* object. Without roles, historical objects entail difficult design problems; for instance, if one wants to avoid redundancy, preserve reuse of unchanged properties through standard inheritance, and avoid changing object identifiers.

Dynamic inheritance: *EmployeeClass* does not inherit statically from *PersonClass*. Instead, role *Employee* inherits dynamically the properties of its *Person* super-role, thus it inherits properties of *PersonClass* indirectly.

Aspects of objects and heterogeneous collections. A challenging problem with classical database object models such as ODMG [32] is that an object belongs to one collection at most. This is contradictory to both multiple inheritance and substitutability. For instance, we can include a *StudentEmployee* object into the extent *Students*, but we cannot include it at the same time into the extent *Employees* (and vice versa). This leads to inconsistent processing. Dynamic roles have a natural ability to model heterogeneous collections: an object is automatically included into as many collections as roles it contains.

Aspect-Oriented Programming. AOP [91] makes it possible to encapsulate cross-cutting concerns within separate modules, namely: history of changes, security and privacy rules, visualisation, synchronisation, and so on. Thus, dynamic object roles have conceptual similarities with AOP or can be considered as a technical facility supporting AOP.

Meta-data support. Meta-data are a particular case of cross-cutting concerns. It is considered in Dublin Core [49] or W3C RDF [42], e.g., authorship, validity, legal status, ownership, or coding can be implemented as dynamic roles of information objects.

Therefore, dynamic object roles have the potential to create new powerful features, which are difficult or impossible to achieve in the classical object model.

3.6.3 A formal model of an object store

For the sake of simplicity, we assume object relativism, i.e., each property of an object is an also object, and consider all properties of the store, including classes, as first-class citizens. The store models a programme/database *state*, and thus does not have types, which we consider a checking utility rather than a materialised property of the state.

Formally, an object is a triple $<i, n, v>$, where i is a unique internal object identifier, n is an external object name, and v is an object value. The value can be atomic, e.g., "*Doe*", a reference to another object, or a set of objects. Classes and methods are objects too. A store model with explicitly defined roles is defined as a 6-tuple $<O, C, R, CC, OC, OO>$, where:

O is a collection of (nested) objects;

C is a collection of classes;

R is a collection of root identifiers (of objects being entries of the store);

CC is a binary relation determining inheritance relationships;

OC is a binary relation determining membership of objects within classes;

OO is a binary relation determining inheritance relationship between roles.

We distinguish *objects* and *roles*. Objects may consist of many roles, and a role belongs to a single object. An object has exactly one *main role*. The name of this main role should reflect semantics of the entire object. Deleting this role implies deleting the entire object. Any role can *inherit dynamically* from another role within the same object; inheritance amongst roles in different objects is forbidden. The inheritance is based on the same rule as inheritance of class properties. A role that inherits from another is called *subrole*; an inherited role is called *super-role*. Relation OO defines two functional aspects: on the one hand, it determines which roles are inherited by other roles; on the other hand, it fixes the semantics of manipulating objects with roles. In particular, copying an object implies isomorphic copying of all of its roles, and deleting an object implies deleting all of its roles. Deleting a role implies that all of its subroles are deleted recursively. Relation OO is thus a pure hierarchy.

In Fig. 3.5, we present an example of the object store with roles; in Fig. 3.6, we present the same object store graphically. Component CC, i.e., the relation determining inheritance between classes, is empty in this case. Each role directly inherits from its class. A role inherits the properties of its super-roles, therefore indirectly inherits the properties of the classes to which these super-roles belong.

The model does not imply problems with multiple inheritance, because no name conflict is possible. The model also shows the reason for multiple inheritance anomalies in classical

***O* – Objects (roles):**
$< i_1$, Person, $\{ < i_2$, Name, "Doe" >, $< i_3$, BirthYear, 1948 > $\} >$
$< i_4$, Person, $\{ < i_5$, Name, "Brown" >, $< i_6$, BirthYear, 1975 > $\} >$
$< i_7$, Person, $\{ < i_8$, Name, "Smith" >, $< i_9$, BirthYear, 1951 > $\} >$
$< i_{13}$, Employee, $\{ < i_{14}$, Salary, 2500 >, $< i_{15}$, works_in, i_{127} > $\} >$
$< i_{16}$, Employee, $\{ < i_{17}$, Salary, 1500 >, $< i_{18}$, works_in, i_{128} > $\} >$
$< i_{19}$, Student, $\{ < i_{20}$, StudentNo, 223344 >, $< i_{21}$, Faculty, Physics > $\} >$
.....
***C* - Classes:**
$< i_{40}$, PersonClass, $\{ < i_{41}$, Age, (...code of method Age...) >,
...other properties of class PersonClass...$\} >$
$< i_{50}$, EmployeeClass, $\{ < i_{51}$, ChangeSalary, (...code of method ChangeSalary...) >,
$< i_{52}$, NetSalary, (...code of method NetSalary...) >,
...other properties of class EmployeeClass... $\} >$
$< i_{60}$, StudentClass, $\{ < i_{61}$, AvgScore, (... code of method AvgScore...) >,
...other properties of class StudentClass ... $\} >$
.....
***R* – Root identifiers:**
i_1, i_4, i_7, i_{13}, i_{16}, i_{19}, ...
***CC* - Inheritance relationships between classes:**
Empty.
***OC* - Membership of roles in classes:**
$< i_1$, i_{40} >, $< i_4$, i_{40} >, $< i_7$, i_{40} >, $< i_{13}$, i_{50} >, $< i_{16}$, i_{50} >, $< i_{19}$, i_{60} >, ...
***OO* – Inheritance between roles:**
$< i_{13}$, i_4 >, $< i_{16}$, i_7 >, $< i_{19}$, i_7 >, ...

Figure 3.5: A state of the object store in the object model with roles.

object models: they are caused because properties of different classes (perhaps incompatible) are not encapsulated, but merged in a single environment.

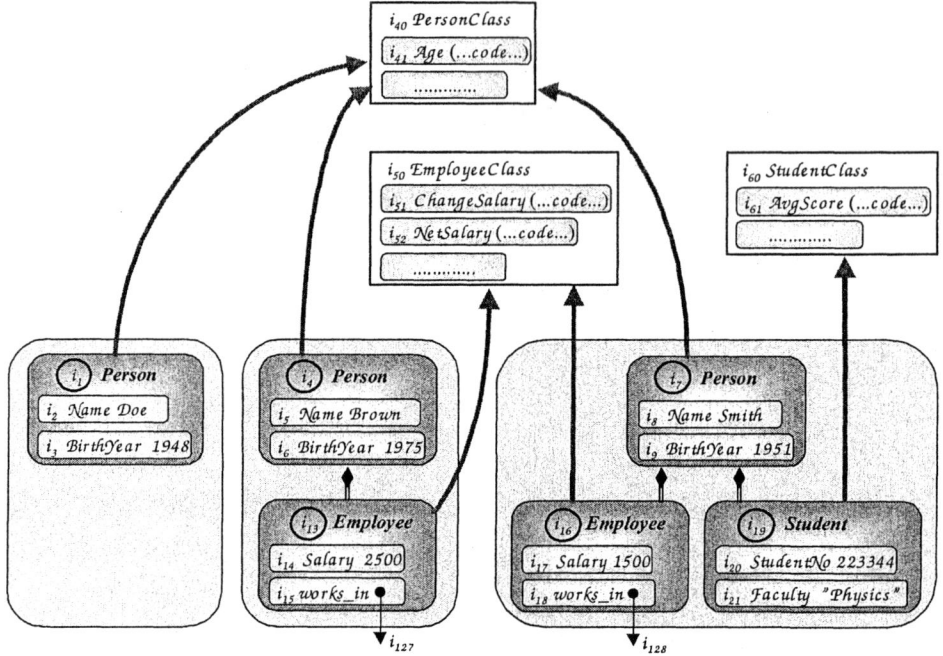

Figure 3.6: Graphical representation of the object store in Fig. 3.5.

Notice that the identifier of each role belongs to the collection of root identifiers R, which are starting points for binding objects. Therefore, name *Person* is bound to i_1, i_4, i_7. The binding concerns exactly the *Person* roles; other roles are invisible. Similarly, name *Employee* is bound to i_{13} and i_{16}; however, after this binding, the corresponding roles *Person* (i_4 for i_{13} and i_7 for i_{16}) become visible, according to relation *OO*. Thus, for instance, *Employee.Name* and *Employee.Age* are correct expressions. Similarly when name *Student* is bound.

The model is consistent concerning references. For instance, when name *Person* is bound references *works_in* are unavailable because the *Employee* roles are invisible. This property holds both if the system under consideration is strongly typed or untyped.

3.7 Specification of Dynamic Roles in Database Schemata

We use the syntax of ODMG ODL (based on IDL CORBA [76]), however, we are more precise concerning defined concepts and semantics.

In our view, *classes* are implementation units that store invariant properties of their members (objects). The invariant properties are usually reduced to names and types of members' attributes, and methods, which can be executed on the member. Other kinds of invariant properties include: a name assigned to a class member, specification of events/exceptions, implementation of reactions to events/exceptions, implementation of integrity constraints concerning the member, specification of exported properties of objects (public properties), specification of imported properties (active and passive side effects), and so on. *Interfaces* allow the programmer to deal with objects as if they were black boxes; thus they should bear all the information that is necessary to deal with objects. A *type* is the main component of an interface, and has constraints on the structure of an object and constraints on the contexts in which it can be used. Multiple interfaces to a single object are possible (as in Java or COM/DCOM). A role of an object is exposed through its interface. Each interface represents an object role; there are no other interfaces.

3.7.1 Building an object scheme with dynamic roles

We use the top-down approach of object-orientedness, i.e., classes are reusable units that can be further specialised by subclasses. In terms of dynamic roles, a class can be closed for modifications, but it can be further extended by new, *ad hoc* defined dynamic roles. Role classes correspond to subclasses of a given class.

A class is an implementation unit registered in the object store by a system or by a database administrator. Each class has a unique name (*AbstractPersonClass, PersonClass, StudentClass,* and so on). The registration of a class entails the following steps:

The code of a class is introduced as a single object into the object store. Methods and other properties of the class are introduced as subobjects of this object.

Meta-information concerning the class (class name, class location, ownership, comments, and so on.) is introduced into the corresponding structure of the catalog.

The *entire interface* to a class is introduced into the catalog. The interface specifies all public properties of the class and is used to build specialised interfaces to class properties. A class interface can be introduced manually by registering the class, or automatically, by means of a registration utility. It can use special keywords and language constructs in the class code, such as keyword "public", signatures of methods, and so on.

Interfaces are defined and identified independently from classes, but they refer to the names of registered classes (more precisely, to the names of their entire interfaces). The approach makes it possible to define several interfaces to a single class.

Any properties relevant to collections of objects being members of a class (class methods and class attributes in the C++ terminology) have to be stored in a separate class (so called a *power-set-of* class), whose members are collections of objects, e.g., *PersonCollectionClass*.

Classes are specified by interfaces, which (as in IDL CORBA and ODL) have the specification of public class properties. Interfaces contain all typing information (types of attributes and signatures of methods), but may also contain information irrelevant to types such as security rules. Interfaces are the subject of inheritance relationships, which can be either static (inheritance concerns properties of a class) or dynamic (inheritance concerns properties of a super-role; see the double line with a black diamond end in Fig. 3.7). Usually, the inheritance amongst interfaces corresponds to the inheritance amongst the corresponding classes. However, this is not mandatory and may depend on the implementation of classes and the conceptual view on the corresponding interfaces.

The relationship between *PersonCollectionInterface* and *PersonInterface*, which is shown in Fig. 3.7 as a dashed, double-line arrow, determines the dependency between a power-set-of class and a class of its elements. Power-set-of classes do not constitute a special kind of classes because they follow ordinary rules, except for the fact that their members are collections of objects.

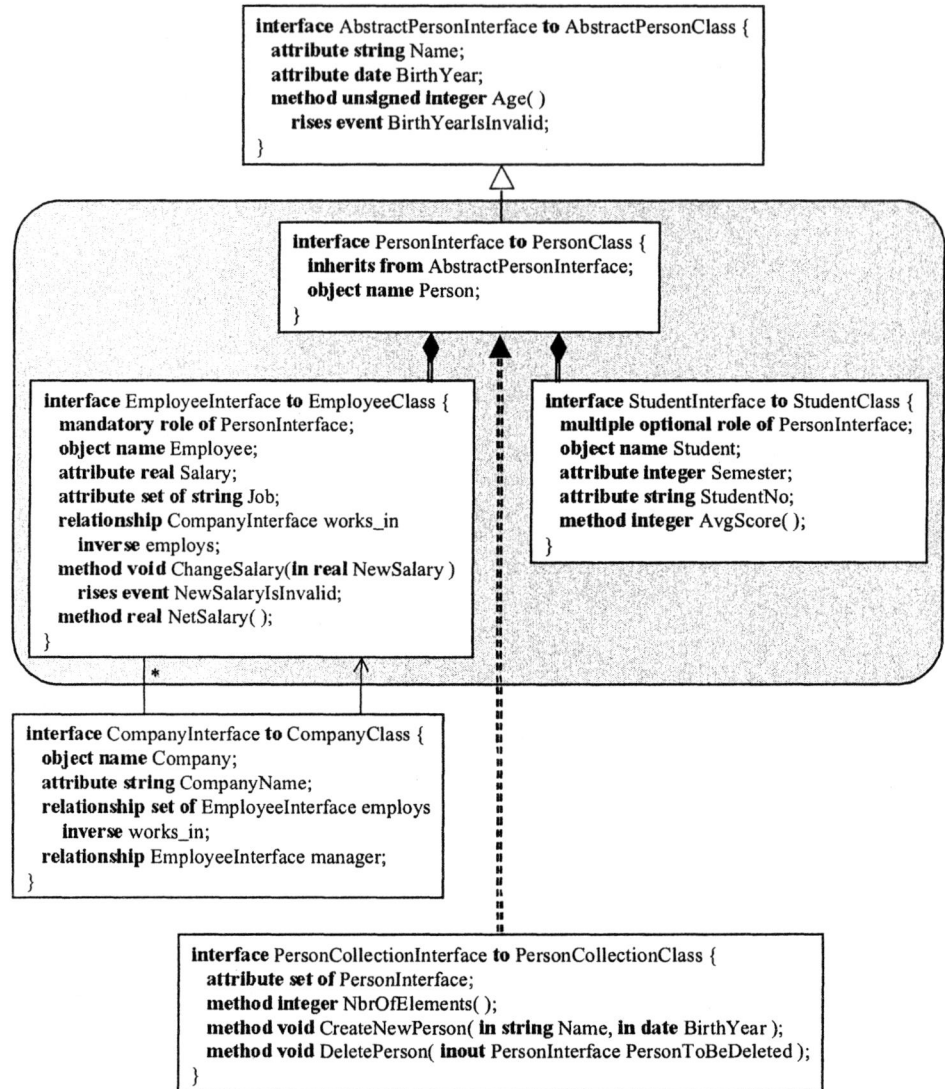

Figure 3.7: Interfaces to database objects with roles.

All the lines, arrows and boxes in Fig. 3.7 are visual comments, and the same information is made explicit inside interfaces. The syntax presented in Fig. 3.7 is an *ad hoc* extension to the ODL syntax. The differences with ODL semantics are the following:

Each interface has a name and is associated with a class name. These names do not determine the names of the corresponding objects. Some interfaces, e.g., *PersonInterface*, *EmployeeInterface*, define the names of the corresponding objects. Interfaces need not determine such a name, e.g., *PersonCollectionClass*.

An interface to a role can be associated with a super-role interface. A role can be mandatory, optional, and/or multiple. A mandatory role means that its super-role must possess it, but roles are usually optional; a multiple role may have many instances within an object.

As in ODL, but unlike UML and the CORBA Relationships Service, relationships are binary and do not have any attributes. In our opinion, more powerful relationships lead to clumsy programming options. Relationships can be bidirectional (with the **inverse** option, e.g., *works_in/employs*), or directed, e.g., *manager*. Independently from the **inverse** option, the system is responsible for keeping referential integrity of relationships so that no dangling references can appear. Unlike ODL, defining attributes with values being references to objects/roles is not allowed; such situations must be stated as directed relationships.

Interface *PersonCollectionInterface* has an attribute that is a set of objects from class *Person*. The name of this attribute is undefined here, because the definition is in *PersonInterface*. An interface like *PersonCollectionInterface* can define more such attributes, what makes it possible to define heterogeneous collections. Such a feature is available in the ODMG standard [32]; however, the semantics is not consistent [8].

3.7.2 Declarations of data structures

The schema presented in Fig. 3.7 maps interdependencies amongst interfaces, but it does not determine which objects are currently stored in the database. Defining stored objects is the main goal of a database schema, as this information is necessary for the application programmer. In ODMG, it is implicitly assumed that some interfaces determine stored objects. Besides the user can use an explicit definition of a stored data structure (*extent*) associated with an ODMG class. The CORBA standard has no clauses determining stored data structures, but it is implicitly assumed that each IDL interface can be used to have access to CORBA objects, whose creation depends on a particular object implementation. An interface definition is bounded with the definition of stored data structures in relational systems. This is materialised in the SQL *create table* statement.

Lack of separation between interfaces/types and declarations/creations of data structures leads to problems in the following cases:

One would like to define an abstract interface (to inherit from it), which has no direct member objects.

One would like to define an interface to an attribute, to a sub-attribute, and so on, i.e., to an object that does not belong to the set of root objects.

One would like to define an interface to a single object (which does not participate in a collection).

One would like to define an interface to a module, i.e., an entity encapsulating classes, interfaces, or types, and, independently, interfaces to objects stored within the module.

The emerging SQL:1999 standard abandons such a solution and assumes that a table type, i.e., an interface, can be defined independently from declarations/creations of stored tables. This entails coming back to the tradition of programming languages. Such an approach supports *reuse* and *encapsulation*: a single definition (perhaps complex, opaque and closed) can be reused to create many data structures. Thus, declarations of interfaces, as shown in Fig. 3.7, are not declarations of stored data structures. They have different information to be stored in the database catalog. In Fig. 3.8, we have declared the following objects:

A single object named *President* (accessed by the *AbstractPersonInterface*);

Two objects named *YoungPersons* and *OldPersons* (being collections of *Person* objects accessed by *PersonInterface*; *Person* objects can be specialised by roles);

A set of *Company* objects, named *Companies*, without a corresponding power-set-of class thus without an interface to the collection. Thus, it is implicitly assumed that such a collection is accessible through a *generic interface* that needs not be defined explicitly by the designer or the programmer. In our approach, any declared structure can be served by a query language that allows for such a generic interface.

The idea presented above concerns the conceptual view on objects, roles, their classes and types.

AbstractPersonInterface *President*;

PersonCollectionInterface *YoungPersons*;

PersonCollectionInterface *OldPersons*;

set of CompanyInterface *Companies*;

Figure 3.8: Declarations of data structures stored in the database.

3.8 Conclusions

In this chapter, we have presented an object model with dynamic roles, which we consider an alternative to the classical database object models, such as the ODMG object model. Dynamic roles can support conceptual models of many applications and do not lead to anomalies and limitations of multiple, repeating or multi-aspect inheritance. We have shown that the classical concepts of the object-orientedness, such as object identity, polymorphism and overriding can be smoothly incorporated into the model. Another advantage of our model is conceptual clarity concerning the level of object store and the mechanisms of data naming, scope control and binding names. The model leads to some new concepts for a schema definition language and meta-data management; this issue requires further research.

The model with dynamic roles and with a corresponding query/programming language is currently being implemented as a repository for intelligent content management systems for distributed web applications, in particular, as an enhanced XML repository.

Acknowledgements

The authors would like to thank their sponsors, who supported part of the work reported in this chapter by means of the 5-th Framework EU project ICONS, IST-2001-32429.

About the authors

Kazimierz Subieta   Andrzej Jodłowski   Piotr Habela   Jacek Płodzień

Kazimierz Subieta is a Professor at the Polish-Japanese Institute of Information Technology in Warsaw, and at the Institute of Computer Science of the Polish Academy of Sciences. He got his Ph.D. in 1973 from the Warsaw Polytechnic University in the area of information retrieval systems, and an Reader Professorship in 1989 from the Institute of Computer Science in the area of database technologies. His research interests include databases, software engineering and distributed systems. He is the author of over one hundred scientific papers and five books.

Andrzej Jodłowski is an fellow researcher at Institute of Computer Science of the Polish Academy of Sciences in Warsaw. He received his M.Sc. degree from the Warsaw Polytechnic University in 1995, in the area of applied computer sciences. His research interests concern object-oriented databases and software engineering. His Ph.D. thesis concerns dynamic object roles in conceptual modeling and databases. He has implemented the prototype supporting dynamic object roles in the stack based approach. He is a co-author of several papers presented at international conferences.

Piotr Habela is an fellow researcher at the Polish-Japanese Institute of Information Technology in Warsaw. He received his M.Sc. degree from the Warsaw Polytechnic University in 2000, in the area of information systems and management. His research interests concern object-oriented databases, distributed systems and software engineering. His Ph.D. thesis concerns metadata management for object-oriented databases. He is a co-author of several papers presented at international conferences.

Jacek Płodzień is a Lecturer at the Institute of Computer Science of the Polish Academy of Sciences in Warsaw and at the Warsaw School of Economics. He received his Ph.D. from the Institute of Computer Science in 2000, in the area of object-oriented database technologies. His research interests include databases, object-orientedness, information systems, and software engineering. He is a co-author of several papers published in international conferences and journals.

In: Technology Supporting Business Solutions
Editors: R. Corchuelo, A. Ruiz-Cortés and R. Wrembel, pp. 73-97
ISBN 1-59033-802-2
© 2003 Nova Science Publishers, Inc.

Chapter 4

Temporal Versioning in Data Warehouses

Johann Eder and Christian Koncilia

4.1 Introduction

A data warehouse is an integrated, materialised view on several data sources, e.g., data that comes from on-line transaction processing (OLTP) systems, from spreadsheets or from the world wide web. Data warehouses are building blocks for many information systems, in particular systems supporting decision making, controlling, revision or customer relationship management (CRM) [83, 174].

Data warehouses are used for analysing data by means of on-line analytical processing (OLAP) tools which provide sophisticated features for aggregating, analysing, comparing, and discovering irregularities in data. Data warehouses differ from traditional databases in the following aspects: they are designed and tuned for answering complex queries rather than for high throughput of a compound of updating transactions, and they typically have a longer memory, i.e., they contain both the actual values (snapshot data) and historical data needed for the above-mentioned purposes. Historical data can be stored either directly as in temporal databases or, more frequently, as aggregated, abstracted data.

OLAP tools are becoming increasingly important on linked-up, complex, heterogeneous markets. According to [130] the OLAP market increased from $1 billion in 1996 to $3.3 billion in 2001. They estimate that the market shall grow up to $5 billion in 2004. The biggest players in this market are currently Hyperion Solutions, Microsoft, Cognos, Oracle, MicroStrategy and Business Objects.

The most popular architecture for data warehouses are multi-dimensional data cubes, where transaction data (called cells, fact data or measures) are described in terms of master data (also called dimension members) that are organised hierarchically into dimensions, where the facts of the upper levels are computed from the facts of the lower levels by defined consolidation functions.

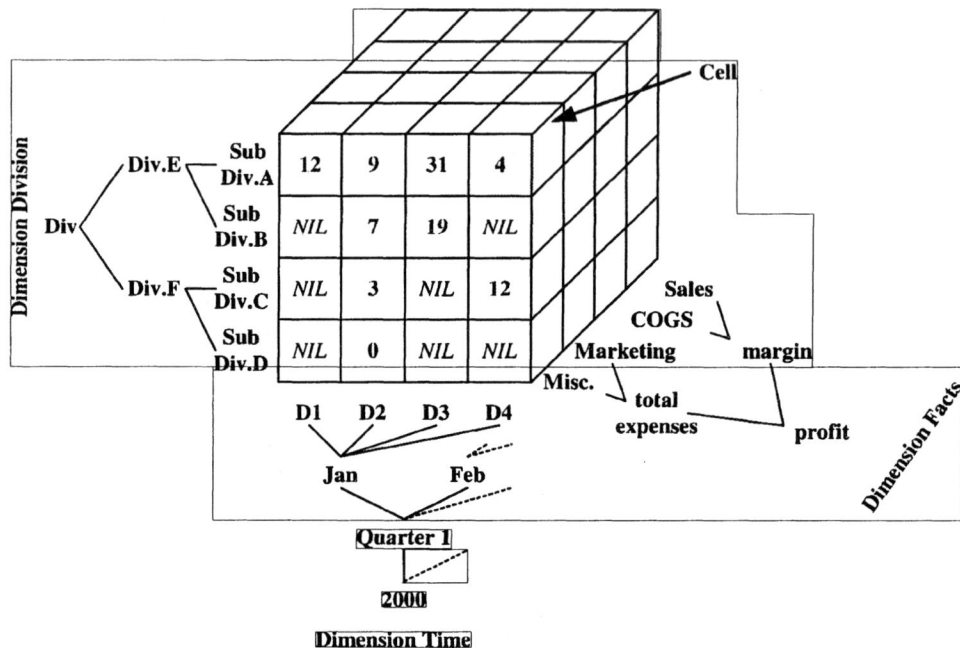

Figure 4.1: An example of a multi-dimensional cube.

A multi-dimensional view on data consists of a set of dimensions that define an n-dimensional data cube [105, 167]. Usually, a data cube is defined by a dimension called *Time*, a dimension called *Facts*, and by several dimensions describing managerial structures such as divisions, products, or branches. Facts and formulas describe what can be analysed, whereas dimensions describe how facts can be analysed. Typical examples of facts are sales, turnover or budget.

The example in Fig. 4.1 shows a data cube with three dimensions called *Facts*, *Time* and *Divisions*. A dimension is a set of dimension members and their hierarchical structure. For instance, *Profit*, *Margin* and *Sales* are dimension members of the dimension *Products*, and they are in the hierarchical relation $Profit \to Margin \to Sales$. The hierarchical structure of all dimensions defines all possible consolidation paths, i.e., it defines all possible aggregation and disaggregation paths.

A cell in such an n-dimensional data cube contains a value, and it is referenced by a vector [96]. For instance, the tagged cell with value 4 in the cube shown in Fig. 4.1 can be referenced by vector $\nu = (Sub\ Div.\ A, D4, Misc.)$

Several OLAP operations like roll-up (aggregation over a selected consolidation level, e.g., summarise from *Quarter* to *Year*), drill-down (disaggregation from a level to a more detailed level, e.g., from *Year* to *Quarter*), slice (bind and unbind specific dimensions), and dice (select a subcube) enable the user to navigate through the multi-dimensional space.

Typical application areas for OLAP tools are marketing (analyse the consumer behavior), financial services (consumer credit analysis), logistics management, optimising operational efficiency, analysing profitability, budgeting and forecasting.

4.1.1 The problem

This multi-dimensional view provides long term data that can be analysed along the time axis, whereas most OLTP systems can only supply snapshots of data at one point in time. Available OLAP systems are therefore prepared to deal with changing measures, e.g., changing profit or turnover.

In spite of their requirement for serving as long term memory, data warehouses are not well-prepared for changes, surprisingly. They cannot represent adequately changes in master data that spans the dimension structures of such cubes, with changes in units, changes in formulas computing derived transaction data, or schema changes. The reason for this disturbing issue is the implicit underlying assumptions that the dimensions are orthogonal. Orthogonality with respect to the dimension time means the other dimensions ought to be time-invariant. This silent assumptions impedes to deal with changes in dimension data properly.

The consequences of this deficiency are the restricted applicability of data warehouse technology in dynamic domains with frequent changes of structural data. The storing of data over several periods, foundational for data warehouses is of rather limited use, if these data cannot be compared and aggregated over these periods to allow for trend computations and multi-period comparisons. Furthermore, we often found incorrect data as results of OLAP analysis, sometimes the users were aware of the errors stemming from structural changes, but more often they were not.

4.1.2 Our contribution

The goals of our research are to make data warehouses more useful in dynamic application areas, and to improve the correctness of OLAP results. For this purpose, we need provisions to answer queries for data in a particular point in time (snapshot data) correctly, and for retrieving data stemming from different periods so that they can be compared or commonly processed further on.

As a result, it is not sufficient to just maintain the schema and the structure of a data warehouse to represent the new view, since this would not allow to answer queries regarding previous periods correctly or restoring the value of data warehouses for revision purposes. Furthermore, just keeping the correct master data and units for the transaction data is not sufficient either, since aggregation over data from different periods would give wrong results.

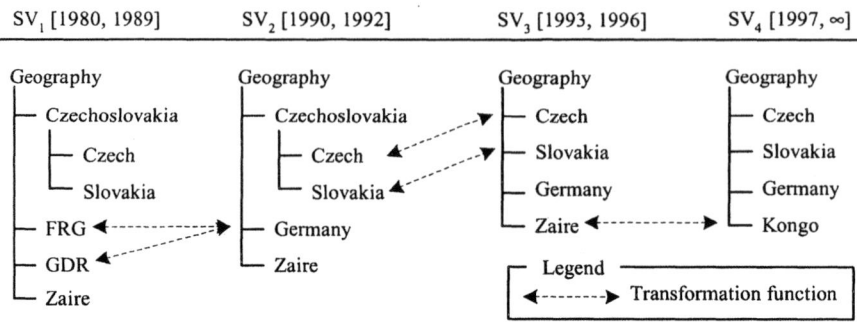

Figure 4.2: Structure versions and transformation functions for *Geography*.

Our approach for a temporal data warehouse architecture extends multi-dimensional data warehouses, and has the following features:

Representation of changes in the schema and instances of data warehouses. Our approach provides time stamps for both the schema and the instances of a warehouse. Therefore, it enables schema and instance versioning.

Identification of structure versions as changeless periods. By providing time stamps for the schema and instances of a data warehouse, our system needs to cope with different versions of structures. We discuss how to identify such different versions of structure as stable, changeless periods.

Provision of mappings of transaction data between structure versions. Our system has to support functions to transform data from one structure version into another.

Supporting queries that entail data spanning several structure versions. Introducing the concept of transformation functions allows us to return correct results for stated queries spanning multiple structure versions.

Analysis of data according to new and old versions of the structure. Our approach allows to transform data from an old structure into the current structure, and also to map data from any structure into any other structure. This is essentially important for correct trend analysis or auditing purposes.

Detect whether the result of a query might be wrong because of changes in structure or schema. Furthermore, our approach allows us to inform the user about what kind of structural modifications took place and what structural changes had an impact on a query.

Consider, for instance, a data warehouse in which we need to store information about sales and profit along two dimensions: *Time* and *Geography*. The instances of dimension *Geography* may change over the time, e.g., Germany reunified in 1990, and Zaire changed its name to Kongo in 1997. Fig. 4.2 visualises the history of dimension *Geography*. Furthermore, it shows the resulting structure versions and the necessary transformation functions to return correct results for queries spanning multiple structure versions.

4.1.3 Outline

The rest of the chapter is organised as follows: In Section 4.2, we discuss several approaches related to our work; we present our concept of a temporal data warehouse approach in Section 4.3; in Section 4.4, we present our $\mathcal{COMET}$ metamodel for temporal data warehouses; the architecture of the prototype we implemented is discussed in Section 4.5; finally, we present our conclusions in Section 4.6.

4.2 Related Work

In contrast to temporal databases, which have been well studied [26, 71, 74], very few approaches for temporal data warehouses are known in the literature [34, 139]. The same applies for schema evolution or versioning of databases versus schema evolution [38, 108] or versioning of data warehouses [25].

An in-depth description of the problem is presented in [140]. In this article, the author proposed a UML-based business metadata model and defined a business concept that affects data warehouses. This concept consists of external events, entities, processes, goals, actions and an evaluation of measures. They propose that business metadata may change over the time, i.e., the business concept may change. Due to the fact that a business user of a data warehouse must be aware of these changes because they may affect the consistency and comparability of the data, the need to make this data consistent and comparable by suitable transformations arises. Although this article gives a very good and detailed description of the model, it does not present any solutions to define such suitable transformations.

Our temporal data warehouse concept builds on the techniques developed in temporal databases [56], schema evolution and schema versioning of databases [63]. However, these approaches are not designed for analytical queries like data warehouses. Therefore, extensions and adaptations to the peculiarities of data warehouses are necessary. In this chapter, we extend the formal model for a temporal data warehouse presented in [52] to enable modifications to both the instance and the schema level.

Other approaches for temporal data warehouses are presented in [25, 34, 166, 175]. They are more or less formal, cf. [175] and [34], respectively. To the best of our knowledge, only [166] deals with both schema and instance modifications. However, this approach supports schema/instance evolution only, not versioning. Furthermore, in contrast to our temporal data warehouse approach [52, 54], none of the articles mentioned supports a mechanism to introduce relationships between instances in different structural versions, i.e., transformation functions for instances between different versions of an structure. Therefore, none of these approaches supports correct results for queries spanning over multiple versions of the same structure.

4.3 A Formal Model for Temporal multi-dimensional Systems

Basically, a multi-dimensional view on data, e.g., an OLAP cube or a data warehouse, consists of a set of dimensions. Typical examples of dimensions frequently found in multi-dimensional databases are *Time*, *Facts* or *Products*. The structure of each dimension is defined by a set of categories, e.g., dimension *Time* can consist of categories *Year*, *Quarter* and *Month*, which are in the hierarchical relation $Year \rightarrow Quarter \rightarrow Month$; for instance, $Year \rightarrow Quarter$ means that a quarter rolls-up to a year.

Each category consists of a set of dimension members. Dimension members define the instances of a data warehouse schema. For instance, *January*, *February* and *March* are dimension members assigned to category *Month*.

In order to extend this description to define a temporal data warehouse that supports valid time relationships, we have to introduce the following elements:

Chronons Usually there is a dimension describes time and represents the valid time in the system [34]. The finest dimension member within this dimension defines the chronon Q. The time axis defined through time is a series of chronons. A chronon is defined as a non-decomposable time interval of some fixed, minimal duration [56].

Time Intervals for Instances Dimensions, i.e., their categories, consist of a set of dimension members, also called nodes, and a set of hierarchical links between them, also known as edges, so that the resulting graph is a tree representing the hierarchical structure of the dimension members. In order to introduce valid time in such a system, all nodes and edges must have a time interval $[T_s, T_e]$, T_s being the beginning, and T_e the end ($T_e \geq T_s$). In [34], only edges have a time interval; however, an additional time interval for nodes is necessary in order to deal with the modification of attributes of dimension members.

Time Intervals for Schemas A multi-cube data warehouse consists of a set of multi-dimensional cubes. The structure of each cube is defined by a set of dimensions, categories and hierarchical relationships between categories. Again, this structure can be viewed as a graph whose nodes are both dimensions and categories, whereas the edges are the hierarchical relationships between categories and the assignments of the top-level categories to a dimension. As described above, all nodes and edges in this schema graph must have a time interval $[T_s, T_e]$ representing their validity periods.

Next, we present a formal description of a temporal multi-dimensional system that supports valid time in order to keep track of the history of modifications. The model is an extension to the model proposed in [52]. These extensions allow modifications on both the instance and the schema level. Furthermore, they support fact-constellation schemas, proportional aggregation and generic dimensionality, cf. Section 4.4.

The schema of our temporal data warehouse approach is defined as follows:

J, the number of dimensions.

A set of dimensions $\mathbb{D} = \{D_1, \ldots, D_J\}$, where $D_i = \langle ID, D_{Key}, [T_s, T_e] \rangle$. ID is a unique identifier of dimension; D_{Key} is a user-defined key, e.g., the name of the dimension, which is unique within the data warehouse for each timepoint $T_s \leq T \leq T_e$; $[T_s, T_e]$ represents the valid period of the dimension. Typical dimensions include *Time, Geography, Products*, and so on.

K, the number of categories.

A set of categories $\mathbb{C} = \{C_1, \ldots, C_K\}$, where $C_i = \langle ID, C_{Key}, [T_s, T_e] \rangle$. ID is a unique identifier of category; C_{Key} is a user-defined key, e.g., the name of the category, which is unique within the data warehouse for each timepoint $T_s \leq T \leq T_e$; $[T_s, T_e]$ represents the validity period of the category.Categories are also known as classification-levels [78, 129], dimension-levels or levels [52]. Typical categories of dimension *Time* include *Year, Month* and *Day*.

A set of assignments between dimensions and categories $\mathbb{A}_{DC} = \{A^1_{DC}, \ldots, A^N_{DC}\}$, where $A^i_{DC} = \langle D.ID, C.ID, [T_s, T_e] \rangle$. $D.ID$ and $C.ID$ represent the identifier of the corresponding dimension and category; $[T_s, T_e]$ represents the validity period of the assignment between this dimension and this category.

A set of hierarchical category assignments $\mathbb{HC} = \{HC_1, \ldots, HC_O\}$, where $HC_i = \langle ID, C.ID_C, C.ID_P \rangle$. ID is a unique identifier of the hierarchical category assignment; $C.ID_C$ is the identifier of a category, $C.ID_P$ is the category identifier of the parent of $C.ID_C$ or $\emptyset$ if the category is a top-level category. Set $\mathbb{HC}$ defines the hierarchical relationships between defined categories. For instance, categories *Year*, *Month* and *Day* are in the hierarchical relation $Year \rightarrow Month \rightarrow Day$.

L, the number of user-defined attributes.

A set of user-defined attributes (UDAs) $\mathbb{U} = \{U_1, \ldots, U_L\}$, where $U_i = \langle ID, U_{Key}, U_{Type},$
T_s, T_e
$, I_{ID} \rangle$. ID is a unique identifier of UDA; U_{Key} is a user-defined key, e.g., the name of the UDA, which is unique within the data warehouse for each timepoint $T_s \leq T \leq T_e$; U_{Type} defines the data type of the corresponding UDA; $[T_s, T_e]$ represents the validity period of the UDA; I_{ID} is the identifier of a dimension or a category. Identifier I_{ID} defines the set of dimension members for which the corresponding user-defined attribute is applicable: each dimension member assigned to the corresponding dimension and/or to the corresponding category may have an assigned value representing the extension of the corresponding user-defined attribute. Therefore, this set of user-defined attributes defines the name and type of all user-defined attributes within our data warehouse. Typical examples of user-defined attributes for dimension *Product* are *Colour* or *Trustee*. Therefore, each dimension member that belongs to dimension *Product* (each product) has a colour and a trustee. Furthermore, we can define a UDA called *Number of Heads* for each dimension member that is assigned to category *VCRs*. Therefore, each videocassette recorder has a colour, a trustee and a specific number of heads.

I, the number of cubes.

A set of cubes $\mathbb{B} = \{B_1, \ldots, B_I\}$, where $B_i = \langle ID, B_{Key}, [T_s, T_e], \mathcal{S} \rangle$. ID is a unique identifier of the cube, similar to oids in object-oriented database systems; B_{Key} is a user-defined key, e.g., the name of the cube, which is unique within the data warehouse for each timepoint $T_s \leq T \leq T_e$; $[T_s, T_e]$ represents the validity period of the cube; $\mathcal{S}$ represents the schema of the cube. The n-tuple $\mathcal{S}$ consists of all dimensions and hierarchical category assignments that are a part of this cube. Therefore, $\mathcal{S}$ is defined as $\mathcal{S} = (\mathbb{D}, \mathbb{A})$, where $\mathbb{D} = \{D_1.ID, \ldots, D_N.ID\}$ and $\mathbb{A} = \{HC_1.ID, \ldots, HC_M.ID\}$.

Our approach supports multi-cube warehouses. In other words, each warehouse may consist of several cubes, e.g., a cube *Fiscal Info* and a cube *Employee Info*. These cubes may or may not share several dimensions. For instance, previous cubes may share dimension *Time*, but only cube *Employee Info* has dimension *Employees*. Furthermore, categories may or may not be shared by different cubes. For instance, both cubes may share category *Month*, which is assigned to dimension *Time*, but if the sources for the fiscal cube support data on a monthly basis only, category *Day* is then assigned to cube *Employee Info* only.

The instances of our temporal data warehouse approach are defined as follows:

P, the number of dimension members.

A set of dimension members $\mathbb{M} = \{M_1, \ldots, M_P\}$, where $M_i = \langle ID, M_{Key}, \mathbb{UV}, \mathbb{CA}, [T_s, T_e] \rangle$. ID is a unique identifier of the dimension member; M_{Key} is a user-defined key, e.g., the name of the dimension member, which is unique within the data warehouse for each timepoint $T_s \leq T \leq T_e$; $[T_s, T_e]$ represents the validity period of the dimension member. $\mathbb{CA}$ represents the set of categories to which the corresponding dimension member is assigned. If a dimension member is assigned to more than one categories and they belong to the same cube for at least one point in time, we then call it a shared member. $\mathbb{UV}$ is a set of tuples that consists of all user-defined attribute values. It is defined as $\mathbb{UV} = \{(U.ID_1, V_1), \ldots, (U.ID_N, V_N)\}$ where $U.ID_i$ is the identifier of the corresponding user-defined attribute, i.e., its definition, and V_i its value, i.e., its extension. For instance, *January* is a dimension member that belongs to category *Month*, and *January, 1* is a dimension member assigned to category *Day*. Furthermore, the set $\mathbb{UV}$ holds all UDA values. For instance, product *VCR 2000* has *Colour* gray and 4 heads.

A set of hierarchical member assignments $\mathbb{HM} = \{HM_1, \ldots, HM_O\}$, where $HM_i = \langle ID, M.ID_C, M.ID_P \rangle$. ID is a unique identifier of the hierarchical member assignment; $M.ID_C$ is the identifier of a dimension member, $M.ID_P$ is the dimension member identifier of the parent of $M.ID_C$ or $\emptyset$ if the dimension member is at the top-level. For instance, dimension members *2002*, *January* and *January, 1* are in the hierarchical relation $2002 \rightarrow January \rightarrow January.1$.

A function $cval : (M_{D_1}, \ldots, M_{D_N}) \rightarrow value$ that uniquely assigns a value to each vector $(M_{D_1}, \ldots, M_{D_N}) \in \mathcal{M}_{D_1} \times \ldots \times \mathcal{M}_{D_N}$. The domain of this function is the set of all cell references. The range of this function are all cell values, i.e., measures of a cube.

4.3.1 Structure versions

Temporal projection and temporal selection, as defined in the Consensus Glossary of Temporal Database Concepts [56], allows us to create a structure version (SV) out of a temporal data warehouse. Intuitively, a structure version is a view on a multi-dimensional structure, its schema definitions and its instances, that is valid for a given time interval $[T_s, T_e]$. All dimensions, categories, dimension members, user-defined attributes and hierarchical relationships within this multi-dimensional structure are also valid for the given time interval. In other words, there cannot exist different versions of a dimension member or a hierarchical relationship within one structure version. Conversely, each modification of a dimension, a category, a dimension member, a user-defined attribute or a hierarchical relationship leads to a new structure version, if a structure version for the given time interval does not exist.

Formally, each structure version is a triple $\langle SV_{id}, T, \mathbb{CD} \rangle$ where SV_{id} is a unique identifier and T represent the validity period of that structure version as a interval of the form $[T_s, T_e]$. $\mathbb{CD}$ represents all cubes (their schema definitions and their instances) that are valid within the given time interval T, i.e., $\mathbb{CD}$ consists of the sets $\mathbb{D}$ (dimensions), $\mathbb{C}$ (categories), $\mathbb{A}_{DC}$ (assignments between dimensions and categories), $\mathbb{HC}$ (hierarchical relationships between categories), $\mathbb{U}$ (user-defined attributes), $\mathbb{B}$ (cubes), $\mathbb{M}$ (dimension members) and $\mathbb{HM}$ (hierarchical relationships between dimension members). Each element in the sets mentioned is therefore valid at each timepoint P with $T_s \leq P \leq T_e$.

On a conceptual level, of course not on an implementation level, we can say that there exists a corresponding set of cubes for each structure version SV. These cubes have the same valid time interval as SV.

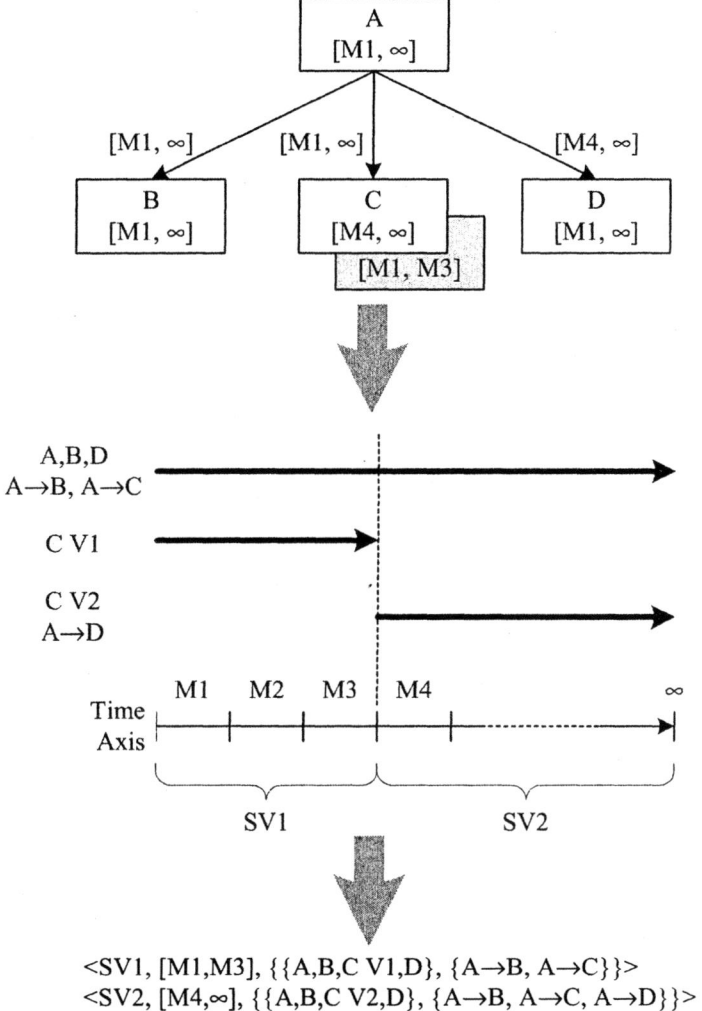

Figure 4.3: Computing structure versions.

The example in Fig. 4.3 shows how to compute the set of valid structure versions. It presents a cube with one dimension. This dimension consists of four different dimension members A, B, C and D, and their hierarchical relationships, e.g., B is a child of A. Furthermore, it depicts the time stamps of all dimension members and all hierarchical relationships between dimension members. Here, we have to deal with two different versions of dimension member C: the former is valid from $Month1$ (M_1) until $Month3$ (M_3), and the latter is valid from M_4 until NOW, which is denoted by ∞. Furthermore, dimension member D is valid from M_1 until NOW, but the hierarchical relationship between A and D is valid from M_4 until NOW. If we represent all time stamps of all modifications within our data warehouse on a linear time axis, the interval between two succeeding time stamps on this axis represents a structure version. Therefore, two structure versions can be identified in this example:

$\langle SV_1, [M_1, M_3], \{\mathbb{M} = \{A, B, CV_1, D\}, \mathbb{HM} = \{A \to B, A \to C\}\}\rangle$;
$\langle SV_2, [M_4, \infty], \{\mathbb{M} = \{A, B, CV_2, D\}, \mathbb{HM} = \{A \to B, A \to C, A \to D\}\}\rangle$.

In this example we have two different structure versions called SV_1 and SV_2. SV_1 and dimension members (A, B, C in version 1 and D); hierarchical assignments ($A \to B, \ldots$) are valid from M_1 to M_3. SV_2, dimension members and hierarchical assignments are valid from M_4 to ∞, i.e., until now. For the sake of readability, we take into consideration the instances of the cube only, and skip the schema definitions in this example. However, each modification of the schema, e.g., when inserting a new dimension or deleting a category, would also be reflected in the set of structure versions.

4.3.2 Structural changes

Once the concept of a temporal data warehouse has been defined, we present the three basic operations to modify the schema and the instances of a temporal data warehouse, namely: INSERT, UPDATE and DELETE.

A given chronon Q defines the granularity of data in the data warehouse regarding time. Therefore, we would not gain any additional information from considering structural changes within one chronon. Therefore, we only have to capture structural changes with the granularity defined through the chronon.

We define a data warehouse (DWH) as a non-empty, finite set of structure versions, i.e., $DWH = \{SV_1, \ldots, SV_n\}$. As mentioned above, version SV_i is a triple $\langle SV_{id}, T, \mathbb{CD} \rangle$. This data warehouse must be a consecutive sequence of tuples $\langle SV_i, T_i, \mathbb{CD}_i \rangle$, where $T_i = [T_{i,s}, T_{i,e}]$ and $T_{i,s} = T_{(i-1),e} + Q$.

The contents of the temporal data warehouse can be modified using operations INSERT, DELETE and UPDATE. In contrast to the definition of these basic operations proposed in [52], the following definitions allow to apply them both to instances and the schema of a data warehouse. The operations are defined as follows:

INSERT This operation inserts a new object (a dimension, a category, a dimension member, a hierarchical relationship between categories, and so on), and it is defined as INSERT(O, T_s). O is the new object, and T_s defines that O is valid in interval $[T_s, \infty]$. A unique identifier O_{id} is assigned to the new element.

UPDATE This operation is defined as UPDATE(O, O', T_s). O is the object that has to be updated, O' comprises the new values for that object, and T_s represents the start of the validity period for the new version of the object. An UPDATE operation entails two actions, namely: modify the existing object, setting the ending time to $T_s - Q$, and insert a new object, setting the valid time interval to $[T_s, \infty]$.

DELETE This operation is defined as DELETE(O, T_e). This operation sets the ending time of object O to T_e.

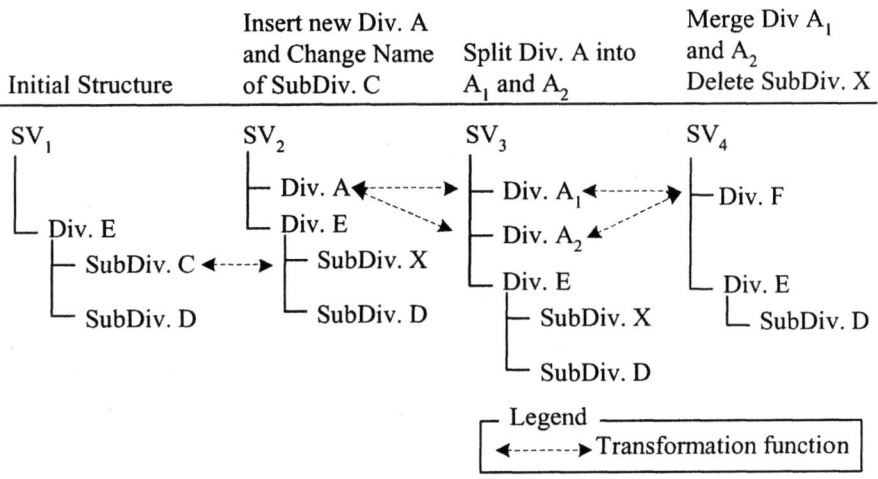

Figure 4.4: An example of structural changes and transformation functions.

If there is not a structure version that starts with the time stamp of the corresponding INSERT, UPDATE or DELETE operation, a new structure version is then generated.

We can modify the schema and the instances of a temporal data warehouse by means of these basic operations. With respect to dimension members, the basic operations defined above may be combined to represent the following complex operations:

SPLIT This operation splits dimension member M into n dimension members, $M_1, \ldots, M_n$. This operation translates into DELETE$(M, T_s - Q)$ and a set of insert operations INSERT(M_i, T_s).

For instance, Fig. 4.4 shows a split operation between structure versions SV_2 and SV_3 in which a division $Div.A$ splits up into two divisions called $Div.A_1$ and $Div.A_2$. We would need one delete operation ($Div.A$) and two inserts ($Div.A_1$ and $Div.A_2$) to deal with this.

MERGE This operation merges dimension members $M_1, \ldots, M_n$ into dimension member M. A merge operation translates into a set of delete operations DELETE$(M_i, T_s - Q)$ and an insert operation INSERT(M, T_s).

A merge is the opposite of a split, i.e., if we split a dimension member along one direction of time, e.g, from the past to the future, this split can then be considered as a merge along the opposite direction of time, e.g, from the future to the past. In the example above, consider that these modifications occur at timepoint T. For each analysis that requires data from a timepoint before T for the structure version which is valid at timepoint T, we would refer to these modifications as splits; for each analysis that requires data from timepoint T for a structure version valid before timepoint T, we would refer to these modifications as merges.

CHANGE An attribute of a dimension member changes, for instance, if the product number (key) or the name of a department (user-defined attribute) changes. Such a modification can be done by using the update operation defined above.

MOVE Modify the hierarchical position of a dimension member, e.g., if product P no longer belongs to product group G_A but to product group G_B. This can be done by changing the DM_{id}^P (parent ID) of the corresponding dimension member with an update operation.

NEW-MEMBER Insert a new dimension member, e.g., if a new product becomes part of the product spectrum. This modification can be done by using an insert operation.

DELETE-MEMBER Delete a dimension member, e.g., if a branch disbands. The new-member and delete-member relationship are also related to the direction of time. Contrarily to a new-member operation, there is a relationship between the deleted dimension member and the following structure version. Consider, for instance, that we delete a dimension member DM_X at timepoint T. If we requested data for the structure version valid at timepoint T from a timepoint before T, we still might get valid data by simply subtracting the data for DM_X from its parent.

4.3.3 Mappings between structure versions

Next, we extend the temporal model of a data warehouse with the definition of transformation functions between structure versions. A structure version is a view on a temporal data warehouse that is valid for a given time period $[T_s, T_e]$. We distinguish between the structure of a structure version (the set of all valid dimension members of the structure version together with their hierarchies) and the data of a structure version (the cube defined by mapping the structure to the value domain).

For answering queries on the data warehouse the user has to define which structure version should be used. The data returned by the query can, however, originate from several, different temporal versions of the cube. Therefore, it is necessary to provide transformation functions mapping data from one structure version to a different structure version.

To assure that queries can be stated in both directions of time, the model has to support two functions for each modification of dimension data; one function to map data from the past into the present, and the converse function. (Terms past and present are used relative to a certain structure version.)

In the rest of this section, we make the following assumptions: (a) relationships between different structure versions depend on the fact under consideration; (b) for sake of simplicity and understandability, we only consider the cube for a single fact, (c) furthermore, the cell values of upper-level dimension members are always computed from their subordinate lower-level dimension members. Therefore, without loss of generality, we do not consider the upper levels here and assume that the dimensions are flat. Roughly speaking, before we transform the data, we select the cube of the dimension members at level 0 (dimension members without any children), and then transform this subset of cell values and compute the upper levels of the resulting cube bottom-up, as usual.

Definition of inter-structure relationships

Transformation functions are used to map data (cell values) for particular numeric facts and a particular dimension member from one structure version into another using a weighting factor. Therefore, we provide an operation called $MapF$ that is defined as $MapF(SV_j, SV_k, DM_{id}, DM'_{id}, \{M^1_{id}, \ldots, M^n_{id}\}, w)$, where:

SV_j and SV_k are different contiguous structure versions. Two structure versions SV_i and SV_k are contiguous if $T_{s,i} = T_{e,k} + Q$ or if $T_{s,k} = T_{e,i} + Q$, where Q is the defined data warehouse chronon, $T_{s,n}$ is the start time of the valid time interval of structure version SV_n and $T_{e,n}$ is the ending time of the valid time interval of structure version SV_n.

DM_{id} and DM'_{id} are unique identifiers for dimension members for which $DM_{id} \in SV_j$ and $DM'_{id} \in SV_k$ is true. DM_{id} and DM'_{id} must be dimension members of the same dimension. $\{M^1_{id}, \ldots, M^n_{id}\}$ is a non-empty, finite set of fact identifiers and $\exists f \cdot f \in F \wedge f_{id} = M^i_{id}$.

w is the weighting factor to map data from one structure version into another.

We implicitly introduce a transformation function with weighting factor $w = 1$ for each dimension member; it does not change from one structure version to another, and it does not have any explicit transformation function. Transformation functions may be applied to map data between contiguous structure versions, e.g., $SV_1 \leftrightarrow SV_2$. Furthermore, transformation functions can be applied to level-0 dimension members only. The data for upper-level dimension members are always computed from the lower level members of the same dimension in the same structure version.

For a split or a merge operation, we need several transformation functions, e.g., if department A splits up into A_1, A_2 and A_3, we need three functions to map data from A to A_n and three functions to map data from A_n to A. We do not restrict the user regarding weighting factor w. This means that the sum of all weighting factors for all functions $A \rightarrow A_n$ (split) does not have to be 1, i.e., 100%. Conversely, not all weighting factors of functions $A_1 \rightarrow A, \ldots, A_n \rightarrow A$ (merge) need to be 1. This allows to represent the effects of structural changes such as product *Personal Computer* is not longer sold as a whole, but separately as *Monitor* and *Desktop Box*. The combined price for both products is higher than the price for *Personal Computer*, i.e., the sum of all weighting factors is greater than 100%.

The example in Fig. 4.4 shows several structural changes in dimension *Divisions*, e.g., *Subdiv.C* was renamed to *Subdiv.X* from SV_1 to SV_2, *Div.A* was split into *Div.A$_1$* and *Div.A$_2$* from SV_2 to SV_3, and so on. This example would result in the following transformation functions for fact *Turnover*:

1. $MapF(SV_1, SV_2, Div.C, Div.X, \{\text{Turnover}\}, 1)$;

2. $MapF(SV_2, SV_1, Div.X, Div.C, \{\text{Turnover}\}, 1)$;

3. $MapF(SV_2, SV_3, Div.A, Div.A_1, \{\text{Turnover}\}, 0.3)$;

4. $MapF(SV_2, SV_3, Div.A, Div.A_2, \{\text{Turnover}\}, 0.7)$;

5. $MapF(SV_3, SV_2, Div.A_1, Div.A, \{\text{Turnover}\}, 1)$;

6. $MapF(SV_3, SV_2, Div.A_2, Div.A, \{\text{Turnover}\}, 1)$;

7. and so on.

This set of functions, for instance, states that for fact *Turnover*, the division A_1 in SV_3 corresponds to 30% of the division A in SV_2 (cf. Function 3). Conversely, the division A in SV_2 is equal to the sum of A_1 and A_2 in SV_3 (cf. Function 5 and Function 6).

Furthermore, the following set of transformation functions is introduced implicitly:

1. $MapF(SV_1, SV_2, Subdiv.D, Subdic.D, \{\text{Turnover}\}, 1)$;

2. $MapF(SV_2, SV_1, Subdiv.D, Subdic.D, \{\text{Turnover}\}, 1)$;

3. $MapF(SV_2, SV_3, Subdiv.D, Subdic.D, \{\text{Turnover}\}, 1)$;

4. $MapF(SV_3, SV_2, Subdiv.D, Subdic.D, \{\text{Turnover}\}, 1)$;

5. and so on.

Next, we discuss how to use matrices to represent transformation functions and to transform data from one structure version into another.

Transformation matrices

Conceptually, we can represent each multi-dimensional cube and the relationships between dimension members of different structure versions as matrices.

Let SV_i be a structure version with N dimensions. Each dimension D_N consists of a set $\mathcal{DM}_N^{L0}$ which represents all level-0 dimension members of that dimension. We can represent this structure version as a $\mathcal{DM}_1^{L0} \times \mathcal{DM}_2^{L0} \times \ldots \times \mathcal{DM}_N^{L0}$ matrix. For instance, a structure version for a 1-dimensional cube results in a vector, whereas a structure version for a 3-dimensional cube results in a matrix of vectors. Fig. 4.5 shows a 3-dimensional cube C_{3D} represented as a matrix, where a_i, b_j and c_k are dimension members at level 0 of the corresponding dimensions A, B and C.

Let SV_1 and SV_2 be two structure versions. We define a transformation matrix $T_{SV_1, SV_2, D_i, F}$ for each dimension D_i and each fact F. Where $T(d_i, d_j)$ is a number representing the weighting factor for mapping F of dimension member d_i of structure version SV_1 to a fact of dimension member d_j of structure version SV_2. These transformation matrices are merely another means to represent the information contained in relation $MapF$. It is worth mentioning that the construction of these matrices is a conceptual view on the transformation. Any meaningful implementation must take into account that these matrices are usually extremely sparse, so they should not be implemented naively.

For instance, consider that cube C represents the structure defined through structure version SV_1 with dimensions $A = \{a_1, a_2, a_3\}$ and $B = \{b_1, b_2, b_3\}$ (a_i and b_j are dimension members). We represent the cell values for a specific fact in this cube as a matrix. Therefore, a value in this matrix represents a cell value in the given 2-dimensional cube.

$$C = \begin{array}{c} \\ b_1 \\ b_2 \\ b_3 \end{array} \begin{array}{c} a_1 \quad a_2 \quad a_3 \\ \left(\begin{array}{ccc} 3 & 7 & 5 \\ 10 & 8 & 6 \\ 20 & 13 & 5 \end{array} \right) \end{array}$$

Temporal Versioning in Data Warehouses

$$C_{3D} = \begin{pmatrix} & & a_1 & & a_2 & \\ b_1 & \begin{matrix} c_1 \\ c_2 \\ c_3 \end{matrix} & \begin{pmatrix} 7 \\ 2 \\ 9 \end{pmatrix} & \begin{matrix} c_1 \\ c_2 \\ c_3 \end{matrix} & \begin{pmatrix} 10 \\ 3 \\ 8 \end{pmatrix} \\ b_2 & \begin{matrix} c_1 \\ c_2 \\ c_3 \end{matrix} & \begin{pmatrix} 5 \\ 3 \\ 8 \end{pmatrix} & \begin{matrix} c_1 \\ c_2 \\ c_3 \end{matrix} & \begin{pmatrix} 9 \\ 2 \\ 6 \end{pmatrix} \\ b_3 & \begin{matrix} c_1 \\ c_2 \\ c_3 \end{matrix} & \begin{pmatrix} 7 \\ 4 \\ 7 \end{pmatrix} & \begin{matrix} c_1 \\ c_2 \\ c_3 \end{matrix} & \begin{pmatrix} 5 \\ 5 \\ 11 \end{pmatrix} \end{pmatrix}$$

Figure 4.5: Example of a 3-dimensional cube matrix.

As mentioned above, we need one transformation matrix for each dimension D_i to map data from structure version SV_1 into structure version SV_2. In the following example, we split the dimension member a_1 into a_{11} and a_{12} and then merge b_1 and b_2 into b_{12}. The functions between SV_1 and SV_2 for a fact are defined as follows:

1. $MapF(SV_1, SV_2, a_1, a_{11}, Fact, 0.3)$;
2. $MapF(SV_1, SV_2, a_1, a_{12}, Fact, 0.7)$;
3. $MapF(SV_1, SV_2, b_1, b_{12}, Fact, 1)$;
4. $MapF(SV_1, SV_2, b_2, b_{12}, Fact, 1)$.

To represent these functions, we define two transformation matrices, namely: T_A for dimension A, and T_B for dimension B. The definition follows:

$$T_A = \begin{matrix} \\ a_1 \\ a_2 \\ a_3 \end{matrix} \begin{pmatrix} a_{11} & a_{12} & a_2 & a_3 \\ 0.3 & 0.7 & 0 & 0 \\ 0 & 0 & 1 & 0 \\ 0 & 0 & 0 & 1 \end{pmatrix}$$

$$T_B = \begin{matrix} \\ b_{12} \\ b_3 \end{matrix} \begin{pmatrix} b_1 & b_2 & b_3 \\ 1 & 1 & 0 \\ 0 & 0 & 1 \end{pmatrix}$$

Non-contiguous structure versions

As presented above, a transformation matrix represents a set of $MapF$ operations defined to map measures between two contiguous structure versions. Transformation matrices between non-contiguous structure versions can be computed automatically by multiplying the corresponding set of transformation matrices between contiguous structure versions.

Let $T_{SV_1,SV_2,D,F}, T_{SV_2,SV_3,D,F}, \ldots, T_{SV_{n-1},SV_n,D,F}$ be a set of transformation matrices to transform measures of fact F along dimension D. Then, $T_{SV_1,SV_2,D,F} T_{SV_2,SV_3,D,F} \ldots T_{SV_{n-1},SV_n,D,F} = T_{SV_1,SV_n,D,F}$, where $T_{SV_1,SV_n,D,F}$ is a transformation function to transform measures from structure version SV_1 into structure version SV_n.

For instance, let $T_A = T_{SV_1,SV_2,D_A,F}$ be a transformation function, as given in the example before, to map measures from structure version SV_1 into structure version SV_2, where dimension member a_1 split into a_{11} and a_{12}. Consider that, for dimension A, dimension members a_2 and a_3 in structure version SV_2 merged into a new dimension member called a_{23} that is valid in structure version SV_3. We represent this in transformation matrix $T_{SV_2,SV_3,D_A,F}$.

$$T_{SV_1,SV_2,D_A,F} = \begin{array}{c} \\ a_1 \\ a_2 \\ a_3 \end{array} \begin{array}{cccc} a_{11} & a_{12} & a_2 & a_3 \\ \left(\begin{array}{cccc} 0.3 & 0.7 & 0 & 0 \\ 0 & 0 & 1 & 0 \\ 0 & 0 & 0 & 1 \end{array} \right) \end{array}$$

$$T_{SV_2,SV_3,D_A,F} = \begin{array}{c} \\ a_{11} \\ a_{12} \\ a_2 \\ a_3 \end{array} \begin{array}{ccc} a_{11} & a_{12} & a_{23} \\ \left(\begin{array}{ccc} 1 & 0 & 0 \\ 0 & 1 & 0 \\ 0 & 0 & 1 \\ 0 & 0 & 1 \end{array} \right) \end{array}$$

The multiplication of these transformation matrices leads to a new transformation matrix $T_{SV_1,SV_3,D_A,F}$ to transform measures from structure version SV_1 into structure version SV_2.

$$T_{SV_1,SV_3,D_A,F} = T_{SV_1,SV_2,D_A,F} T_{SV_2,SV_3,D_A,F} =$$

$$= \begin{array}{c} \\ a_1 \\ a_2 \\ a_3 \end{array} \begin{array}{ccc} a_{11} & a_{12} & a_{23} \\ \left(\begin{array}{ccc} 0.3 & 0.7 & 0 \\ 0 & 0 & 1 \\ 0 & 0 & 1 \end{array} \right) \end{array}$$

Transformation of warehouse data

The goal of this transformation is to map the warehouse data (cube) of a certain structure version SV_1 to the structure of a different structure version SV_2. We first define a function to transform the cube in one dimension: $f_{SV_1,SV_2,D,F}$ transforms the values of fact F of structure version SV_1 to structure version SV_2 in dimension D as follows:

$$f_{SV_1,SV_2,D,F}(C_{D=j}) = C'_{D=i}$$

with

$$C'_{D=i} = \sum_{j \in DM_{D,SV_1}} T_{SV_1,SV_2,D,F}(i,j) C_{D=j} \text{ for all } i \in DM_{D,SV_2}$$

where C is a cube with the dimension members of SV_1 in dimension D, and C' is the transformed cube where all values in the cube have been transformed to the members of dimension D in structure version SV_2 according to transformation matrix T. $C_{D=j}$ is the $(n-1)$-dimensional subcube of an n-dimensional cube associated with member j in dimension D. Obviously, transforming a cube in dimension D_x first, next in dimension D_y yields the same result as the converse transformation:

$$f_{D_y}(f_{D_x}(C)) = f_{D_x}(f_{D_y}(C))$$

given that

$$\forall i, k \cdot C'_{D_x=i,D_y=k} \sum_j T_{D_x}(i,j) \sum_l T_{D_y}(k,l) C_{D_y=l,D_x=j} =$$
$$= \sum_l T_{D_y}(k,l) \sum_j T_{D_x}(i,j) C_{D_y=l,D_x=j} = f_{D_x}(f_{D_y}(C))$$

The transformation of a fact F in cube C from structure version SV_1 to structure version SV_2 is now defined as a sequence of functions that transform the cube in all dimensions D_i successively:

$$f_{SV_1,SV_2,F} = f_{SV_1,SV_2,D_1,F}(f_{SV_1,SV_2,D_2,F}(\ldots f_{SV_1,SV_2,D_n,F}(C_{SV_1})\ldots))$$

According to the observation above, the result does not depend on the sequence of transformations used. Again, we emphasise that this is the specification of a transformation function, and the actual implementation should exploit the sparseness of the matrices involved adequately.

For instance, we are now able to transform data from SV_1 into SV_2 by means of these transformation functions. Cube C and transformation matrices T_A and T_B were presented in the example in Section 4.3.3.

$$C' = f_{SV_1,SV_2,D_A,F}(f_{SV_1,SV_2,D_B,F}(C)) =$$
$$= \begin{matrix} & a_{11} & a_{12} & a_2 & a_3 \\ b_{12} & \begin{pmatrix} 3.9 & 9.1 & 15 & 11 \\ 6 & 14 & 13 & 5 \end{pmatrix} \\ b_3 & \end{matrix}$$

Matrix C' represents the cube with the structure defined through structure version SV_2 and the values of structure version SV_1.

4.4 The $\mathcal{COMET}$ Metamodel

We now adapt the concept presented in Section 4.3 to the Unified Modeling Language (UML) [77]. The result was published previously in [54].

4.4.1 Goals and features

In contrast to well-known modelling techniques for data warehouses, e.g., Star Schema, our model allows to model data warehouses that evolve over the time. It offers the following features for the definition of data warehouses:

Temporal Data Warehousing $\mathcal{COMET}$ allows us to keep track of modifications on both the instance level and the schema level.

Instance Level: instances, i.e. dimension members may change over the time. For instance, new products may become a part of the product port-folio of a company, divisions may split into several subdivisions or the way to compute facts may change over the time.

Schema Level: The schema of the defined data warehouse may change over the time. For instance, dimensions may be deleted or categories may be inserted.

Multi-period Comparisons Transformation functions allow to define so-called inter-structure relationships. Therefore, measures stored in a cube can be transformed from one version of the cube into another and thus allow us to answer queries spanning multiple periods correctly, even after a modification to the structure.

Extended Fact-Constellation Schemas Frequently, all measures and dimensions cannot be captured in a single schema. Usually, a data warehouse consists of several fact tables described by several (shared or non-shared) dimensions. $COMET$ allows to set up fact-constellation schemas (also known as galaxy schemas) [3]. Thus, it allows for shared dimensions, e.g., dimension *Products* may be part of several cubes.

In contrast to fact-constellation schemas, $COMET$ allows to share dimensions amongst different cubes, as well as parts (subsets of dimensions) of dimensions only. For instance, two cubes may share categories *Year* and *Month* of dimension *Time*, but only one cube may have category *Day*.

Proportional Aggregation Our model supports correct aggregation even if dimension members are not disjunct. This means that one dimension member may belong to several parents, e.g., the fifth calendar week of the year 2002, which is a dimension member of category *Weeks*, belongs to January and February: days 4–7 belong to January, and days 3–7 belong to February. Our model supports proportional aggregation to enable correct aggregation of non-disjunct dimension members.

Generic Dimensionality In contrast to the different OLAP models proposed so far, ours fulfills Codd's sixth OLAP rule of generic dimensionality [39]. According to this, each dimension must be equivalent in both its structure and operational capabilities.

For instance, we deal with dimension *Time*, which is usually a part of every data warehouse. Furthermore, we represent the facts of a data warehouse as a dimension called *Facts*. Although there are discussions about Codd's sixth OLAP rule, it allows to apply the whole functionality of our approach even to dimension *Time* or *Facts*. For instance, dimension *Time* can become finer or coarser, i.e., we can insert or delete a new leaf category (days instead of weeks). Obviously we have to register such changes and transform values back and forth.

4.4.2 The elements of $COMET$

The core of $COMET$ is composed of a set of classes to represent cubes (class `CubeVersion`), dimensions (class `Dimension`), categories (class `Category`) and dimension members (class `Member`). A cube consists of several dimensions and each dimension consists of several categories, as shown in Fig. 4.6 by means of multiplicity symbols.

Temporal Versioning in Data Warehouses

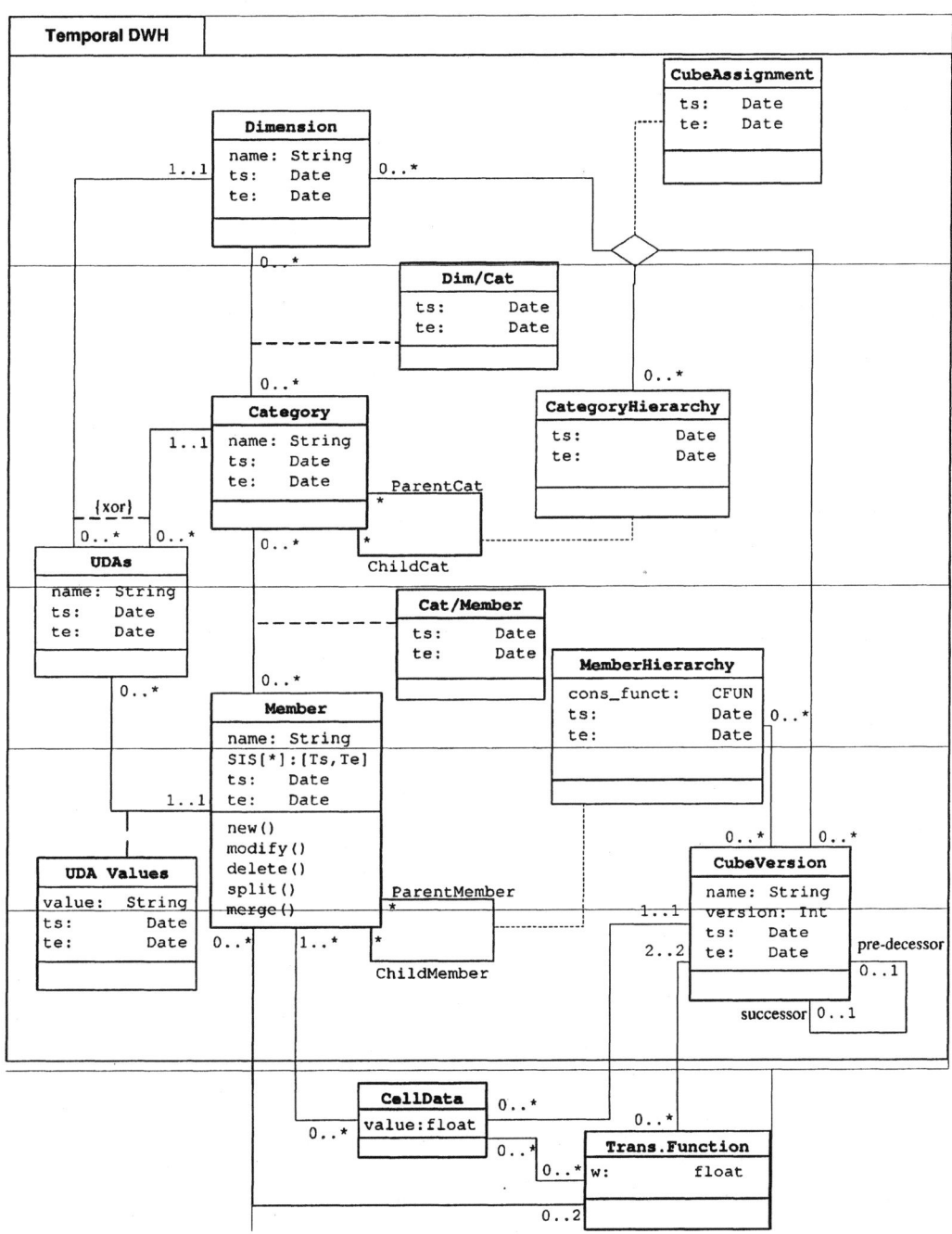

Figure 4.6: The $COMET$ model (using UML).

Categories are represented by class `Category`, and they are ordered hierarchically. For instance, categories *Country*, *State*, *Region* and *City* are ordered as follows: *Country* → *State*, *Country* → *Region*, *State* → *City* and *Region* → *City*, were $X \rightarrow Y$ means that Y rolls up to X. This is represented by the recursive association of class `Category`.

The same applies for dimension members. For instance, dimension members *USA*, *Texas*, *South* and *Dallas* are ordered according to $USA \rightarrow Texas$, $USA \rightarrow South$, $Texas \rightarrow Dallas$ and $South \rightarrow Texas$.

Given that both hierarchical relationships between categories and between dimension members may change over the time, we have to represent the validity period of these relations with a time stamp in classes `CategoryHierarchy` and `MemberHierarchy`. Furthermore, we have to represent how data may be aggregated. We represent this with attribute `cons_func` in class `MemberHierarchy`. Furthermore, this attributes allows the representation of proportional aggregation functions for non-disjunct members. For instance, an salesman may be assigned to two divisions *Div1* and *Div2*. The amount of sales attained by this salesman may be assigned with factors 40% and 60% to divisions *Div1* and *Div2*.

Another important issue with which $COMET$ has to deal is that the relationship between dimensions and categories may change over the time. The same applies for the relationship between categories and dimension members. This is represented with time stamps (attributes t_s and t_e) in association classes `Dim/Cat` and `Cat/Member`.

We have to deal with different versions of a cube because the schema and/or instances of a cube may change over the time, and $COMET$ supports both schema evolution and schema versioning. Each version of a cube may have a preceding and a succeeding version, and each version is valid for a given validity period. We represent that with class `CubeVersion` and its recursive relationship.

$COMET$ supports transformation of data from one structure and/or schema version into the (immediate) succeeding or preceding version. We represent these transformation functions within class `Trans.Function`. Each transformation function transforms several cell data entries from exactly one version into its preceding or succeeding version. Furthermore, several transformation functions may be defined to transform a cell value from one version into its preceding and succeeding version.

Transformation functions are allowed between contiguous cube versions only. Versions V_i and V_k are contiguous if $T_{s,i} = T_{e,k} + Q$ or if $T_{s,k} = T_{e,i} + Q$, where Q is the defined chronon of the data warehouse. As described in Section 4.3.3, we can represent these transformation functions by matrices. In order to increase query performance, we are able to compute transformation matrices between two non-contiguous versions by multiplying all corresponding transformation matrices. Consider, for instance, two transformation matrices $M_{1\rightarrow 2}$ to transform data from structure version SV_1 into version SV_2 and $M_{2\rightarrow 3}$ to transform data from version SV_2 into version SV_3. We can compute a transformation function $M_{1\rightarrow 3}$ to transform data from version SV_1 into SV_3 by multiplying these transformation matrices.

As described before, $COMET$ allows us to assign different dimensions to a cube. Furthermore, each dimension may be assigned to several cubes in order to allow fact-constellation schemas. Furthermore, if a dimension is assigned to more then one cube, it may consist of a different structure, i.e., a different set of categories and their hierarchical assignments in each cube. This is represented by the ternary association between classes `CubeVersion`, `Dimension` and `CategoryHierarchy`.

Furthermore, each dimension member may have different user-defined attributes (UDA), e.g., the products stored in the data warehouse may have a *Colour* and a *Weight*. Therefore, UDAs are attributes that describe a dimension member. In contrast to dimensions, UDAs

Temporal Versioning in Data Warehouses 93

do not allow the application of OLAP functionality, e.g., drill-down, roll-up, slice, and so on.

$\mathcal{COMET}$ allows the definition of UDAs for each defined dimension or category. The UDAs defined for a certain dimension define the UDAs applicable for all dimension members assigned to this dimension (all dimension members that are assigned to a category that is assigned to the specific dimension). The UDAs defined for a certain category define the UDAs applicable to all dimension members assigned to this category. For instance, one may want to assign a *Colour* to each product and thus define this UDA through dimension *Products*, but only products that belong to category *Video Cassette Recorder* have UDA *Number of Heads*. Attributes t_s and t_e in class UDAs represent the validity period of a UDA.

The association class UDAValues specifies the value of a specific UDA for a specific dimension member. Attributes t_s and t_e in class UDA Values represent the validity period of a value defined for a specific UDA and a specific dimension member.

The measures of a data warehouse are stored in class CellData. As mentioned before, a measure, i.e., a cell in an n-dimensional data cube contains a value and is referenced by vector $\nu = (DM_{D_1}, ..., DM_{D_N})$, where DM_{D_i} is a dimension member that is assigned to a dimension D_i [96]. For instance, $\nu = (Sales, Drinks, Toronto, Jan.\ 2001)$ references the sales of drinks sold in Toronto in January 2001 in a four-dimensional cube. One can consider the validity period of a specific measure by defining dimension *Time*, which is usually a part of every data warehouse, i.e., multi-dimensional cube.

Due to the temporal extensions $\mathcal{COMET}$ offers, integrity constraints have to be taken into consideration. $\mathcal{COMET}$ comprises 23 integrity constraints. A description and a formal definition were presented in [54].

4.5 Implementation

We implemented $\mathcal{COMET}$ as a layer between data warehouse sources and a standard front-end such as Hyperion Essbase, Oracle Express or Cognos PowerPlay. (Currently, we are using Hyperion Essbase v6.1). The main advantage of this approach is that it does not require a front-end implementation. In [53], we discussed several approaches to query the data stored in our temporal data warehouse model. We implemented one of these approaches, namely the indirect approach.

The indirect approach can be easily integrated into an existing data warehouse architecture. As we use a standard OLAP database as front-end, each data mart generated offers the whole OLAP functionality, e.g., drill-down, roll-up, slice, dice, and so on. The performance of queries is not affected by this modification of the data warehouse architecture because it depends on the OLAP database system used.

The main idea of the indirect approach is, as shown in Fig. 4.7, that the transformer generates one data mart for each structure version the user needs. In most cases, this is be the current structure version only. Each data mart consists of all fact data that are valid for the same time interval as the corresponding structure version, and fact data that can be transformed by the set of $MapF$ functions defined. Therefore, the user defines his or her base structure version by selecting a specific data mart.

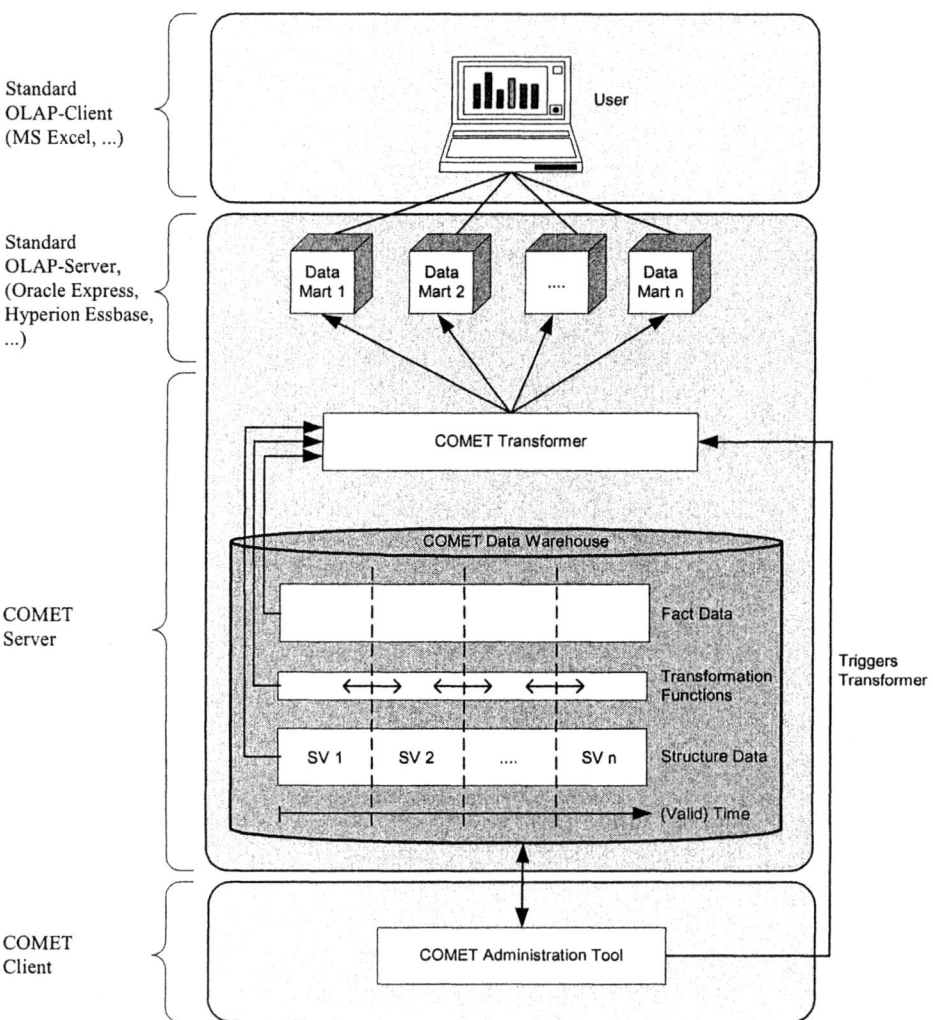

Figure 4.7: Architecture of the indirect approach.

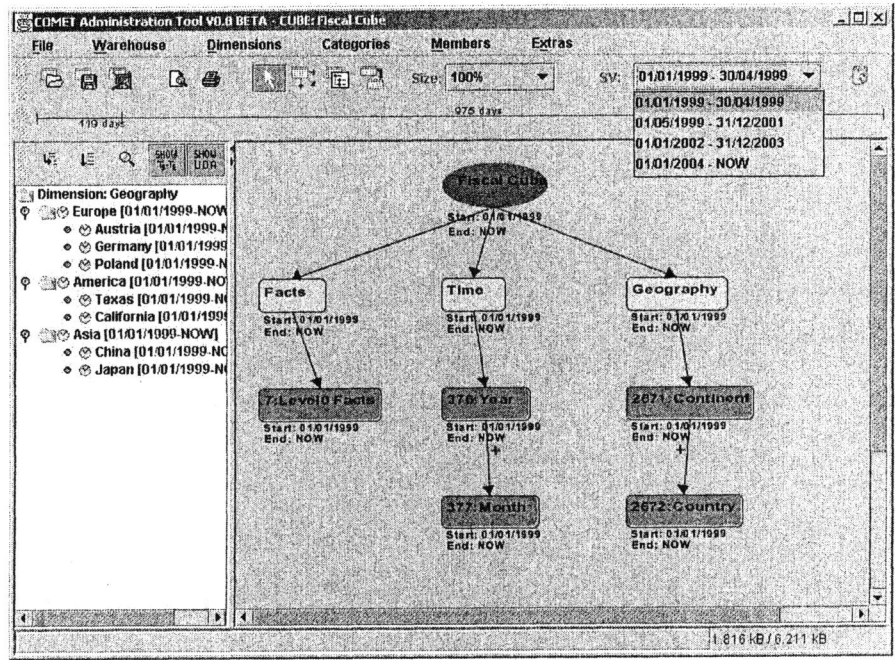

Figure 4.8: A cube built with the administration tool.

Fig. 4.7 shows the parts of the indirect approach, namely:

Administration Tool It allows an administrator to import new cell data into the temporal data warehouse and, of course, to perform modifications of the multi-dimensional structure at the schema and instance levels. The administration tool is implemented in Java.

Fig. 4.8 shows a screen shot. The instances of dimension (*Geography*) are shown as a tree on the left; the schema of the selected cube, i.e., its dimensions and categories and their hierarchical relationships, are shown on the right.

Temporal Data Warehouse It holds the information required about the schemas and instances of the cubes defined, its structure versions, cell data and transformation functions as described in Section 4.3. We use a standard relational database management system (tested with Oracle 8.1) as the basis for our temporal data warehouse.

Transformer It transforms all required cell values from all required structure versions into the chosen base structure version by using the transformation functions defined, i.e., by using all necessary $MapF$ functions. The transformer is implemented in Java. We used the Java Native Interface (JNI) to gain access to the application programming interface (API) of Hyperion Essbase.

We call this approach indirect because the transformer is triggered by the administration tool, not by the user. In other words, it starts to generate data marts only after a new structure version has been generated or new measures have been imported. In both cases, it has to recalculate all existing data marts in order to return consistent information.

As we use a standard OLAP database for each data mart, the main advantage of the indirect approach is that each data mart offers the whole OLAP functionality, e.g., drill-down, roll-up, slice, dice, and so on.

4.6 Conclusions

Data warehouses are dynamic with respect to the measures they store and the structure of dimensions. Modifications to the structure may, for instance, stem from legal changes or organisational changes, from changes in the way economic figures such as unemployment rate or consumer price indexes are computed, or from changes in units, e.g., from Austrian Schillings to Euros.

Unfortunately, data warehouses used currently are not able to deal with changes to the structure. In this chapter, we have discussed our approach to deal with the temporal behavior of data warehouse structures, called $COMET$. We have shown how our approach keeps track of changes to the schema and the instances of a data warehouse. Furthermore, it allows to answer queries spanning multiple structures by introducing transformation functions. Furthermore, our approach allows us to inform the user about changes to the structure that have an impact on a query.

We have discussed the formal $COMET$ model and its implementation. The main advantage of this implementation is that it does not require a front-end implementation. In fact, it may be viewed a layer between data warehouse sources and a standard front-end. Therefore, it can be easily integrated into an existing data warehouse architecture. As we use a standard OLAP database as front-end, each data mart generated offers the whole OLAP functionality. The performance of a query is not affected by this modification of the data warehouse architecture because it depends on the OLAP database system used.

About the authors

Johann Eder   Christian Koncilia

Johann Eder is a Professor of information and communication systems at University Klagenfurt, Austria. Currently, he is the head of the Department of Informatics-Systems, and serves as a member of the board of the Austrian Science funds. His research interests include databases, information systems and knowledge engineering. Current research projects include workflow management systems, in particular time management and exception handling, temporal data warehouses, and inter-organisational business processes. He (co-)authored one book and over eighty papers published in international journals and conference proceedings. He served in many program committees for international conferences, as well as an editor or a referee for international journals and conferences.

Christian Koncilia received a MS degree in computing science and a Ph.D. degree in computing science from the University of Klagenfurt, in 1999 and 2002, respectively. He is a Lecturer at the Department of Informatics-Systems at the University of Klagenfurt. His research interests include temporal databases, data warehousing, multi-dimensional databases and data mining. He published several papers in international conference proceedings. During his MS studies he worked as project manager for a large Carinthian company with over 7000 employees. Amongst other duties, he was responsible for the introduction of an OLAP system.

Part III

Data and Applications Integration

Chapter 5

Identification of Missing Information in Integrated Database Systems

Bogdan D. Czejdo and Kenneth Messa

5.1 Introduction

Typically, information contained in data integration systems is incomplete. This is manifested in various omissions, misleading the user of the system, which is unacceptable for serious business solutions. The solution discussed in this chapter is to provide explanations together with answers to user queries. We discuss the process of performing selections, projections and joins where the values for crucial attributes are missing. We classify data incompleteness situations and show how to generate appropriate explanations for each case.

Our solutions are applicable both for federated database systems and data warehouses. In federated database systems, some data sources might not be available or some attributes that are crucial for business decisions might not be present in some data sources. In well-established data warehouses, the problem of unavailability of some data sources appears hardly; however, some attributes that are crucial for user queries might not be present in some data sources. Furthermore, during data warehouse evolution, some automatic assistance may be necessary in order to provide additional explanations for new data warehouse users.

Some aspects of these problems were initially identified in [103], but they were more extensively described in [121]. The latter publication refers to federated database systems where some data sources might not be available. They describe the solutions, based on defining a new query difference operator. The role of this operator is similar to our explanation method. However, we go much beyond performing selections where the values for the crucial attributes are missing. In addition, we differentiate between temporary and permanent data unavailability and generate explanations accordingly.

In this chapter, we also discuss the tools that are part of our system, called *LODA*. They provide accurate answers and explanations for user queries in a variety of data in-

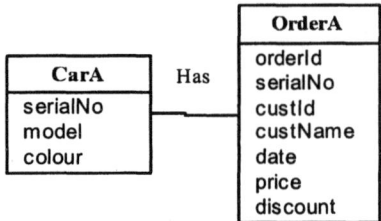

Figure 5.1: Schema diagram for dealer A.

completeness situations. The LODA system has a graphical interface [45, 46, 55, 119, 120] based on UML diagrams that allows to specify queries in a visual language called UML-VL. These queries are analysed and translated into object-oriented code and an explanation of the results is provided. In addition, a query that identifies potential solutions, called the *unavailability query*, is generated with an explanation.

The chapter is organised as follows: a description of data unavailability cases and sample UML-VL queries and their answers are given in Section 5.2; in Section 5.3, we describe the process of object-oriented code generation based on graphical queries; in Section 5.4, we describe how to generate explanations and additional object-oriented code generation for data integration systems; finally, we present some conclusions in Section 5.5.

5.2 Unavailability Cases and Sample Queries

There are many reasons why information may be unavailable. They can generally be classified into those causing either temporary or permanent data unavailability. Let us first discuss permanent data unavailability, namely:

Values for the attributes that are used for selection conditions;

Values for the attributes that are used for projections;

Values for the attributes that are used for join conditions;

Values for the attributes that are used for aggregations.

As an example, we consider some data schemas for automobile dealerships similar to those given in [67]. The first dealer, referred to as A, maintains two tables: *CarA* to store information about all cars, including colour, and *OrderA* to keep information about all orders, including data for the customers, as shown in Fig. 5.1. The second dealer, denoted as B, maintains three tables: *CarB* to store information about all cars, except for their colours, *OrderB* to keep information about all orders, and *CustomerB* to keep information about customers and their involvement in an order, as shown in Fig. 5.2.

The schema integration process is then performed in order to obtain the global schema. (Schema integration is beyond the scope of this chapter.) In our example, a global schema can be designed as shown in Fig. 5.3.

5.2.1 Incomplete attributes in selection conditions

Let us consider some examples of queries involving conditions that are based on unavailable data. Fig. 5.4 shows the graphical query that requests a list of cars (serial numbers) that

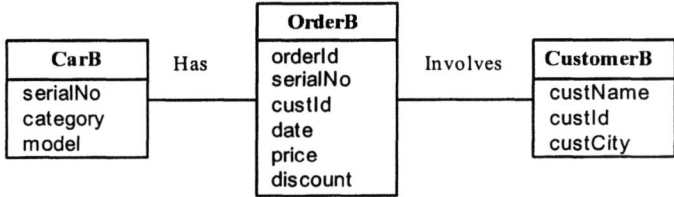

Figure 5.2: Schema diagram for dealer B.

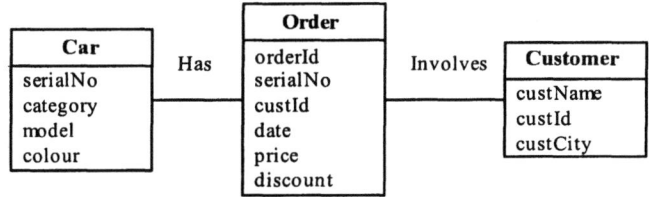

Figure 5.3: Global schema diagram.

are red. It should be noted that in UML-VL, key words begin with "@". The key word **@print** denotes that the serial numbers that are obtained by the query must be printed on the default printing device, e.g., the system console.

As a result of executing this query, we get red cars only from dealer A, since data source B does not contain any information about the colour that can be used for the selection condition. The correct business solution should include the resulting data as a first component, and additional components that fully informs the end user about it. In this case, we have to provide three extra components. The second component is an explanation about the source of data. In our example, this would be that the answer data was taken only from dealer A. The third component shall list all potential results produced by the unavailability query, whereas the fourth component shall provide an explanation of these potential results, that is, a list of data sources that cause incompleteness. In our example, this third component would include all objects from dealer B with the fourth component being an explanation that only some of them can satisfy the condition that they might be red. A complete business solution for the above query might be represented textually as follows:

A list of serial numbers of cars that are red;

The explanation: "These are all taken from the dealer A";

A list of serial numbers of cars from dealer B;

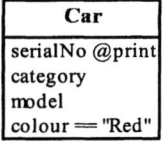

Figure 5.4: UML-VL query to find the set of red cars.

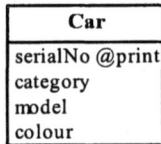

Figure 5.5: UML-VL query issued for data source B.

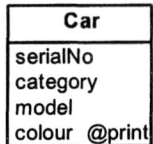

Figure 5.6: UML-VL query to find the set of colours of all cars.

The explanation: "Some of these might not satisfy the query."

Our graphical language approach allows for a graphical explanation without resorting to SQL or the generation of complex statements in a natural language. In our example, we specify the unavailability query as the graphical query issued for dealer B as shown in Fig. 5.5.

5.2.2 Incomplete attributes in projections

Let us next discuss the second case when values for the projected attributes are unavailable. Fig. 5.6 shows the graphical query requesting a list of all colours.

As a result of executing this query, we get only colours from dealer A, since data source B does not contain any information about the colour. The correct business solution includes an additional explanation and data that fully informs the end user about it. Specifically, four components, similar to the ones described in previous section, are provided as an answer. In our example, we would explain that we can obtain colours only from dealer A and we would then list the serial numbers of all cars whose colour is unknown and the explanation that the data is taken from source B. The attribute *serialNo* was chosen, since this is the key attribute of the table whose attribute values were requested.

5.2.3 Combined incompleteness

Queries involving join conditions that are based on unavailable data can be processed similarly to queries with incompleteness of selection. Similarly, queries involving aggregations that are based on unavailable data can be processed similarly to queries with incompleteness of projections.

In real situations we might have all cases combined, as shown in the query "list colours of all cars ordered by customers in New Orleans" (cf. Fig. 5.7).

In this UML-VL diagram, the directional symbol "@<" is appended to the relationship name to indicate the direction of processing. As a result of executing this query, the answer shall have no data, since data source A does not contain a customer city and, therefore no cars shall be selected, and data source B does not contain any information about the colour.

Identification of Missing Information in Integrated Database Systems 105

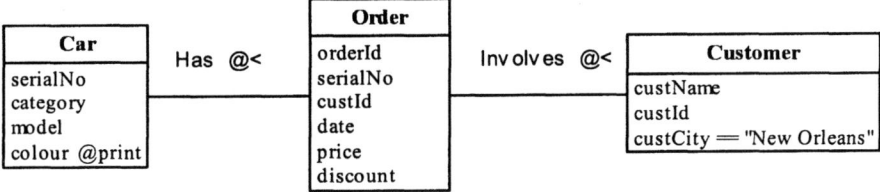

Figure 5.7: UML-VL query "list colours of all cars ordered by customers in New Orleans".

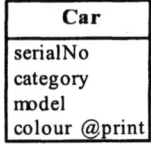

Figure 5.8: UML-VL additional query issued for data source A.

The correct business solution should include an additional explanation and data to fully inform the end user about the available answer data. Specifically, in this case, it means that we shall also have five extra components in addition to the first component of the answer. The second component shall contain, in this case, an explanation that the answer data could not be taken from any data source. The third component shall list all objects from data source A with the explanation that only some of them can satisfy the condition. The fifth component shall list selected objects from data source B with the appropriate explanation.

In our example, the third component shall be a list of colours that could potentially be ordered by a customer from New Orleans with appropriate explanation. In addition, the fifth component shall list cars that were ordered by a customer in New Orleans with the explanation that the colour of these cars is unknown.

Our graphical language approach allows for a graphical explanation without resorting to SQL or generation of complex statements in a natural language. In this example, we can specify the third and fifth components as graphical queries issued for dealer B as shown in Fig. 5.8 and Fig. 5.9, respectively, in addition to the explanations.

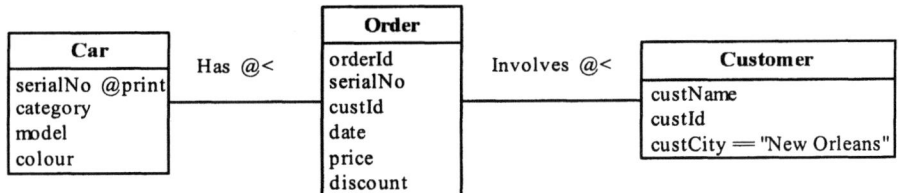

Figure 5.9: UML-VL additional query issued for data source B.

5.2.4 Temporary unavailability of data sources

Let us next discuss the case when there are data sources that are temporarily unavailable. We assume that this can be determined dynamically. For instance, let us consider Fig. 5.6 that shows the graphical query that requests a list of all colours. As a result of executing this query, we obtain colours only from dealer A, since data source B is not available at this moment. The correct business solution should include an additional explanation that fully informs the end user about the answer data. Specifically, in this case, it means that, in addition to the first component of the answer, we shall have two extra components. The second component shall contain an explanation about the source of data, and the third component shall list all unavailable data sources. In our example, it should state that the answer data was taken only from dealer A, and other results can be found in dealer B, but it is currently unavailable.

5.3 LODA Tools for Data Retrieval

A UML class diagram represents the underlying structure of the data and queries as discussed in previous section. The UML model views the world as consisting of objects (entities) and associations and other relationships amongst those objects. Objects and associations/relationships are classified into object collections and relationship collections, respectively. We use the term *OType* to refer to an object type or object class and the term *RType* to refer to a relationship type or relationship class. An OType is a class, in an object-oriented (UML) sense, and also a collection (called the *base collection*) of objects or instances of the class. If the base collection is a set, then an OType is an object set, in a database/ER sense. Attributes can be either instance attributes or class attributes. Instance attributes refer to any object in the OType. Class attributes refer to the OType or base collection as a whole, not to the individual objects in the base collection. Class attributes are represented by underlining the attribute name. Generally RTypes are binary relationships, but can also be ternary or higher order relationships. RTypes can also have attributes.

The generated code shall be from LODA (the Library of Object-oriented Database Abstractions). This library is a collection of Java messages and classes that allow to manipulate the underlying application [119], however; the code can be generated in any language.

Once the UML schema diagram has been built, it can be used as a template within the other CASE tools [29, 81] to construct message and other diagrams. The message diagrams are written in a visual language that is based on a transformation of UML, called UML-VL. The UML-VL message diagrams can include queries, updates, and other messages by converting the schema diagram into a directed acyclic graph, and attaching various expressions and symbols. In order to convert the schema diagram into a directed acyclic graph, we identify source or root OTypes and make all links of RTypes directional. The direction symbol indicates the order in which processing is done. Expression and symbol groups added to OTypes and RTypes of the class diagram include selection expressions and symbols, modification expressions and symbols, projection symbols, variables, external operators, and others. Class diagram components that are not part of the diagram can be hidden. The order in which the items are listed in the schema diagram can be altered and OType and RType icons can be expanded or collapsed.

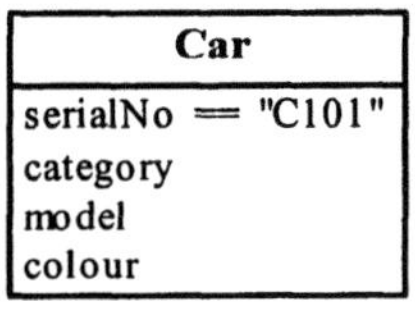

Identification of Missing Information in Integrated Database Systems

```
┌─────────────────────┐
│        Car          │
├─────────────────────┤
│ serialNo == "C101"  │
│ category            │
│ model               │
│ colour              │
└─────────────────────┘
```

Figure 5.10: Instance attribute selection.

5.3.1 Establishing an initial collection

The source or root of a directed UML-VL diagram indicates the icon or icons where diagram processing is to begin. The source OType can be represented explicitly by appending **@root** to the OType name or it can be derived automatically. In the examples in Fig. 5.7 and Fig. 5.9, we assumed automatic derivation. When we have a single OType in a query, it is obviously the root. When we have several related OTypes, the direction of processing may indicate the root. In these cases, the root need not be specified explicitly. Processing of the source begins by using the base collection for the given class. This is the initial collection used in the generated code.

For display purposes, the visibility and types of attributes and methods have been omitted from the diagrams presented here.

5.3.2 Selection using attributes

Selections can depend on the values of an attribute. Generally, the result of a selection operation shall consists of the objects from a particular collection whose attributes have the desired range of values. If the collection is a set, then the selection returns a subset of the set. A selection expression is indicated by appending a condition symbol, which includes a comparison operator such as "==" or "<", and a value expression to the appropriate component. Selections can be either attribute selections or class selections. Instance selections are represented graphically by appending a condition symbol and a value to an attribute, as shown in Fig. 5.10, where attribute *serialNo* has condition symbol "==" and value "C101".

Attribute selections generate the LODA message *select()*. The instance version of this message requires three parameters, namely: the name of the attribute that is being selected, a comparison operator, and a value. For instance, the query in Fig. 5.10 generates the following code:

collOfCar = collOfCar.select("serialNo", "==", "C101");

This piece of code selects all items from a particular collection of cars and chooses those whose number is equal to "C101". There can be any number of selection expressions in a diagram and any number for a particular attribute. If more than one selection expression is attached to the same attribute, then they are listed in sequence and processed according to "and" and "or" logical operators; for instance, *serialNo* == *"C101"* || *"C102"*.

5.3.3 Printing the values

Returning the results from a query can be specified by attaching the **@print** key word to the attributes chosen. An example is shown in Fig. 5.11. Processing this query would involve

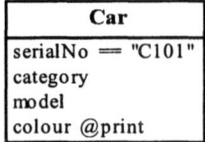

Figure 5.11: Example of query that prints attribute values.

first generating the code for the selection, as discussed in previous section. Next, the print directive would be processed and the following code would be generated:

collOfCar.print("colour");

5.3.4 Processing relationships

In a directed UML-VL diagram, a directional symbol "@>" or "@<" is appended to the RType name to indicate processing from the source OType through the RType to the target OType. The relate operation returns the collection of all objects from the target collection that are related to the source collection. This collection may be empty. Relate operations generate the LODA message called *relate*(). The relate message has the name of the RType as a parameter, as follows:

collOfOrder = collofCustomer.relate("Involves");

The processing of subclass/superclass relationships is very much like the processing of ordinary relationships. If the processing proceeds from the superclass to the subclass, then an intersection of all members of the initial collection from the superclass with all members of the subclass is formed. The reverse processing embeds the collection of subclass members into a collection of superclass members.

A directional symbol can also be added to subclass/superclass links to indicate the direction of processing. In this case, as well as for relationships, the relationship line is required to have a horizontal component where the directional symbol is attached.

5.3.5 Summary of diagram processing

The processing of a given diagram proceeds as follows: (a) begin at the source and process it; (b) follow the directed links through an RType to the next OType; (c) repeat these steps until all OTypes and RTypes have been processed.

If there are several sources, the processing begins at any of them. Processing proceeds as above until a node in which all the requisite information is not currently available is reached. Processing of this path is suspended, whilst another source is processed. When a node that was previously suspended is reached, and all information is known, then processing continues. This is repeated until all sources have been processed.

Processing of each OType involves several steps that use the information from the diagram to generate code. Generally, each process step generates one or more statements of LODA code. For each OType, the processing proceeds as follows: (a) start with an initial collection obtained by selecting all objects, selecting those derived from a previous relate operation or from an input variable; (b) perform all selections; (c) handle OType exceptions; (d) perform assignments of collections or instances; (d) execute any external operators on the resulting collection (it is expected that these operators shall not change the resulting collection); (e) compute projections; (f) perform any updates; (g) return the output variable or result.

Process each RType as follows: (a) start with the initial collection obtained from the source OType; (b) filter it through attribute condition; (c) perform the relate operation.

A more detailed description of diagram processing can be found in [120].

5.4 Processing and Analysing Incomplete Queries

Processing and analysing graphical queries, explanation and unavailability query generation can be described by means of a meta-database schema as shown in Fig. 5.12. Such a meta-database contains information about the source and integrated databases, including their tables and attributes. The meta-database should be enhanced to accommodate the graphical representation of the queries that includes conditions, projections and so on. The meta-database containing this information is referred to as MDB. The MDB is populated by our graphical interpretation system, which translates the graphical components of a UML-VL diagram into objects that are stored in the MDB.

Let us describe a simplified MDB in some detail. *L_DATABASE*, *L_TABLE*, *L_RELATIONSHIP*, and *L_ATTRIBUTE* are meta OTypes. *L_DATABASE* is used to store information about the source and integrated databases. It has a user-defined name (*name*), a unique, system-generated identifier (*id*), an attribute (*dbAvail*) indicating whether the database is available or not, and an attribute (*source*) that specifies whether it is a source or the integrated database. All LODA OTypes have a class variable, called the *all-collection*, which contains the collection of all instances of the OType. In particular, *allDatabases* represents the collection of all databases.

The meta OType *L_TABLE* contains information about tables. It has a user-defined name (*name*), a unique, system-generated identifier (*id*) and an attribute (*tabAvail*) indicating whether the table is available or not. The attribute *display* is used to display (or hide) a table icon. A user may wish to hide certain tables that do not participate in the query in order to improve readability.

The meta OType *L_RELATIONSHIP* contains information about relationships. In addition to the attributes *id* and *name*, which are attributes of all meta OTypes, it has attributes *ref1* and *ref2* that contain references to the participating OTypes. It also has attribute *display*, amongst others.

The meta OType *L_ATTRIBUTE* contains information about attributes. In addition to the attributes *id* and *name*, it has an attribute (*dType*) that indicates its data type, *condition*, which indicates that it is participating in a query, *projection*, which indicates that its value is to be projected, and others. If it is a condition attribute, then it also needs to store the condition operator and its value. Therefore, there are attributes *operator* and *value* for this purpose. It also has an attribute (*source*) that specifies whether it belongs to a source or the integrated database and *display*. The collection of all attributes is stored in class variable *allAttributes*.

There are several meta RTypes connecting the meta OTypes. The meta RType *D_HAS_T* connects each database with its tables; *T_HAS_A* connects each table with its attributes; *R_HAS_A* connects each relationship with its attributes; *T_FROM_R* and *T_TO_R* connect

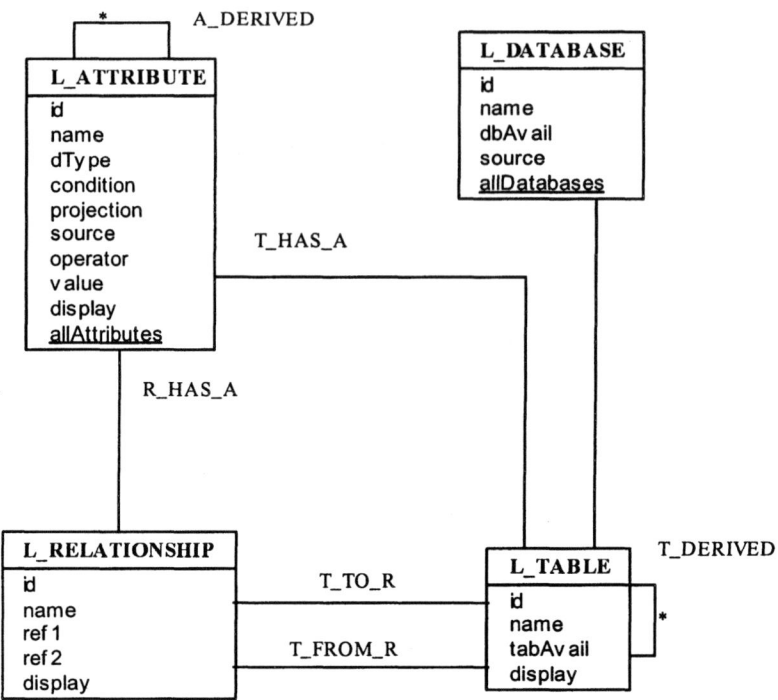

Figure 5.12: Meta-database schema for MDB.

the participants of each relationship; *A_DERIVED* connects an attribute to those attributes from which it is derived; Similarly *T_DERIVED* connects tables.

As an example, let us consider the diagram in Fig. 5.4 and, specifically, the attribute *colour*. The information about colour would be stored in *L_ATTRIBUTE* in MDB as follows:

id = *a system-defined string*;
name = "colour";
dType = "String";
condition = false;
projection = true;
operator = "==";
value = "Red";
source = true;

5.4.1 Processing and generating queries

MDB is used to process and analyse queries, as well as to process explanations and unavailability queries. Let us first describe the generation of the initial query. Once again, we use the simple query listed in Fig. 5.4. Through the rest of this section, we assume that all tables and databases are available.

Identification of Missing Information in Integrated Database Systems

First, we identify "global" condition attributes:

integAttr = allAttributes.select("source", "==", false);
condAttr = integAttr.select("condition", "==", true);

Now, for each condition attribute *cond*, we obtain its name:

condName = cond.project("name");

We use similar code to obtain the condition operator ("==") and the value ("Red"). The name of the table from which the condition attribute is derived can be determined as follows:

derivedTable = cond.relate("T_HAS_A");
tableName = derivedTable.project("name");

We also identify the projection attributes as follows:

projAttr = integAttr.select("projection", "==", true);

We obtain their names as described above. This information can now be used to generate the query where the items in bold were determined during processing:

collOf**Cars** = all**Cars**.select("**colour**", "==", "**Red**");
collOf**Cars**.print("**serialNo**");

5.4.2 Analysing queries

The information stored in the MDB can be used to analyse a query to determine if there is missing information. In this case, we can generate explanations about the resulting query. Here, we assume that all tables and databases are available. For instance, using the query in Fig. 5.4, one of the source database tables (*CarB*) does not have information about the colour of the cars it stores. We should then include an explanation about the source data, in addition to the basic query.

First, however, we must evaluate the graphical query to determine if an explanation is needed. The code below illustrates the evaluation method for any given condition attribute, *cond*:

allSources = allDatabases.select("source", "==", true);
derivedAttr = cond.relate("A_DERIVED");
derivedTables = derivedAttr.relate("T_HAS_A";
derivedDBs = derivedTables.relate("D_HAS_T");
return derivedDBs.equals(allSources);

Thus, if a condition attribute is derived from fewer than all source databases, then an explanation should be generated. Variable *derivedDBs* provides the list of source databases that contribute to the query. By obtaining their names, we can formulate the proper explanation.

5.4.3 Generating unavailability queries

If there is missing information, in addition to providing the user with an explanation, we would also like to generate a list of data sources that might contain other answers and an unavailability query. In order to determine the list of data sources, the following code is used for each condition or projection attribute *attr*:

```
integTables = attr.relate("T_HAS_A");
allDerivedTables = integTables.relate("T_DERIVED");
derivedAttr = attr.relate("A_DERIVED");
derivedTables = derivedAttr.relate("T_HAS_A");
missingTables = allDerivedTables.minus(derivedTables);
```

The unavailability query partially satisfies the original query using the information that is available. We need to consider the two cases of condition and projection separately.

For conditions we refer to the query from Fig. 5.4. In this case we should generate a list of all cars from source database B that could possibly have colour red. To do this, we would use the following algorithm:

Make a copy of the original query;

Remove the condition that is based on an incomplete attribute;

Identify all missing tables as described above;

Send this new query to the data integration system for processing on the identified databases.

For projections, we refer to the query from Fig. 5.6. In this case we should generate a list of all serial numbers from source database B. To do this, we would use the following algorithm:

Make a copy of the original query;

Identify all missing tables;

For each such table, add a projection to its key attribute. Remove the projection from the incomplete attribute;

Send this new query to the data integration system for processing on the identified databases.

5.4.4 Generation of explanations

So far in this section, we assumed that all tables and all databases were available. If a database is unavailable, then all of its tables are also unavailable. Therefore, it is enough to consider only the case in which tables are unavailable. To generate the explanation about available tables, one computes the collection of derived tables as described in previous sections, and then executes the following statement:

```
sourceTables = derivedTables.select("tabAvail", "==", true);
```

The names of these tables can be used to formulate the appropriate explanation. To provide an explanation of the databases that have unavailable tables, one needs only to obtain the names of the databases selected. The code is similar.

5.4.5 Creating visual queries in UML-VL

Not only allows our system to analyse and process queries, but also to generate executable code. A description of the code generation process can be found in [120]. Furthermore, our system generates visual queries using the UML-VL visual language as shown in Fig. 5.5, Fig. 5.8, and Fig. 5.9.

The algorithm below outlines the process of generating visual unavailability queries:

Set the display attribute of all components to false;

Process the query as above;

Set display to true for each source table and attribute that participates in the unavailability query;

The UML-VL environment shall display only the components of the unavailability query.

5.5 Conclusions

In this chapter, we have discussed the need for more accurate answers to user queries in integrated databases. We have discussed how to perform selections, projections and joins when the values of crucial attributes are missing. We classified data incompleteness situations and showed how to generate appropriate explanations for each case. Our solutions are applicable both for federated database systems and data warehouses. In our solution for federated database systems, we assumed that the information about unavailability of tables and data sources is dynamic. Our research can lead to extending data warehouses to allow for proper operation with temporary unavailability of tables and data sources.

We have also discussed the tools that are part of our system, which provide accurate answers and explanations to user queries in a variety of data incompleteness situations. The LODA system has a graphical interface based on UML diagrams that allows query specifications in our visual language, UML-VL. These queries are analysed and translated into object-oriented code, and an explanation of the results is provided. LODA is currently a stand-alone system, and it can also be used to allow better query processing in an existing federated database system. This is a topic for further study. The federated database system performs query decomposition. In this process, information about data unavailability can be taken into account and query decomposition can be optimised.

Acknowledgements

We would like to thank Marc Minock. Our discussions with him and Ref. [121] convinced us about the importance of dealing with incomplete information.

About the authors

Bogdan D. Czejdo   Kenneth Messa

Bogdan D. Czejdo is a Professor in the Department of Mathematics and Computer Science at Loyola University in New Orleans. He received the M.S. and the Ph.D. degrees from the Warsaw Technical University in 1972 and 1975, respectively. His research interests include distributed database systems, database and visual languages, and software for web-based cooperation. He has published over one hundred referred technical papers in these areas. He is a member of the ACM and the IEEE.

Kenneth Messa is a Professor in the Department of Mathematics and Computer Science at Loyola University in New Orleans. He received the Ph.D. degree from Tulane University, New Orleans, La. USA in 1972. His research interests include object-oriented systems, graphical languages and software development. He has published numerous technical papers in these areas. He is a member of the ACM and the IEEE.

Chapter 6

Application Integration Patterns

Matjaž B. Jurič, Ivan Rozman, Tatjana Welzer, Marjan Heričko, Boštjan Brumen, and Vili Podgorelec

6.1 Introduction

The information systems of virtually any enterprise consist of a number of applications, which may be partially integrated, or, more commonly, not at all. They are part of such systems for historical, technical, technological or purely political reasons. With the demanding requirements for ubiquitous information access and e-business solutions, the need for integrated applications is increasing at a quick pace. It is widely accepted that enterprise application integration (EAI) concerns are becoming the key factors for successful information systems [87]. First, the applications a company has need to be integrated, which we call intra-EAI; next, there are increasing needs to ensure inter-EAI or business-to-business (B2B) integration [87].

At first, the integration problems and the solutions provided seem to be different. However, a careful analysis of several integration projects shows some similarities. Software engineering came up with patterns that describe a general solution in a given context [36, 65, 66]; in our case, such patterns allow to identify common integration problems and their solutions.

This chapter presents the results of the analyses and the experiences gained with several integration projects. We describe several common integration solutions and call them integration patterns. They present an idea of different design solutions and architectures for the integration task; thus, they may also be viewed as design and architectural patterns. They allow the selection of the best solution to a problem, and enlighten the integration problems from a different perspective, from a certain abstraction level. The patterns we present provide a sound solution for intra-EAI as well as for inter-EAI problems. They can be used for the component-based approach to EAI problems, as presented in [87]. As mentioned before, the patterns are given at a certain abstraction level, and are thus platform- and language-independent. Therefore, they can be used on virtually any platform with any programming language. The patterns were verified in more than three large-scale integration projects in which they proved to be quite suitable.

The review of the field of integration patterns we present reveals that there is not too much work in this area, chiefly on the definitions of the design and architectural integration patterns. In [113], the authors define two integration patterns called Access Integration and Application Integration. They are process patterns, so they cannot be compared to the design and architectural patterns with which we deal in this chapter. In [47], the author defines the Data Access Object (DAO) Pattern to provide access to the data of the existing data stores. DAO was included in the J2EE design patterns catalog maintained by Sun Microsystems, and it is the basis for the integration patterns presented in this chapter. In [27], two additional process patterns were presented, namely: Scenario Partitioning and State Machine Integration. In [176], the author gives a one-paragraph description of the Direct Data Mapping Pattern, which is comparable to our Data Mapping Pattern, the Hierarchical Multi-Step Pattern, which is similar to our Integration Mediator Pattern, the Direct Request Pattern, which compares to our Integration Façade Pattern, and the Peer Service Pattern, which resembles our Integration Mediator Pattern. The descriptions in [176] are given without the necessary formalisation and usual elements of a standard pattern description. In [177], the author presents four B2B patterns, namely: the Direct Application B2B Pattern, which shows how to integrate cross-company applications directly, the Data Exchange B2B Pattern, which presents an XML-based architecture for data transfers between companies, the Closed Process Integration B2B Pattern, which identifies the main participant responsible for the managerial processes, the Open Process Integration B2B Pattern, which introduces the notion of shared processes. Last two patterns are process patterns, so they do not compare to the patterns in this chapter. The Direct Application and Data Exchange patterns, however, focus on point-to-point integration and are not formally defined. They are also very different from the patterns in this chapter, which are broker- and mediator-based. Additionally, the patterns we present can be used for inter- and intra-EAI problems.

The rest of the chapter is organised as follows: Section 6.2 presents a short introduction to application integration; in Sections 6.3–6.8, we present our patterns, namely: Integration Broker, Integration Wrapper, Integration Mediator, Virtual Component, Data Mapping, and Process Automator (the description is informal, which is a common practice in this field, e.g., [12]); in Section 6.9, we present the application of our integration patterns to a case study; finally, we report on our main conclusions and future research directions in Section 6.10.

6.2 Application Integration Patterns

Application integration, or EAI (Enterprise Application Integration), is the competitive advantage a company gains when their applications are integrated into a unified information system able to share information and support business workflows. From a technical perspective, EAI amounts to integrating different applications and data to enable sharing of data and integration of business processes without modifying existing applications too much. EAI needs to use methods and activities that enable it to be effective in terms of costs and time [87].

The major challenge with EAI is that companies are faced with inter-related, heterogeneous existing systems on which they depend, but, unfortunately, they were not usually designed uniformly. This heterogeneity becomes apparent through:

Combinations of monolithic, client/server, and multi-tier applications;

Mix of procedural and object oriented solutions;

Mix of programming languages;

Different types of database management systems (relational, hierarchical, object-oriented);

Different middleware solutions for communication (message-oriented middleware, object request brokers, remote procedure calls);

Multiple information transmission models, including publish/subscribe, request/reply, and conversational;

Different transaction and security management capabilities;

Different procedures to share data;

Use of EDI, XML and other proprietary formats for data exchange.

Differences in programming models make it difficult to integrate solutions, and they are sometimes an obstacle for communication between developers. The answer to the demands of EAI is to build a robust, scalable integration architecture. We use a layered approach to address this problem step by step. The idea is to break the problem into several smaller problems and to solve each sub-problem step by step. Therefore, today's integration can be viewed as if it was composed of several layers. The most important are the following:

Data-level integration;

Application interface integration;

Business method integration;

Presentation integration;

Inter-EAI integration.

A combination of both application interface and business method integration is sometimes referred to as business-level integration, because they share some of the concepts. Defining a robust application integration architecture is the major challenge in EAI. Integration patterns, which describe proven methods and processes used for integration within enterprise or beyond, provide valuable guidance. Integration patterns emerge from classification of common integration solutions. Each integration pattern defines a common integration problem and a sound solution.

The integration patterns covered in this chapter are independent from the underlying architecture, and they can be applied to the above-mentioned integration layers. In the following chapters, we present the following integration patterns: Integration Broker, Integration Wrapper, Integration Mediator, Virtual Component, Data Mapping, and Process Automator.

6.3 The Integration Broker Pattern

6.3.1 Context and problem definition

The simplest way to integrate different applications consists of connecting them with each other. It is very simple, but it is not an option since it increases the dependencies; in particular, complexity and maintenance become a nightmare. In the point-to-point integration, the application interaction logic is interwoven with all integrated applications. Such a solution makes applications highly dependent on each other, thus complicating their maintenance, which becomes also very time consuming. A small change to an application might imply modifications to the whole set of applications connected to it. For this reason, maintaining such a system is more time-consuming and costly than maintaining the applications separately, which hides the benefits of the integration process. In a typical integration scenario there are usually more than fifty applications to be integrated. In these cases, the point-to-point approach is not an option because it increases complexity exponentially.

6.3.2 Forces

The following list gives a set of goals that should be achieved when integrating several applications:

Separation of responsibilities for different operations is required, i.e, we need to identify the operations performed by each application to be integrated;

An application should provide a common integration interface, which reduces complexity and does not require building interoperability interfaces for each integration scenario;

The integration logic should be separated to ease maintenance;

Clients should not be aware of the details of integration;

Clients should not be aware of the internal structure of the applications being integrated;

The communication model should not be constrained, rather the best solution should be used for each application.

6.3.3 Solution

The architectural approach to integration of many different applications is presented by the Integration broker. It avoids the disadvantages of point-to-point integration because it minimises the dependencies between the applications being integrated and implements one or more communication mechanisms. It is an abstraction for middleware technologies and it is implemented with a combination of means offered by the underlying software platform. It offers services such as transactions, security, naming, life cycle management, scalability, rules, routing or brokering.

The Integration Broker Pattern has to be used by the applications to be integrated so that the integration can be achieved at different levels. Applications have transparent access to the integration broker by means of adequate interfaces, either programmatically or declaratively. Programmatically means that applications have to implement code to use the infrastructure services; conversely, declaratively means that the integrator can designate relevant applications and declare which services they should use. The infrastructure takes care of the details necessary to invoke a service. The transparency of the services available depends on the technology selected. Communication, brokering, and routing services can be implemented transparently by means of object request brokers, which hide remote method invocations so that they look as if they were local to the developers. On the contrary, a message-oriented middleware requires the applications to create messages and parse incoming ones properly. Declarative transaction and security services can provide services to applications without adding any code to the application.

The Integration Broker Pattern allows to build the integration layers step by step, and enables the reuse of previous results. It is not based on point-to-point communication between applications, and the n-to-n multiplicity is reduced to n-to-1. Therefore, complexity

Application Integration Patterns

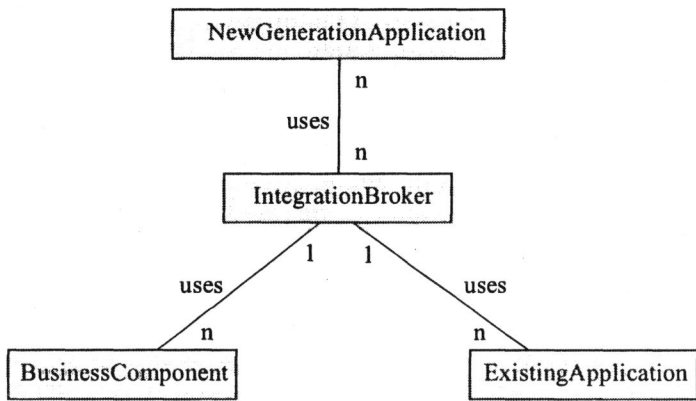

Figure 6.1: The Integration Broker Pattern.

is reduced, too, which consequently eases maintenance. The structure of the Integration Broker Pattern is shown in Fig. 6.1.

The Integration Broker Pattern defines the roles of each application for a certain integration interaction. In an interaction, an application may require a service from another application. The applications that require a service are called client applications, whereas those that provide it are called server applications. The role an application plays depends on the interaction in which it participates, which can change during an execution. Usually, an application has both roles because it acts as a server application in some interactions, and as a client application in others.

The Integration Broker Pattern connects applications and also contracts them. The integration is based on contracts, which are usually expressed as interoperability interfaces. Interoperability interfaces define the services client applications can request from a server applications. Furthermore, they define the relationships between the applications on which an application depends. The coupling between a set of integrated applications can be viewed as long-term contracts. They provide a façade through which client applications can have access to interoperability services. As long as the interfaces do not change, we can replace the parts or the whole server application without disturbing client applications. Therefore, the definition of interoperability interfaces requires a great deal of effort.

An integration broker should support one of the following communication models at least:

Synchronous one-to-one communication if clients can require immediate responses from servers and have to wait for them;

Deferred synchronous one-to-one communication if clients do not need answers to be provided immediately; they must be able to ask servers for the status of their answer, and should be notified when it is ready (call back or event);

Asynchronous one-to-one communication if clients do not require an immediate answer and servers are not required to be on-line continuously;

Asynchronous one-to-many communication if a single client can communicate with several servers. This model is also referred to as publish-and-subscribe.

The Integration Broker Pattern is used typically in common middleware technologies such as remote method invocations (object-request brokers) and message-oriented middlewares. It requires one or more middleware products to implement its functionality, but allows to achieve a high level of abstraction. For this reason, it is not modelled at design time; contrarily, it must be taken into account during the design of the architecture so that it can adapt communication requests between components.

6.3.4 Consequences

The consequences of using the Integration Broker Pattern are the following:

The number of connections between applications is reduced, which also reduces the level of coupling between the applications being integrated;

If the interfaces are carefully designed, we can replace the parts or the whole application without any impact on other applications;

The dependencies between the applications are defined as contracts referred to as interoperability interfaces;

Location transparency is achieved;

The maintenance effort and the costs are reduced to an acceptable level.

The disadvantage of this pattern is that it introduces an abstraction layer, which amounts to communication overhead. Therefore, the most appropriate communication modes have to be selected carefully, performance and scalability need to be assessed and optimisations should be implemented, e.g., local communication and collocation of components.

This pattern is related to the rest of integration patterns presented in this chapter. It is also related to the GoF Mediator Pattern [66].

6.4 The Integration Wrapper Pattern

6.4.1 Context and problem definition

In order to reuse the functionality provided by existing applications in new solutions, it is necessary to have programmatic access to them. The most obvious way is to have access to existing functionality by using existing application programming interfaces (APIs). Sometimes, however, existing applications do not provide any APIs to have access to their functionality, not even proprietary ones. Sometimes, they provide only a subset of their functionality through APIs, but it is necessary to have access to the whole functionality.

6.4.2 Forces

The following list presents a set of goals that need to be achieved when wrapping several applications:

For integrating and reusing existing applications, we need to have programmatic access to them;

We can reuse data and functionality provided by existing applications by means of APIs;

Having access to an application by means of an API is better than retrieving data from its database directly because its business logic is active during this process;

Application Integration Patterns

Figure 6.2: The Integration Wrapper Pattern.

6.4.3 Solution

The Integration Wrapper Pattern is a layered approach to adding APIs to existing applications. The services and the functionality they provide can thus be exported to other applications, thus enabling interoperability and integration. Its motivation lies in the Adapter Pattern (GoF) [66]; its goal, however, is to provide reusable interfaces for multiple clients so that they can have access to the wrapper simultaneously. To develop the wrappers, we need to build a layer around existing applications and add the necessary interfaces. These interfaces are called wrappers, and the existing applications that need to be modified are called "wrapped existing applications".

The Integration Wrapper Pattern has two major goals: it provides open, reusable interoperability interfaces, and it converts calls to reuse the services and the functionality of existing applications. The structure of this pattern is shown in Fig. 6.2.

The wrapper can add APIs either intrusively or non-intrusively. There are two ways to add wrappers to existing applications: we can modify them so that they are wrapped, or we can use screen scraping or terminal emulation to have access to their functionality through the user interfaces they expose. The decision on which technique should be used depends on the availability of source code. If the source code, the tools required or the libraries necessary to build an executable are not available, our only choice shall be to wrap the user interface. Furthermore, this technique is adequate to reduce the risk to introduce a bug because we might well not be familiar with the source code of the application.

Before we select any of these choices, we have to identify the operations by means of which we can have access to the functionality provided by existing applications. The Integration Wrapper Pattern is tightly related to the Integration Broker Pattern. The structure of the wrapper depends on the type of communication. For instance, if we use synchronous communications such as remote method invocation, the infrastructure shall then force typed communication and shall check the signatures of the operations. If we use asynchronous communication, the wrapper would be responsible for decomposing the messages it receives.

6.4.4 Consequences

The consequences of using the Integration Wrapper Pattern are the following:

It allows to reduce complexity and decouples clients from servers;

It allows to reuse the services and the functionality provided by existing applications;

It enables programmatic communications with existing applications;

It hides the details of internal structure of existing applications, their technologies, the programming model and the communication details.

This pattern might have some disadvantages in some cases:

The interfaces of a wrapper need to be designed carefully, otherwise we shall not be able to reuse them once existing applications are replaced by next-generation systems.

Frequently, existing applications have not been designed to be used concurrently. Wrappers provide programmatic access to existing applications, thus increasing the number of total users. Therefore, we have to pay attention to scalability.

If we develop several layers of wrappers, we have to take the overhead this may produce into account because it shall have an impact on the performance of the whole system.

When wrappers have access to existing applications through an user interface, we have to ensure that we catch all possible exceptions.

This pattern is related to the Integration Broker, the Virtual Component, and the GoF Adapter patterns.

6.5 The Integration Mediator Pattern

6.5.1 Context and problem definition

The integration logic to be applied needs to be separated from the applications to be integrated and also needs to be encapsulated. The dependencies are thus minimised, the chances to reuse them are increased, and the maintenance process is simplified.

There are many cases in which existing applications need to be integrated with each other, or a common functionality is distributed amongst several applications and/or duplicated. In these cases, we need to produce a piece of integration logic to deal with these problems so that a service or a piece of functionality can be exposed to its clients uniformly. The clients should not be aware of the complexity inside any mediator.

6.5.2 Forces

The following list presents a set of goals that need to be achieved:

Existing applications often need to be integrated with each other;

The functionality is distributed over more than a single existing application;

The functionality is duplicated in more than one existing application;

The interaction between the applications is complex;

The clients should not be aware of the complexity of the mediators.

6.5.3 Solution

The Integration Mediator Pattern acts as a controller for existing applications and provides an interface for their clients. It should be aware of existing applications and include some interaction logic to fulfill some high-level operations, which require complex interaction with existing and/or new applications. The integration logic can be used at different integration levels. For instance, it can be used at the data level integration or at the function and method level integration. However, the Integration Mediator Pattern should not have direct access to existing applications; instead, it should use integration wrappers. The structure of the Integration Mediator Pattern is shown in the Fig. 6.3, and shows the client, the integration wrappers, and the mediator.

Generally, integration mediators come in two different forms: single step or stateless, and multi-step or stateful. Stateless mediators are used if it is not necessary to keep the state during an interaction with an existing application. In this case, the way the mediator works

Application Integration Patterns

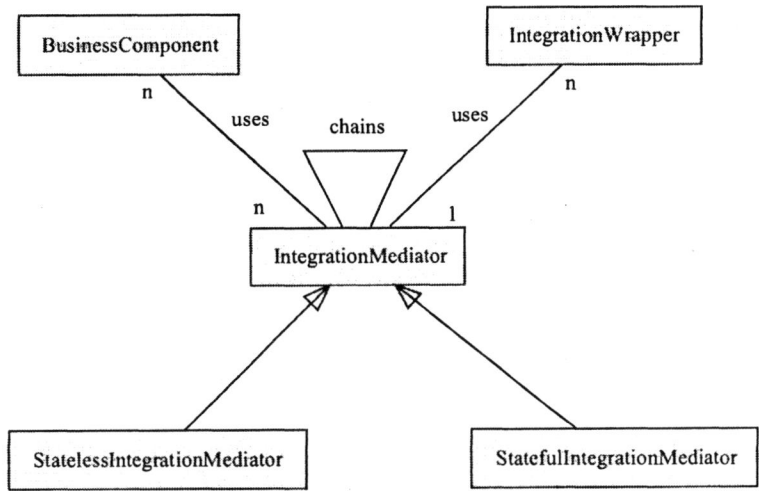

Figure 6.3: The Integration Mediator Pattern.

depends only on the response from the existing applications. Examples include routing, brokering and vocabulary transforming. An XSLT engine, for instance, is a stateles mediator. Conversely, a stateful integration mediator must be used if it is necessary to keep track of the interactions with an application before a new one can be started. Stateful integration mediators are based on events, and they are able to record past events. They perform an action as long as all of the events required have been triggered. Stateful integration mediators need to manage the state of the interactions they control; sometimes, it needs to be persistent, chiefly if long-term interactions with the existing applications need to be carried out and they need to be able to recover from system shutdowns or crashes. The interactions can last from a few minutes to hours, or even days, and can be very complex.

6.5.4 Consequences

The consequences of using the Integration Mediator Pattern are the following:

The integration logic is encapsulated and decoupled from the participating existing applications, as well as new clients;

Maintenance is simplified as the integration logic is centralised rather than distributed amongst existing applications;

Services can be built on top of the functionality provided by the mediator, thus they do not have to be aware of the complexity of existing applications;

Application dependencies are minimised.
In turn, it might have some disadvantages:

We should include integration logic into mediators only;

We have to identify the most efficient way to chain mediators;

Stateful mediators have to implement recovery algorithms to be able to recover from a system shutdown or crash.

This pattern is related to the Integration Wrapper, the Virtual Component, the GoF Mediator, and the GoF Façade patterns.

6.6 The Virtual Component Pattern

6.6.1 Context and problem definition

The way to have access to an integrated information system can vary, chiefly if the integration system uses several different existing applications, implemented using different technologies. Having access to these services directly requires the availability of the knowledge about the internal structures of the information system on the client's side. A workaround for this problem is to use virtual components, which provide a common, unified access point to the services. Virtual components act as a façade to existing applications.

Client applications that need to have access an integrated information system should not be aware of the complexity of the existing applications and should not have direct access to them. The integrated information system is more than a simple set of connected existing applications. An integrated information system should have added value and should provide new services and functionalities. These new services need to be exposed to the clients uniformly. If client applications need to have access to existing applications directly, they are too tightly coupled with them, which results in difficult maintenance problems; replacement, for instance, is almost unfeasible.

6.6.2 Forces

We next list the goals to be achieved:

Clients should use high-level services;

Existing applications do not provide the high-level services and functionalities a client may require;

Clients should not be aware of the complexity of the underlying information system.

6.6.3 Solution

The Virtual Component Pattern aims at integration. It provides reusability capabilities and the ability to re-engineer and replace the applications behind a virtual component with actual, modern implementations. The pattern has its motivation in the Façade Pattern [66]. An integrated information system that is based on the Virtual Component Pattern is a system that looks like a completely new information system, although its functionality provided by an underlying existing application.

From a client's point of view, virtual components do not differ from new ones because they provide the same functionality through interfaces. The concept of virtual components allows us to hide the actual implementation of existing applications and makes them look like new components. It also allows to merge existing and new applications.

The details about how existing applications satisfy the requests and the methods by which they are satisfied are hidden by the Virtual Component Pattern. On one hand, a

Application Integration Patterns

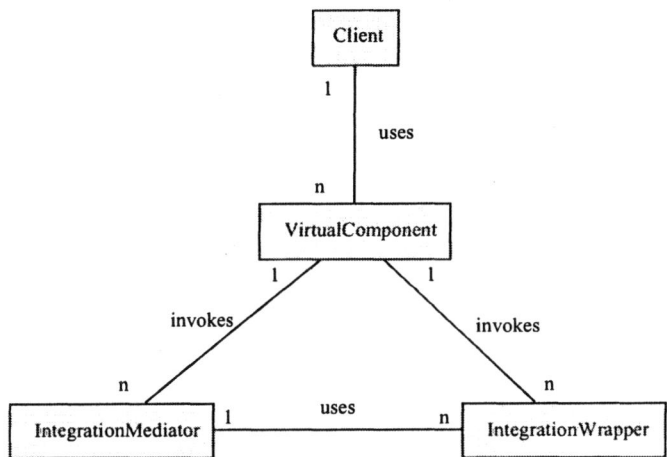

Figure 6.4: The Virtual Component Pattern.

virtual component exposes an exiting application through abstract interoperability interfaces; on the other had, a virtual component communicates with integration wrappers and integration mediators as shown in the Fig. 6.4.

For instance, a virtual component can be a payment system that provides a simple interface to fill in a payment record and has access to an existing system, e.g., an accounting system, a banking system, and so on. A virtual component, together with several abstract interoperability interfaces, exposes an implementation-independent view to its clients. If the abstract interface is kept, other applications do not see any changes to the original application. This way, there is no need to modify the applications that depend on the original application when a change is made. A client of a virtual component is unable to determine how it is implemented.

The way a virtual component is actually implemented is defined by the Integration Broker Pattern. A virtual component encapsulates the complexity of existing applications because the high-level business functionality is implemented in the background. Virtual components are deployed on the business-logic tier. They must be built step by step during the integration. Different virtual components can expose interfaces that offer different abstraction levels to have access a given functionality. Virtual components are therefore organised into several subtiers at the business-logic tier.

Virtual components at a lower level take care of the underlying technology used, whereas virtual components at higher levels transform high-level business requests into a series of lower-level calls to different low-level virtual components. High-level virtual components also perform some data conversions to implement the required functionality by reusing existing applications.

Virtual components are typically used to implement some combinations of the functionalities listed below:

The functionality of existing applications is encapsulated by virtual components. For instance, a virtual component can expose exactly the same functionality provided by existing application APIs, i.e, they simply encapsulate technological differences; they are thus called lower-level virtual components.

Lower-level virtual components implement the code that translates method invocations into one or more calls to the APIs provided by existing applications and database access components. Lower-level virtual components can act as adapters between new and existing applications.

Furthermore, virtual components can provide a high-level interface and hide how existing applications implement their APIs. Such virtual components are called high-level virtual components, and their interfaces should be defined on a global design model; we report on it later.

Virtual components can encapsulate several existing applications and help maintain transaction integrity and security.

Virtual components are also useful to encapsulate or abstract persistent data. For this purpose, virtual components can have access to EIS databases, directly or through protocols, and they often implement the validation logic. A virtual component can keep a database consistent because of its additional security level.

Virtual components can provide a unified access to several EIS databases and can handle different combinations of databases in the background. Alternatively, they can use APIs to have access to the data they need as long as those APIs are provided by the underlying applications.

Virtual components are often layered; thus high-level virtual components aggregate the behaviours of lower-level virtual components and provide the higher level of abstraction required for multiple levels of abstraction of EIS application functionality.

Virtual components can also be used to map technical differences. A particularly useful scenario is to adapt synchronous and asynchronous communication models.

6.6.4 Consequences

The consequences of using the Virtual Component Pattern are the following:

A unified view on the services and the functionality of integrated information system is provided by virtual components;

Virtual components abstract the details of the underlying information system, thus providing a sort of façade to the clients;

Virtual components provide high-level, business-process-oriented interfaces for interoperability;

They enable the replacement of old components with new components as long as the interfaces remain unchanged.

It may, however, have some disadvantages:

Virtual components should not include the functionality of integration mediators and wrappers;

When dealing with transactions and security, virtual components can be too complex. They can be broken into several layers, which can introduce communication overhead;

The interfaces have to be carefully designed in order to keep the interfaces invariable when replacing virtual components with new components;

The related patterns are Façade, Integration Wrapper, Integration Mediator, and Integration Broker.

6.7 The Data Mapping Pattern

6.7.1 Context and problem definition

Data often need to be moved from one application to another during the integrating of several existing applications. The access to the databases of the existing applications varies depending on type of data store used, e.g., relational, object-oriented, hierarchical, or flat files, or the way to have access to the data they store, e.g., directly, through an application, or physically.

The data mapping logic of an application can be very complex, and it should be encapsulated and independent from existing applications. This way the data mapping logic is less coupled with the existing applications, which improves the maintenance and eases replacement of components.

6.7.2 Forces

The following list gives a set of goals that need to be met:

Data need to be moved between existing applications;

Data are stored in different formats;

The method to have access to data depends on the type of storage and the technology selected;

The data mapping logic should be kept separated from the applications.

6.7.3 Solution

The Data Mapping Pattern is used to encapsulate and abstract the data mapping logic for transferring, replicating and updating data between several related applications that need to be integrated. This pattern allows to have access to the data store, either directly or by means of wrappers.

The Data Mapping Pattern comes in two forms: the Direct Data Mapping Pattern, and the Multi-Step Data Mapping Pattern. The former, handles mappings in which data need to be moved from one data store to another without any transformations; the latter also transforms the data it handles. The structure of this pattern is shown in the Fig. 6.5.

6.7.4 Consequences

The consequences of using the Data Mapping Pattern are the following:

The data mapping logic is encapsulated and decoupled from the existing applications and their data stores;

Data dependencies are minimised;

When the data mapping logic is centralised maintenance is simplified;

Business components can use the functionality provided by the Data Mapping Pattern. They thus do not have to be aware of the data complexity of the applications to be integrated.

The list of disadvantages include the following:

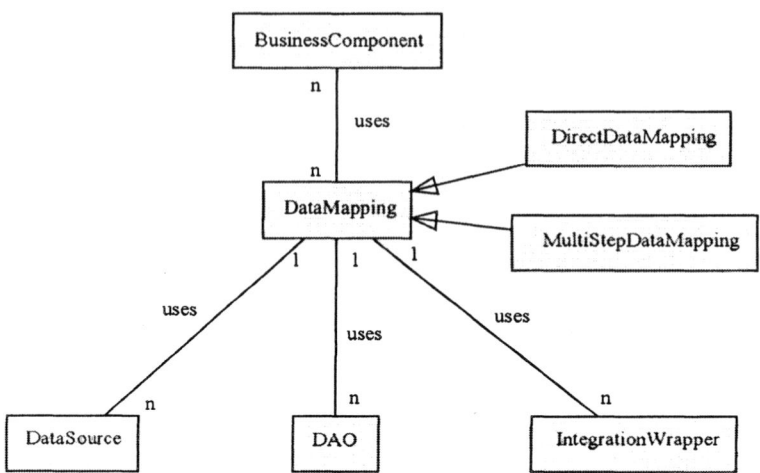

Figure 6.5: The Data Mapping Pattern.

The data mapping logic can get complex and can require considerable resources to carry out a mapping. This can reduce the overall scalability of the information system. Data mapping should therefore be carefully planned, implemented and scheduled.

Data mapping components have to be prepared to raise exceptions due to database errors or failures.

The related patterns are Integration Wrapper, Integration Mediator, and Data Access Object.

6.8 The Process Automator Pattern

6.8.1 Context and problem definition

A process controller should hide and abstract system interactions. The dependencies between the business process controllers and the system logic of the information system should also be minimised. The clients should see the services of an integrated information system by means of high level methods only. An interaction with different virtual components and integration mediators is typically required by a business process method. The interaction should not be delegated to the clients since this solution increases complexity, complicates maintenance, and does not allow to use declarative transaction management.

6.8.2 Forces

The following list presents a set of goals that need to be achieved:

Services of an integrated system should be exposed as high-level business-process methods;

The business-process interaction logic should be abstracted and encapsulated at the middle tier;

Application Integration Patterns

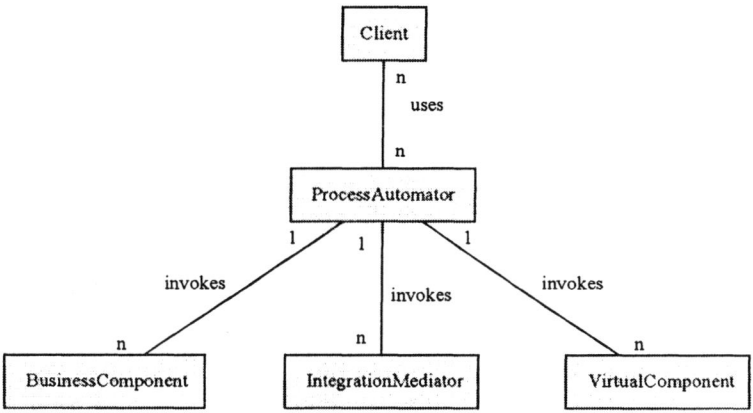

Figure 6.6: The Process Automator Pattern.

Clients should not care of the operations that need to be invoked;

The business-process logic should be performed inside appropriate transactions;

The dependencies between the process automation control and the information system technology should be minimised.

6.8.3 Solution

The Process Automator Pattern gathers and encapsulates the business-process logic. A process automator controller hides the underlying interactions. This pattern allows to improve the quality of a business process and also reduces the execution cost. Therefore, this pattern is highly appropriate for defining integration processes within and between companies.

The Process Automator Pattern sequences the activities of a business process and delegates the tasks to the corresponding parts of the integrated information system. This is done by a set of virtual components and integration mediators through which automator components have access to the functionality provided by existing applications. A process automator can, indeed, have access the new components as well. Its structure is shown in Fig. 6.6.

The Process Automator Pattern is commonly used for the definition of business activities, timers and process-context reporters. It has two variants: the Closed Process Automator Pattern, and the Open Process Automator Pattern, and the difference is how they interpret both types of the processes. The Closed Process Automator Pattern implements a process that is managed internally and externalises key process activities by means of data exchange only. Its clients are able to monitor the activities within the process, but cannot participate in them actively. Conversely, the Open Process Automator Pattern allows to share business processes between several clients. Such processes are managed by more than one client and are particularly useful for inter-EAI, i.e., B2B integrations, in which a single process is shared by more than one company.

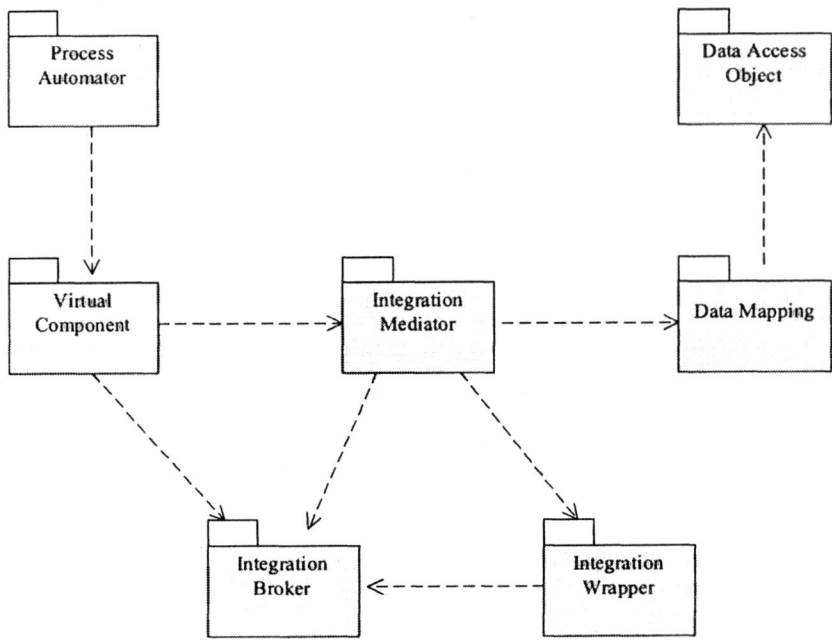

Figure 6.7: Relationships amongst integration patterns.

6.8.4 Consequences

The consequences of using the Process Automator Pattern are the following:

The architecture facilitates analysing business processes, their bottlenecks, utilisation, and downtime;

Business processes can be redefined flexibly;

Process automator components allow to reduce the semantic gap between the technology used and the managers of a business;

A highly-flexible integration architecture can be defined by connecting virtual components and integration mediators.

It might have several disadvantages, however:

The development of process automation components can become a complex task; thus, errors are likely to sprout, which has an impact on the whole information system in which such components are integrated.

It is necessary to guarantee high availability of process automation components, which can be realised with clustering and replication. This is particularly necessary if they are used for inter-EAI.

Process automation components are the entry points to the integrated information system, therefore we have to make a point of identifying security holes.

The related patterns are the Virtual Component, and the Integration Mediator.

6.9 A Case Study

6.9.1 Case study description and analysis

Fig. 6.7 shows the most important relationships between the integration patterns described in this chapter. In this section, we present a case study that shows them at work. It consists of an application in the context of a company that provides services for digital (GSM) mobile telephony. The information system is not integrated and uses a set of non-connected or partially-connected applications (existing applications in our terminology).

The primary applications that the operator uses are the following:

An application to handle information about customers. This includes entering new customers, updating existing customers, and adding data about their accounts.

An application that manages the balance of each account. It allows to enter data about the money a user spends and the money that is paid in his or her account, which can correspond either to an invoice or an advanced payment. It also allows to search for accounts that have negative balance, as well as for accounts that have had null balance for a given period, which are unsubscribed automatically. Please, notice that this application is not integrated with the one described above, and they require an human operator to control their execution.

An application that prints invoices every month. It scans subscriber accounts and prints the invoices according to their consumption.

An application that evaluates national mobile phone calls. It calculates the consumption for each account based on the data transferred from the mobile phone exchange, but only for national calls.

An application that calculates the cost of international mobile phone calls. It is similar to the above-described application, but it does not have a direct connection with the mobile phone exchange. Instead, it receives input data formatted from each roaming partner.

An application that manages information about rates. It includes functions to enter and display rates, e.g., rate policies, rate classes, and costs per minute for voice and data communications.

Some of the primary applications are not integrated at all. Therefore, their users have to enter manually the same data to different applications several times. There are other primary applications that facilitate simple data exchange based on sharing files with data that is formatted using a proprietary format.

Such set of applications cannot fulfill several needs and does not provide the efficiency that could be achieved with an integrated information system. However, we cannot cover the details about the integration of the whole system in this chapter. Instead, we focus on the two most important functionalities, which are not provided by the existing system, namely:

Mobile phone users should be able to check their balance on line, at any time; they can use their mobile phones (WAP or SMS) or PCs (Internet browser). The information provided should be accurate and include all national and international calls, as well as any discounts applied. Discounts are typically based on how often a phone is used and the average duration of calls during the last six months, for instance.

Mobile phone users should be able to pay money in their phone accounts using their mobile phones or PCs. Money should be charged to the credit card the user provided when he or she hired his or her phone. The payment should be performed as long as it is authorised.

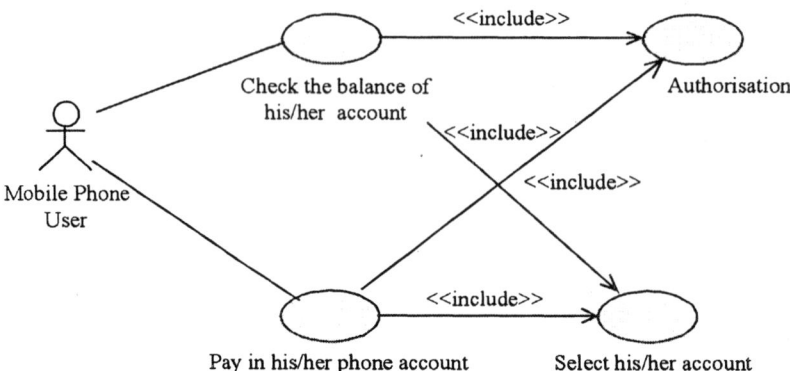

Figure 6.8: Use case diagram for our integration scenario.

Both use cases have to perform authorisation and selection of the account first. The use case diagram is shown in Fig. 6.8. To demonstrate the identification and application of integration patterns we present in this chapter, we focus on these two use cases: authorisation (having access to the information of a customer) and checking the balance of an account.

6.9.2 Checking authorisation

From the perspective of integration, authorisation is related to having access to the information the system has about customers. Therefore, we need to look at how to present information about customers stored in the existing applications. We use the following integration patterns: Virtual Component, Data Mapping Pattern, Data Access Object (DAO), and Integration Wrapper.

We now need to identify components. High-level components can be identified from the analysis model, which is not a trivial task. Selecting the adequate components has a long-term impact on an information system as a whole [87]. The selection also determines how suitable the integration architecture is to re-engineer existing applications and replace them with new solutions. In our example, we use virtual component *CustomerVC* to display information about customers.

Next, we have to identify the dependencies amongst existing applications and databases. The required data is stored in the account balance management database and in the customer information application. This is shown in Fig. 6.9.

To have access to the application that manages balances, we use the Integration Wrapper Pattern. Given that we only need to have access to data, we can abstract this interaction with a DAO. We also use a DAO to have access to the information about a customer in the existing database. To extract, compare, and merge the data produced by these applications, we use the Data Mapping Pattern. This leads us to the model shown in Fig. 6.10.

Next, we have to select the appropriate technologies to integrate our systems, and there are several choices. One of them is the Java 2 Enterprise Edition platform, which allows us to use entity beans with bean managed persistence (BMP) for virtual component *CustomerVC*. Entity beans are best suited to represent entity components, which store transaction state

Application Integration Patterns 133

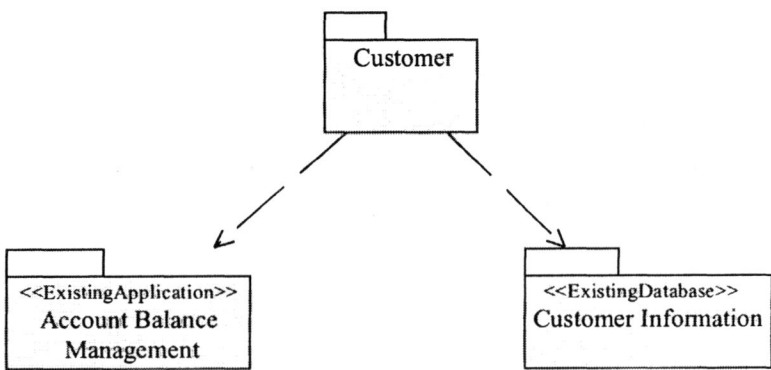

Figure 6.9: Relationships to existing applications for the customer virtual component.

and are shared between clients. We use BMP because we need to have access to existing applications and map the data from two different applications. Therefore we cannot use CMP (Container Managed Persistence). We can use the Multi-step Data Mapping Pattern, which we can implement as dependent objects. We use dependent objects for both DAO objects, too. This allows us to build coarse-grained entity beans that minimise remote method invocation overhead. This approach is suitable for EJB 1.1 and EJB 2.0. An alternative is to use local interfaces and container-managed relations, but it is available in EJB 2.0 only and results in slightly lower performance because containers are involved in local method invocations. Finally, we have to implement *CustomerInformationWrapper* as a CORBA integration wrapper. Using CORBA allows us to develop the wrapper in a different programming language and we need the synchronous access to the existing application.

6.9.3 Checking the balance of an account

Checking the balance of an account requires interaction with several existing applications. Therefore, we need to have access to them appropriately and coordinate the whole interaction logic. We also need to present this functionality as a high-level service to which other clients must be able to have access. We use the following patterns: Process Automator, Virtual Component, Integration Mediator, and Integration Wrapper.

We have to identify high-level components based on the analysis model class diagram, not shown here. We can identify the following components:

Component *CheckBalance* must implement the Process Automator Pattern;

Component *AccountVC* (Account entity component from the analysis) must implement the Virtual Component Pattern.

To identify other components, we first need to identify the relationships with existing applications. We focus on the operation that allows to check the balance of an account. The existing applications certainly support this functionality; however, this functionality is not provided by a single existing application. Therefore this component depends on more than one existing application. To calculate the current balance of an account, the component has to interact with existing applications. The dependencies are shown in the diagram in Fig. 6.11.

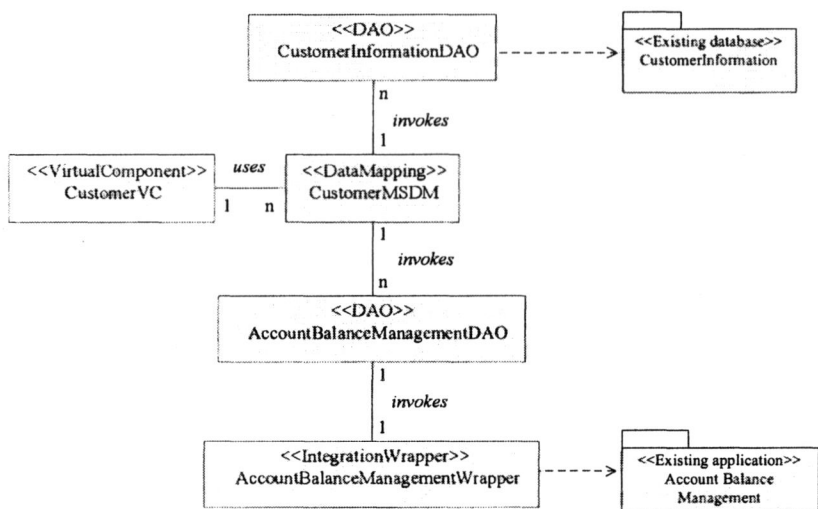

Figure 6.10: Application of the patterns to customer virtual component.

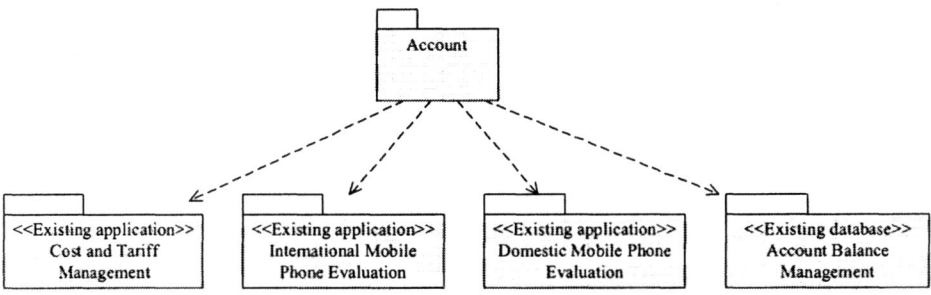

Figure 6.11: Relationships to existing applications for checking the balance of an account.

These dependencies allow us to identify additional components. To interact with existing applications we use integration wrappers, which provide programmatic access to them. For national and international mobile phone evaluation, we also use an Integration Mediator Pattern, which coordinates the interaction logic with both existing applications. This leads us to the design shown in Fig. 6.12.

We have several choices regarding the technologies to be used. Java 2 Enterprise Edition might be a good solution, and it would lead to:

A session bean for the *CheckBalance* (Process Automator Pattern). A session bean is well suited for stateless as well as stateful process automator components. Our scenario requires synchronous request/response communication; this is the reason why a session bean is the optimal choice. Alternatively we can use message-driven beans if we need asynchronous communication.

An entity bean with BMP for *AccountVC* (Virtual Component Pattern). We use entity

Application Integration Patterns

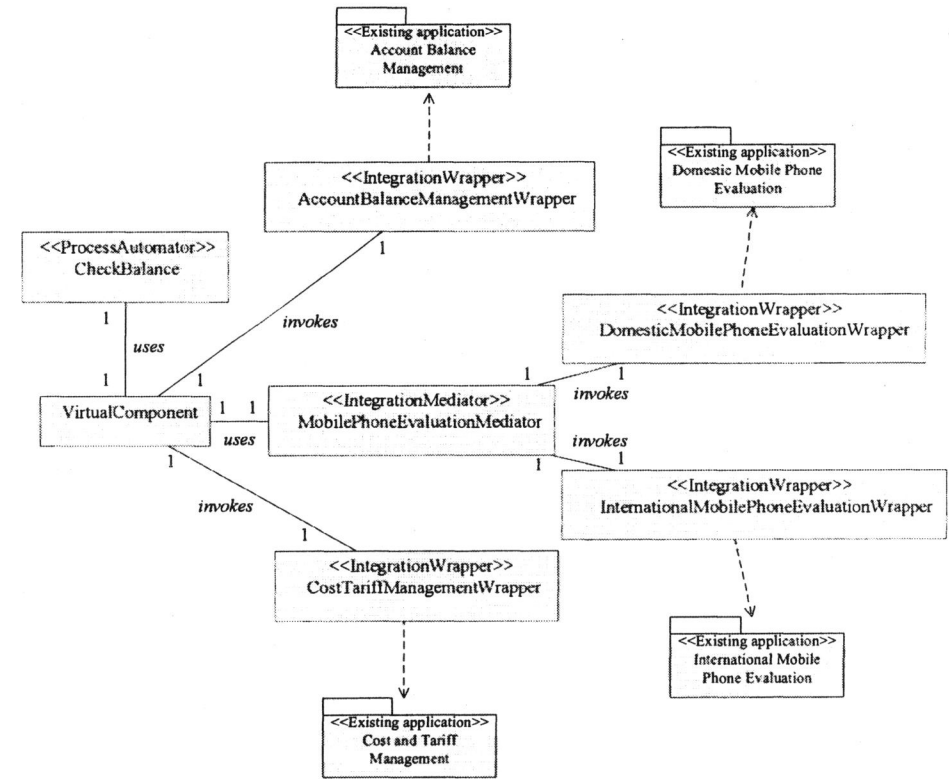

Figure 6.12: Application of the patterns to checking the balance of an account.

beans, because AccountVC should represent shared, transaction state. Entity beans are best suited for this purpose. *AccountVC* must gather data from different existing applications. Therefore we cannot rely on CMP and have to use BMP.

An RMI-IIOP distributed object called *MobilePhoneEvaluationMediator* (Integration Mediator Pattern). We chose RMI-IIOP because we do not want to incur in extra container overhead; it might also require thread control and synchronization in more complex scenarios. Alternatively, we can use session beans or CORBA, but we think that this is also a good interoperability demonstration.

CORBA wrappers for our integration wrappers. We use CORBA because we need synchronous communication. CORBA provides interoperability with RMI-IIOP, and is not limited to Java, which is important for developing wrappers.

The selection of the technology to implement integration wrappers depends primarily on the architecture of existing applications. However, we chose CORBA because it is widely used in this context, and it supports a variety of programming languages, operating systems and platforms.

In this use case, we have shown how to use our integration patterns for the integration of applications within a company (intra-EAI). The same patterns are suitable for intra-enterprise integration, too. Here, we build on the principle that successful inter-EAI and

B2B integration can be based on well-defined intra-EAI only. Therefore, we think that the patterns we have presented have to be applied step by step: first, to enable intra-EAI integration; next, we should build B2B interactions on top of an integrated architecture. In this context, our patterns play an important role.

6.10 Conclusions

In this chapter, we have presented six new integration patterns: Integration Broker, Integration Wrapper, Integration Mediator, Virtual Component, Data Mapping, and Process Automator. They are design and architectural patterns and can be used both for intra-EAI and inter-EAI (B2B) integration. We arrived at these results largely thorough a systematic analysis of common integration problems. They have been implemented successfully in several integration projects, and differ considerably from other proposals in the field of integration patterns.

In order to integrate B2B application successfully, we first need to integrate intra-company applications since inter-EAI needs well-defined intra-EAI first. For this reason, our integration patterns have to be applied step by step, first to enable intra-EAI, next to enable inter-EAI. The B2B interactions are to be placed on top of an enterprise-wide integrated architecture. To develop an integrated architecture, all the patterns presented are important. However, in the B2B context, the Process Automator Pattern is a special case. This pattern was designed to be applied when implementing the shared business processes amongst several enterprises.

In future, we shall describe how to apply these patterns using most prominent component-based architectures, e.g., Java 2 Enterprise Edition, CORBA, and .NET Component Services.

About the authors

 Matjaž B. Jurič
 Ivan Rozman
 Tatjana Welzer
 Marjan Heričko
 Boštjan Brumen
 Vili Podgorelec

Matjaž B. Jurič holds a Ph.D. in Computer and Information Science and he is an Assistant Professor at the University of Maribor. He has been involved in several large-scale object technology projects. In cooperation with the IBM Java Technology Centre, he worked on performance analysis and optimisation in RMI-IIOP development, an integral part of the Java 2 Platform. Matjaž has co-authored J2EE Design Patterns Applied, Professional J2EE EAI and Professional EJB, all from Wrox Press, and has published a chapter in More Java Gems, from Cambridge University Press. He has published articles in journals and magazines, such as Web Services Journal, EAI Journal, Java Developer's Journal, Java Report, Java World, ACM journals; he has also made contributions to conferences such as OOPSLA, XML Europe, SIGS Java Development, Wrox Conferences, BEA Forum, SCI, and others. He is also a reviewer, program committee member and conference co-organiser.

Ivan Rozman is the dean of the Faculty of Electrical Engineering and Computer Science of the University of Maribor since 1999, and he also heads the Institute of Informatics at this university. His research interests include Engineering Management, Software Development Methodologies, Software Process and Software Quality, which are also the topics of his lectures. Results of his research activities have been published in over 500 publications. The most outstanding publications are: three books and fifteen original scientific papers published in international scientific journals ranked in JCR (Journal Citation Reports) by ISI (Institute for Scientific Information), conference papers, professional papers and project reports. Since 1990, he has been the project leader of over 40 projects, implemented in cooperation between the academia and the industry. He is also the leader of COT (Object Technology Centre).

Tatjana Welzer holds a Master Degree in Electrical Engineering and a Ph.D. degree in Computer Science. She is with the University of Maribor Slovenia, Faculty of Electrical Engineering and Computer Science as an Associate Professor. She is lecturing different courses on databases and security. As a guest professor, she has lectured in Finland, Portugal and Spain. Her main research topics are databases, reusability, quality dimensions of reusable components, data mining and data warehouse as well as education in Computer Science. Results of those researches were presented and published in IASTED, IEEE and ICSC conferences. Some of the results were also published as independent chapters in books (MCB University Press, University of Vaasa Publication Unit, IOS Press). The newest results and research are related to medicine, medical informatics (based on data reusability) and e-commerce, and they have been published in Journal of Medical Informatics (Elsevier) and Journal of Medical Systems (Plenum Press).

Marjan Heričko is an Assistant Professor at the University of Maribor. He has been involved in several large-scale projects with object technology and is an expert in object design, EAI, software quality, and component development. He is the technical leader of COT and the program chair of the annual OTS conference. He has contributed to several important conferences.

Boštjan Brumen is a researcher at the University of Maribor. His research includes data mining, sub-sampling methods, data preparation, predictive model-oriented data mining, electronic commerce, and data security.

Vili Podgorelec received a M.Sc. degree and a Ph.D. degree in Computer Science from the University of Maribor in 1999 and 2001, respectively. Currently, he is an Assistant Professor with the Faculty for Electrical Engineering and Computer Science, University of Maribor. His main research interests include intelligent systems, software engineering, medical informatics, and computational intelligence. He has participated in many national and international research projects, and he is the author of several journal papers on computational intelligence, medical informatics and software engineering. He has received several international awards and grants for his research activities, including IEEE Region 8 Best student paper award in 1999 for his work on automatic medical diagnostic decision support model.

Part IV

Data Analysis and Knowledge Discovery

Chapter 7

Agents, Personalisation, and Intelligent Applications

Giovanni Semeraro, Fabio Abbattista, Marco Degemmis, Oriana Licchelli, Pasquale Lops, and Fabio Zambetta

7.1 Introduction

Internet services evolve quickly, leading to both a constantly increasing number of web sites and improvement in their functionality. Nowadays, companies are developing new business portals and providing large amounts of product information. The largest e-commerce sites offer millions of products for sale and choosing amongst so many options is difficult for customers. Customer satisfaction and loyalty is inevitably reduced due to the time they spend at searching for the information they need. A useful e-commerce application should mimic traditional catalogues, order forms and other printed material that used to be the basis of communication between consumers and suppliers. Furthermore, the inherent potential for interactive data processing and man–machine dialogue should be used by e-commerce applications to meet a user's need for immediate situation-specific responses, instantly available problem-specific advice, and better ways to have access and inspect the offers provided by a supplier. However, current graphical user interfaces in widespread use, which rely on classical WYSIWYG (What You See Is What You Get) mechanics, require a considerable cognitive overhead. The main problem of most web sites is that they offer manifold navigation options and search functions, but leave it up to users to find their way through the set of interface functions. This may be tolerable to frequent users, but can deter casual users in many cases.

The interface should use best-practice solutions to achieve a high degree of dialogue intelligence, and use an appropriate graphical design. Currently available mechanisms for easing orientation and usability include (quasi) natural language input and simple forms of context-sensitive help. Still, they often offer too little situation-specific and strategic support for solving substantial tasks. In order to offer useful, proactive advice and react cooperatively, a system should have access to a large and varied repository of dialogue rules and strategies [116], including descriptions of logical steps for solving a dialogue goal, as well as monitoring and evaluating the dialogue history of individual users, with a view to offer interactive, personalised advice. These requirements have been discussed in the literature for some time, but the need for practical solutions and commercially-available systems has given rise to several projects aiming at producing intelligent agents, also called personas [17].

In this chapter, we present an application developed within the European Union project called COGITO; it combines several advanced technologies to enhance consumer–supplier relationships through intelligent personalised agents that can serve as virtual assistants for customers. Such technologies include an advanced user interface based on natural language processing, personalisation systems exploiting the knowledge about the users accessing the services, and modules for flexible data representation using XML. The rest of the chapter is organised as follows: Section 7.2 describes problems and requirements for adaptive systems in the field of electronic commerce; a thorough description of the results of the COGITO project for developing an architecture able to deal with these problems and requirements is presented in Section 7.3; Section 7.4 generalises the outcome of the COGITO project in order to build a modern, advanced infrastructure for e-business applications; finally, related work is described in Section 7.5, and some conclusions are drawn in Section 7.6.

7.2 Adaptive Systems in E-commerce

Compared to other applications, there are many special requirements for adaptive shopping systems on the web. The most important ones are the following:

Privacy As the web can be accessed really world wide, with varying degrees of security, many users are wary of giving private data. Companies must guarantee not to give personal data to a third party and should provide customers with suitable technical means to rectify user model items [92].

Fun Electronic shopping malls on the web are a new form of marketing. It is very important not to bother the customer with questions and psychological tests to build a user model.

Speed The adaptation of the presentation should occur very quickly [99], so that it becomes an individual presentation for everybody, including new customers.

Simplicity To produce personalised advertising, the integration of user modelling and adaptation components in electronic catalogues should be simple.

Furthermore, the process of buying products and services on the Internet often implies a high degree of complexity and uncertainty. Some important problems concerning e-commerce in general and shopping at Internet bookstores in particular are the following:

Surfing and buying experience One problem related to the use of the Internet is getting people to start web surfing and, more specifically, to make their first purchase. Many people's lack of experience with computers impedes the exploitation of e-commerce sites.

Transfer of traditional shopping behaviour Using traditional metaphors for shopping on web sites may create advantages as well as problems. The obvious advantages are the possibility of recalling known patterns, thereby facilitating decision-making. Furthermore, users can experience uncertainty when confronted with the differences that, despite the resemblance with traditional shops, lie within the Internet way of shopping.

Degree of involvement in the product There is more interest in buying on-line products with a low degree of involvement, such as groceries. In general, the users are motivated to buy this kind of product on the Internet because it relieves their shopping burden and because the products are identical to those they can find in local stores. Problems arise when e-commerce sites are concerned with products with a high degree of involvement, such as clothes or books. The physical sense of touching the product and the visual representation are of utmost importance in deciding whether to buy or not.

Lack of trust Internet stores frequently offer several opportunities to the users to get tailored recommendations, create personal lists, and obtain news from the shops. In order to do so, users should submit information about their personal preferences, e-mail addresses, and, in the case of buying items, a credit card number is imperative. Two problems arise: one concerns the creation of a user profile and the other regards the handling and use of the information given. Some people are not interested in being confronted with choices that are based on information about earlier choices or interactions. They feel that this could constrain their action possibilities, even though they might enjoy the personalisation.

Non-transparent interfaces A problem that is often encountered on the Internet is the lack of well-arranged sites. Generally, they are messy and overloaded with information, so users are forced to scroll, even though this way of exploring a site is tiring.

The common theme for the above-mentioned problems is uncertainty. It is necessary to overcome these problems to facilitate the use and acceptance of e-commerce.

7.3 Intelligent, Personalised Web Services

In the e-commerce field, applications offer a wide range of functions nowadays. Considering the vast selection of offers, it is particularly important to give the customers personal advice that reflects their individual needs and interests. Therefore, advanced features are necessary to tailor the presentation of a web site to the customer's personal tastes. Nevertheless, current interface technology provides only limited solutions for specific e-commerce related requirements. For instance, the interface should support affective marketing communication, allow for interactive guided tours, and dynamic FAQs. Thus agents and personalisation become the key factors to enhance personal assistance, e.g., in cross- and up-selling. The use of agents and personalisation could satisfy or deal with most of the requirements and problems described in previous section (cf. Table 7.1).

7.3.1 Virtual dialoguing agents

Intelligent agents can converse with the user in written natural language and can be regarded as an alternative interface metaphor to the contemporary GUI technology, which can be used to implement many of the advanced requirements of e-commerce effectively. Natural language dialogues are easy to understand, the users may express their needs in an

Table 7.1: Requirements and problems dealt with agents and personalisation.

Requirements	Agents	Personalisation
Privacy	✗	✓
Fun	✓	✗
Speed, simplicity	✓	✓
Problems	**Agents**	**Personalisation**
Surfing and buying experience	✗	✓
Transfer of traditional shopping behaviour	✓	✓
Degree of involvement in the product	✓	✗
Lack of trust, non-transparent interfaces	✓	✓

unrestricted form, and it is possible to produce sophisticated system behaviour. Conversational interfaces that simulate a virtual dialogue partner have been around for decades, but they have been mostly confined to very limited functions, such as database querying. Apart from such simplistic approaches, a variety of research projects [116] have yielded a rich background of methods, algorithms and representation formats which can be used to transform the limited capabilities of these agents into more advanced interaction tools called chatterbots.

A chatterbot is able to engage in a conversation with a user, sometimes accompanied by cartoons expressing emotions. Simple chatterbots only simulate conversation without using any knowledge about the individual users and their actual behaviour during on-line sessions. For instance, A.L.I.C.E., which is available at http://www.alice.org, has become popular on the web and with the specialised press, despite it has no theoretical background. Such simple chatterbots are not powerful enough to serve as a medium for customer advice. Even those with a sophisticated repertoire of conversational skills shall fail to be more than entertaining if they do not treat a user as an individual having specific needs and preferences. This means that, in addition to some of the abilities already available, a further reaching dialogue management shall be needed to help reach two major goals: first, in order to achieve an adequate, non-stereotypical repertoire of reactions, the individual dialogue situation must be interpreted; furthermore, dialogues that are more complex allow goal-directed strategies to be pursued (cooperative behaviour, convincing argumentation). Whilst being important, the increased ergonomic usability and personalisation of chatterbots are only the first steps. By being able to take the initiative, rather than simply reacting to user input and commands, a system can take on the role of an independent agent during dialogue. In addition, the look and feel of a virtual advisor can be a direct and useful complement to the proposed dialogue approach: this shall contribute to a relaxed atmosphere and an increased attractiveness of the service.

The MS Office assistants deserve to be mentioned because of their widespread use, even though they are quite shallow in some respects. Sometimes they are too invasive and do not exhibit a very complex behaviour; however, they suffice to help the inexperienced user in many situations. They are based on the Microsoft Agent technology that enables multiple applications, or clients, to use animation services such as loading a character, playing a specified animation and responding to user input. Spoken text appears in a word balloon but several TTS (text-to-speech) engines must be used to play it. Another example of a Microsoft Agent is IMP (Instant Messaging Personalities), available at http://www.e-clips.com.au, which gives a very good idea of how an agent can help the users handle Microsoft Messenger features such as mail checking, instant messaging, and so on. The agents have lip-synchronised faces pronouncing the messages the user receives, and they tell the user whether any of his or her contacts have just gone on-line, off-line, or away, for instance.

7.3.2 Personalisation

Personalisation has become an important business strategy in the e-commerce field, where a user explicitly wants the site to store information such as preferences about himself or herself. Exploiting the underlying one-to-one marketing paradigm is essential to be successful in the increasingly competitive Internet marketplace. A key issue in personalisation of a web site is the automatic construction of accurate machine-processable customer profiles. This is called the user modelling process. User modelling simply means ascertaining a few bits of information about each user, processing that information quickly and providing the results to applications without intruding on the user's consciousness. The final result is the construction of a user model or a user profile.

The user model is a collection of information about an individual and should be able to recognise the user, know why he or she did something, and guess what he or she wants to do next. Profiles can be used to deliver personalised contents to the user. The main advantages of using the one-to-one personalisation paradigm based on user profiling in the e-commerce field are attractiveness for users, customer trust and confidence, as well as customer loyalty [162].

Personal recommendations, individual purchase incentives, and assistance are facilitated by establishing a learning relationship between a customer and a supplier. In fact, the use of the profile provides the customer with more effective recommendations, leading to an increase of the interaction with the system. Consequently, more information about the user's preferences is collected and an improvement in both the quality of the personalisation process and the profile itself is gained.

7.3.3 The architecture of COGITO

The COGITO project aims at bringing together appropriate technologies from different fields of artificial intelligence, information retrieval, electronic publishing and commerce and human factors research; the goal is to reach a hypothesis for an architectural framework for advanced e-business applications. The combination of the technologies we considered includes: user guidance in conversational interaction, personalisation and profile extraction, as well as proactiveness through intelligent retrieval.

The project aims at improving the usability of the BOL web site, an on-line media shop specialised in books, CDs and gifts [1]. BOL Medien is a partner of the COGITO consortium, and it is one of the European subsidiaries of Bertelsmann AG, Europe's largest media company.

The general architecture includes six macro modules shown in Fig. 7.1, namely: BOL's web server, the eBrain chatterbot, the Profile Extractor, the Prompter, the XML Content Manager, and the Connector. The system provides access to relevant product information or helps the user find appropriate offers. Thus, a considerably more precise search in the BOL product database is accomplished. The interaction with users interested in some products is managed by the eBrain chatterbot by Logica pdv, which is able to engage in conversations with users as long as the conversations concern topics in the knowledge bases to which the chatterbot has access; they are referred to as contexts, too.

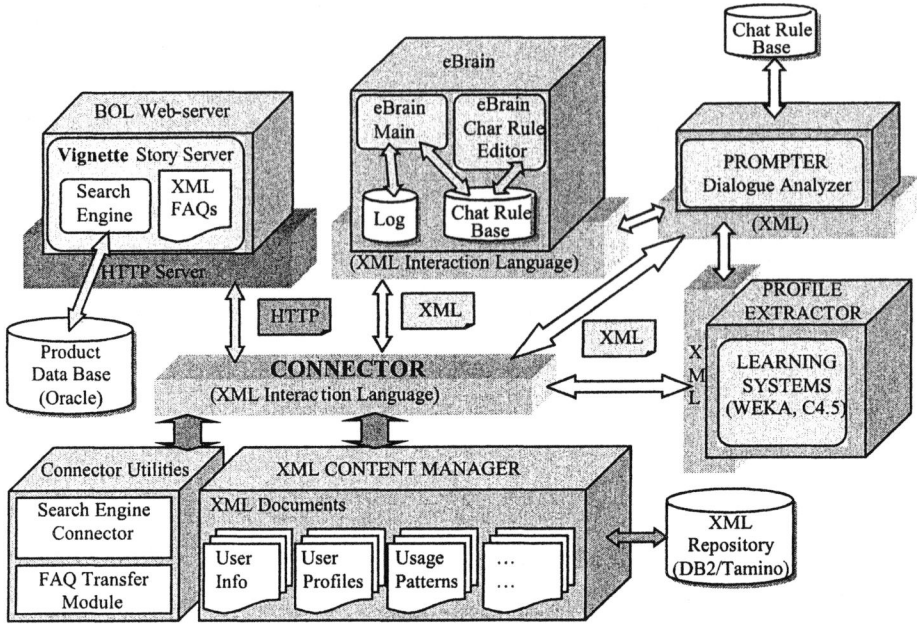

Figure 7.1: The architecture of COGITO.

A significant part of the project is concerned with the use of machine learning techniques to improve the personalised interaction of the users with the eBrain chatterbot and, consequently, with the BOL site. The Profile Extractor is the module that represents the main result of the accomplished analysis: its primary function is to implement the user profiling mechanism of the system. The output of the Profile Extractor, user profiles, is used to fit the search in the BOL product database to the user interests and preferences.

The Prompter is an intelligent information retrieval component invoked in situations which are either problematic or caused by unknown phrases, highly specialised vocabulary, or ambiguous words. A situation can be problematic if some unexpected result of a search is given or the general problem solving competence embedded in the chatterbot's rule base is not sufficient to fulfill a user's request. In such cases, a reasonable system response requires specialised knowledge and skills. Therefore, the Prompter uses search heuristics that enable it to re-formulate the original request, either automatically or by initiating a clarification dialogue with the user. The automatic re-formulation is performed by an appropriate set of rules which use both the domain knowledge and the user profile to add, modify or clarify the terms occurring in the current query to be submitted to the system [164]. This process is usually named query expansion and consists of an improvement in the criteria used for the specification of a query.

Another requirement dealt with during the development of the COGITO system involves matters about representing information in a homogeneous and structured format, exchanging information between distributed components of a system, and storing information in distributed, shared repositories. An optimal solution to these problems is provided by the eXtensible Markup Language (XML). The system responsible for the management of XML data is the XML Content Manager. The integration with back-end systems and the inter-

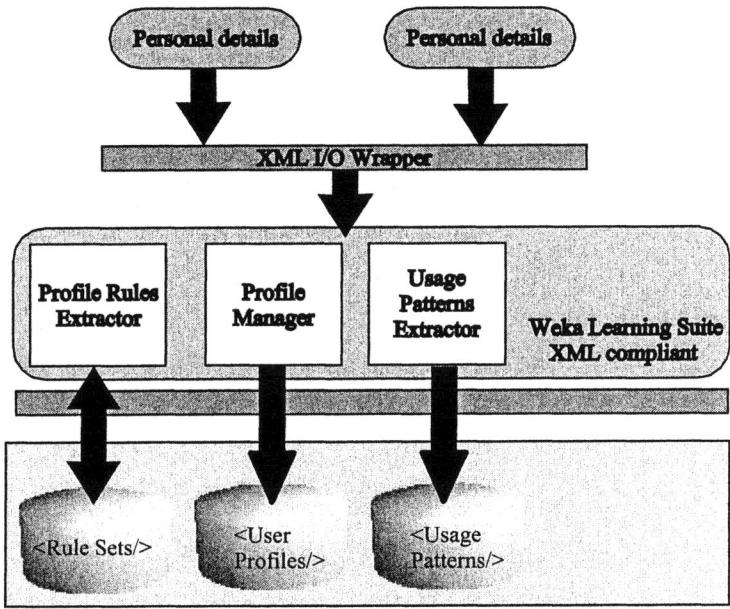

Figure 7.2: The architecture of the Profile Extractor.

nal architectural modules is based on a connector that comprises components enabling the system to have access to external services and knowledge sources. It relies on a standard XML-based communication protocol, namely SOAP (Simple Object Access Protocol).

7.3.4 Extracting user profiles

In the first phase of the COGITO project, the analysis of the requirements led us to adopt machine learning techniques for the implementation of a profiling system able to build profiles through the analysis of past user interactions. The Profile Extractor is a highly reusable module that classifies the users that enter a web site. It uses supervised and unsupervised learning techniques. The former are exploited to induce a set of rules, used by a classification module, whereas the latter are exploited to group users into communities (clusters) and to discover association rules used to identify common trends underlying the data set.

The system is able to analyse data gathered from sources such as data warehouse or transactions, for instance, in order to infer rules describing the customer/user behaviour and more general usage patterns. Profiles can be useful to support one-to-one marketing actions, whereas communities can be useful to address clusters of users by means of mass-marketing campaigns. The architecture of this module is shown in Fig. 7.2.

Some preliminary work is needed to establish a formal description of the features and attributes that are needed to accomplish the given task; we can use the results to define the representation language of the entire learning framework. The other main problem concerns the definition of meaningful classes that characterise the corresponding kind of interaction. The Profile Rules Extractor and the Profile Manager are the main modules involved in the profile generation process; the Usage Patterns Extractor implements both

Table 7.2: Description of the attributes used to represent examples.

Attribute	Description
User_id	Unique identifier of each user
Access_date	Identifies the date of the last access performed by the user
Connections_num	Total number of connections to the site performed by the user
Search_num_⟨CategoryName⟩	Number of searches for a specific category
Search_freq_⟨CategoryName⟩	Frequency of searches for a specific category
Purchase_num_⟨CategoryName⟩	Number of purchases for a specific category
Purchase_freq_⟨CategoryName⟩	Frequency of purchases for a specific category

a clustering algorithm and a technique for extracting association rules. It groups dialogue sessions in order to infer some usage patterns that can be exploited for understanding trends useful to further market studies and for grouping single users, sharing the same interests and preferences, into user communities [127]. The XML I/O Wrapper is the layer responsible for the integration of the inner modules with external data sources using the XML protocol; it is also responsible for the extraction of data required for the learning process. During a session, user dialogues with the eBrain agent are stored in log files. The dialogue analyser presented in Fig. 7.1 receives the log files of past sessions and processes them in order to produce a structured dialogue history, containing some transactional data.

The input to the Profile Extractor is represented by the XML file coming through the Connector from the dialogue analyser module. The XML I/O Wrapper is responsible for extracting all relevant information from the file in order to set up the examples for the learning components.

The complete set of attributes used to represent the examples is listed in Table 7.2. (⟨CategoryName⟩ denotes each of the ten main book categories of the BOL web site, namely: Belletristik, Computer und Internet, Kinderbücher, Kultur und Geschichte, Nachschlagewerke, Reise, Sachbuch und Ratgeber, Schule und Bildung, Wirtschaft und Soziales, Wissenschaft und Technik[1]. This information is arranged into a set of unclassified instances, where each one represents a single customer. The subset of the instances chosen to train the learning system has to be pre-classified by a domain expert: this is the actual input to the Profile Rules Extractor, which infers a set of classification rules for each book category presented in Fig. 7.3.

The actual user profile generation process is performed by the Profile Manager on the grounds of the user history and the set of rules induced by the Profile Rules Extractor. When the domain expert decides to generate or update user profiles, the related structured dialogue history is arranged into a set of instances that represents the input to the Profile Manager. On the basis of the classification rule sets inferred, the classifier predicts whether the user is interested in each book category. These classifications, together with the interaction details,

---

[1] N.T.: Fiction, Computer and Internet, Children's Book, Culture and History, Reference Book, Travel, Monographs and Guidebooks, School and Education, Economics and Law, Science and Technique.

There are 11 rules extracted for class Kinderbücher:

if search_num_Kinderbucher > 1.0
    and purchase_number_Schule_Und_Bildung <= 38.0
    and search_freq_Schule_Und_Bildung <= 0.26 **then**
  Class: yes
else if purchase_freq_Kinderbucher > 0.24
    and purchase_number_Computer_Und_Internet <= 29.0
    and purchase_number_Computer_Und_Internet > 5.0 **then**
  Class: yes
else if purchase_freq_Kinderbucher > 0.25
    and purchase_number_Schule_Und_Bildung <= 24.0
    and purchase_number_Kultur_Und_Geschichte <= 18.0 **then**
  Class: yes
else if search_num_Kinderbucher <= 1.0
    and search_number_Reise <= 3.0
    and search_freq_Nachschlagewerke <= 0.33
    and purchase_freq_Nachschlagewerke > 0.14
    and search_number_Reise <= 2.0
    and search_number_Sachbuch_Und_Ratgeber > 0.0 **then**
  Class: no
else if
...
Otherwise Class: no

Figure 7.3: An example of classification rules for category Kinderbücher.

are gathered to form a user profile similar to the one in Fig. 7.4.

After the training phase, once a user enters the BOL web site, his or her dialogue history file is generated or updated by the system. The file is then exploited to produce a new example that the Profile Extractor classifies on the grounds of the rules inferred. The system is thus able to track user behaviour evolution and, consequently, customer profiles are updated across multiple interactions.

The Profile Extractor is built on an intelligent component, called Learning Server, developed in the context of a digital library service [147]. The core of the Profile Extractor is WEKA [171], a machine-learning tool that was developed at the University of Waikato (New Zealand). WEKA provides a uniform interface to many learning algorithms, along with methods for pre- or post-processing, as well as for the evaluation of the results of learning schemes.

The WEKA learning scheme may be used in various ways. Indeed, it provides an implementation of state-of-the-art learning algorithms, which can be applied to a data set expressed in a tabular format called ARFF. WEKA also includes an implementation of algorithms for unsupervised learning, mining association rules and tools for the evaluation of the inferred models. In the COGITO system, we developed XWEKA, an XML compliant version of WEKA that is able to represent input and output in XML format.

For the purpose of extracting user profiles, we focused on supervised machine learning techniques. Starting from pre-classified examples of some target concepts, these techniques

Profile for User: 117						
CONNECTIONS_NUM	23	Belletristik	yes	0.9902	no	0.0098
SEARCH_NUMBelletristik	3	Computer_und_Internet	yes	1.0	no	0.0
SEARCH_FREQBelletristik	0.2	Kinderbucher	yes	0.0	no	1.0
PURCHASE_NUMBelletristik	23	Kultur_und_Geschichte	yes	0.7902	no	0.2098
PURCHASE_FREQBelletristik	0.35	Nachschlagewerke	yes	0.0	no	1.0
SEARCH_NUMComputer_und_Internet	1	Reise	yes	0.0038	no	0.9962
SEARCH_FREQComputer_und_Internet	0.2	Sachbuch_und_Ratgeber	yes	0.6702	no	0.3298
PURCHASE_NUMComputer_und_Internet	13	Schule_und_Bildung	yes	0.0	no	1.0
PURCHASE_FREQComputer_und_Internet	0.24	Wirtschaft_und_Recht	yes	0.0	no	1.0
SEARCH_NUMKinderbucher	0	Wissenschaft_und_Technik	yes	0.0	no	1.0
SEARCH_FREQKinderbucher	0					
PURCHASE_NUMKinderbucher	0					
PURCHASE_FREQKinderbucher	0					
SEARCH_NUMKultur_und_Geschichte	1					
SEARCH_FREQKultur_und_Geschichte	0.2					
PURCHASE_NUMKultur_und_Geschichte	23					
PURCHASE_FREQKultur_und_Geschichte	0.34					
SEARCH_NUMNachschlagewerke	0					
SEARCH_FREQNachschlagewerke	0					
...	...					

Figure 7.4: An example of a user profile.

induce rules that are useful for predicting the classification of further unclassified examples. The antecedent, or precondition, of a rule is a series of tests, just like the tests at nodes in decision trees, whereas the consequent, or conclusion, gives the class that applies to instances covered by that rule (cf. Fig. 7.3).

The learning algorithm adopted in the profile generation process is based on PART [64], a rule-based learner that produces rules from pruned partial decision trees built using C4.5 heuristics [133]. Other interesting implementations of different classifiers based on the naive Bayes probabilistic technique, as well as on an implementation of the k-neighbours classifier, are also available. Although these methods have been applied to user modelling [24], we chose to adopt PART on the basis of the results of the experiments conducted in order to evaluate the most suitable learning system to embed into the Profile Extractor. See next section for further details.

PART combines the divide-and-conquer approach for decision tree learning with the separate-and-conquer one for rule learning in an attempt to avoid their respective problems. The divide-and-conquer approach is used in order to build a partial decision tree as the basis for the subsequent extraction of the classification rule. Then, the method adopts the separate-and-conquer strategy in that it builds a rule, removes the instances it covers, and continues creating rules recursively for the remaining instances until none are left.

It differs from the standard approach in the way each rule is created. In essence, to make a single rule, a pruned decision tree is built for the current set of instances, the leaf with the largest coverage is turned into a rule and the tree is discarded. Using a pruned tree to obtain a rule, instead of building it incrementally by adding conjunctions one at a time, avoids the over-pruning problem of the basic separate-and-conquer rule learner. Furthermore, combining the separate-and-conquer methodology with decision trees adds flexibility and speed. The key idea is to build a partial decision tree instead of a fully explored one. A partial decision tree is an ordinary tree that contains branches to undefined subtrees. To generate such a tree, construction and pruning operations are integrated in order to find a subtree that cannot be further simplified. Once this subtree has been found, the building process terminates and a single rule is extracted from the decision tree. PART builds a rule considering the path from the root to the leaf with the largest coverage. The internal nodes represent the tests that must be verified for that rule to be fired, whereas the leaf represents the classification given to the instance if the rule is fired. The instances covered by the rule are subtracted, and the process continues creating rules recursively for the remaining instances until none are left. The main advantage of this method is not performance but simplicity: it produces good rule sets without any need for global optimisation.

7.3.5 Experimental results

In this section, we present the results of the experimental evaluation conducted in order to choose the most suitable learning system for the profile generation process.

We carried out two experiments: first, a comparison between two different approaches for rule learning within WEKA was performed. Specifically, we compared PART with J4.8, an algorithm that implements a later and slightly improved version of C4.5. Then, the most efficient method was compared with another learning system, IBK, thus evaluating the use of a different learning paradigm, namely instance-based learning.

In both experiments, we considered the 10 main book categories of BOL as target concepts for the classification task, which consists of labelling each user with thematic categories from a predefined set. For each of the categories, the system was trained in order to infer proper classification rules. Each instance in the training set contains information on the interaction of a user with the web site and is preclassified by a human expert who decides whether it refers to a user interested in that category. For the sake of truth, customers used to train the system were chosen from those who had already filled in a form concerning their preferred book categories, since they had already registered with service MyBOL. Thus, their preclassification did not require the intervention of a human expert.

For classification problems, it is straightforward to measure the performance of a classifier in terms of its error rate. The classifier predicts the class of each instance and it counts a success if it is correct; if not, it is an error. The error rate is just the ratio of errors made over the whole set of instances, and it measures the overall performance of the classifier.

The error rate on the training data is called the re-substitution error because it is calculated by re-substituting the training instances into a classifier that has been constructed from them: it is not a reliable predictor of the true error rate on new data. To predict the performance of a classifier on new data, we have to measure its error rate on an independent data set that has not been involved in the construction of the classifier, that is the test set. Consequently, each data set is analysed by means of a 10-fold cross validation.

Experiment 1: PART versus J4.8

We used three sets of 400, 500 and 600 instances, respectively, to train both PART and J4.8, considering the error rate produced by each learning method. Each instance was described by means of 43 attributes, as shown in Table 7.2. Both unpruned and pruned trees were inferred in order to evaluate the different error percentages.

The results are shown in Fig. 7.5.a. It is worthwhile to note that the error rate decreases as the number of training instances grows. The reason is that the larger the set of instances is, the more the classifier increases its predictive accuracy. Another result is that PART

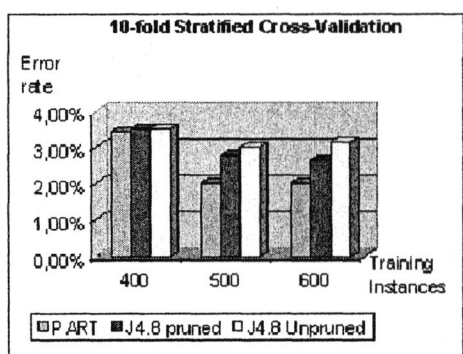 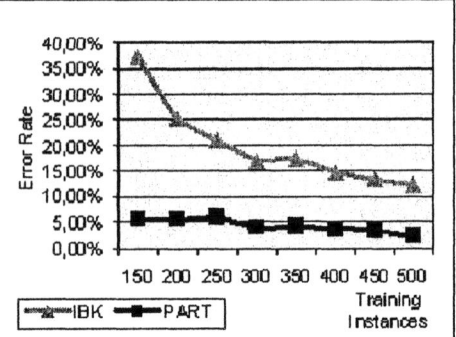

Figure 7.5: (a) PART versus J4.8; (b) PART versus IBK.

Table 7.3: Wilcoxon test performed between PART and IBK.

Training inst.	PART err. rate	IBK err. rate	Difference	Rank
150	5.40	37.24	(-)31.84	(-)8
200	5.51	25.27	(-)19.76	(-)7
250	6.03	21.06	(-)15.03	(-)6
300	3.81	16.91	(-)13.10	(-)4
350	4.06	17.35	(-)13.29	(-)5
400	3.65	14.70	(-)11.05	(-)3
450	3.30	13.29	(-)9.99	(-)2
500	2.20	12.17	(-)9.97	(-)1
				W=-36

turns out to be more accurate than J4.8, regardless of the size of the training set. This is due to the different approaches they adopt: divide and conquer for J4.8 and a hybrid method for PART.

Experiment 2: PART versus IBK

IBK is the implementation of the k-nearest-neighbour classification scheme available in the WEKA suite [6]. By default, IBK uses just one-nearest-neighbour, i.e., $k = 1$. If more than one neighbour is selected, the predictions of the neighbours can be weighted according to their distance from the test instance.

We used 8 sets of examples, ranging from 150 to 500 instances. The results of 10-fold cross validation are shown in Fig. 7.5.b. In this experiment, the non-parametric Wilcoxon signed rank test was used to evaluate the difference between the error rate of PART and IBK, since the number of folds or independent trials is relatively low and does not justify the application of a parametric test, such as the t-test [126]. The results are shown in Table 7.3.

Table 7.4: Wilcoxon results.

Significance level	0.1	0.05	0.02
Result	H_0 rejected	H_0 rejected	H_0 rejected

Agents, Personalisation, and Intelligent Applications 153

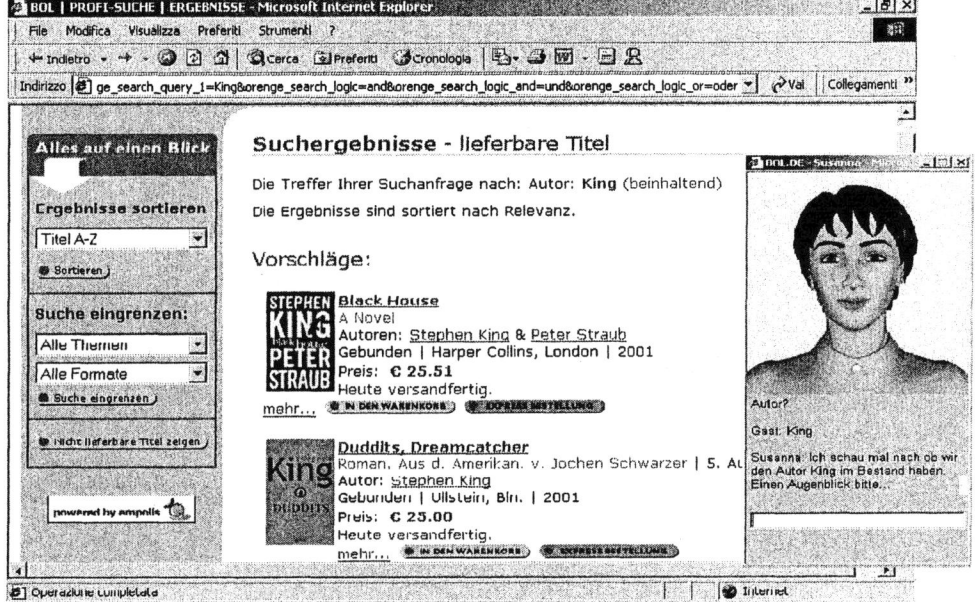

Figure 7.6: Susanna offers a list of books written by King.

The two hypotheses are the following:

H₀ the error rates of IBK and PART are not significantly different;

Hₐ the error rates of IBK and PART are significantly different.

The null hypothesis is accepted or rejected according to the W statistic related at different levels of significance. On the basis of the values of the W statistic calculated above, the comparison between IBK and PART shows that PART is clearly more efficient than IBK, for each significance level considered, as shown in Table 7.4.

7.3.6 The retrieval process in COGITO

The name of the chatterbot in the COGITO prototype is Susanna. It offers a better support to customers during the interaction, providing personal recommendations, purchase incentives and helping users in problematic situations during the search. This improves usability of the BOL web site, as demonstrated in the following scenarios.

Scenario 1: unknown user

A user is known by the COGITO system if he or she completes the BOL registration procedure. This step provides each customer with a personal identification number that is necessary both for recognising a user and for collecting data on his or her preferences and for generating or updating his or her profile.

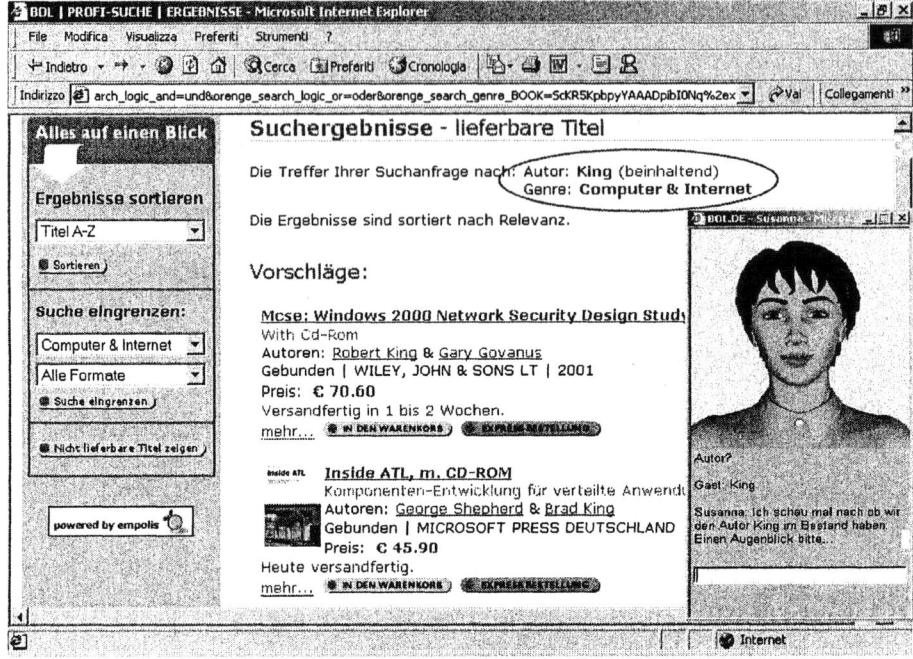

Figure 7.7: List of books by selected authors and category.

In the first scenario, an unknown user asks the chatterbot for a book by the author named King. Susanna finds several books by this author through a remote call (deep linking) to the search engine available at the BOL web site, and displays them as shown in Fig. 7.6. Notice that the books that rank at the top are authored by Stephen King. Books by other authors are found further down the list, which means that the user must scroll down a long list if he or she is not looking for a book by Stephen King. The customer not looking for a book by Stephen King can now choose to either refine the search by using an advanced search function or continue to chat with Susanna about different fields of interest.

Scenario 2: registered user

In the second scenario, the user has already been chatting to Susanna about some of his or her interests. Therefore, a profile of this user is available to the system, which can exploit it to accomplish a more precise search in the product database. Consider that the profile of such a user is the one presented in Fig. 7.4 and the query submitted by the user is the same as in the previous scenario. Now, the first book displayed is a book about Windows 2000 co-authored by Robert King (cf. Fig. 7.7). This result is due to the fact that the original query about King has been automatically expanded by the system into "Author:King AND Genre:Computer&Internet" (highlighted by the circle in Fig. 7.7), since Computer und Internet is the category with the highest degree of interest in the profile of the user (cf. Fig. 7.4). This process is called query expansion.

When a user asks the chatterbot for a book by King, it dynamically builds an XML message containing this value and sends it to the Prompter module (cf. Fig. 7.1) to expand the original query by using the favorite book categories stored in his or her profile. The query expansion process consists of an improvement of the criteria used for the specification of a query. This is usually achieved by adding search terms to an already defined query. The additional terms may be taken from different sources and the Prompter is responsible for determining a suitable query expansion method to be used, according to the information available in the message. The decision process is described in [97]. The information sources invoked for expanding a query are the following:

Product Thesaurus Products like books or other kinds of media are usually characterised by a textual description. The most relevant words contained in these descriptions are clustered according to their relation to those that appear most frequently, thus generating a thesaurus of terms.

User Profiles They are accessed to identify the book categories preferred by a user, which can be enclosed in a query for a more specific result identification, as already described in the second scenario.

Usage Patterns The application of association rules to a specific user can lead to the inference of this user's possible interest in a product or service. The chatterbot can thus decide which dialogue context to use when the dialogue comes to a dead end, i.e., when the user does not want to either take the initiative or mention a specific topic of discourse.

7.4 An Architectural Framework Hypothesis

In this section, we try to outline the main components of a general framework architecture for developing e-business applications; it is based on a generalised view of the COGITO system (Fig. 7.8). The general architecture includes the macro-modules listed below; for each one, an idea of the role they play in the architecture is provided, in an attempt to generalise functions and requirements.

Web Site It accommodates the search engine, which can be used by the agent component by means of a remote call to browse information and navigate the contents of the site. This approach distinguishes the functions provided by the framework from the main services offered by the site and simplifies the integration of the site content with the effective implementation of the services provided by the framework.

Conversational Agent It has a chatterbot component and a 2D/3D character. The former is exploited to converse with a user to serve his or her needs and to collect data from the dialogue. The latter elicits non-verbal cues occurring during a face-to-face conversation, thus endowing the system with a higher-level human-computer interaction. This mechanism tries to mimic a human-like communicative metaphor [2].

Personalisation Suite It extracts the knowledge about users to personalise the content and the interaction with the web site. The knowledge can be extracted from different sources, e.g., the interaction logs, the searching history or the purchasing history. Another important source of information is represented by the chat logs, containing the dialogues between the users and the conversational agent. Different techniques can

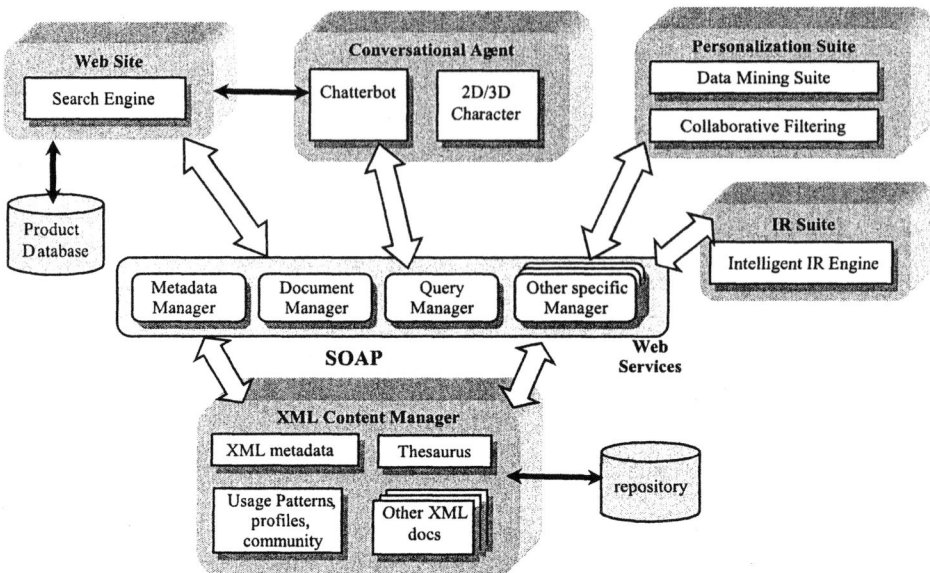

Figure 7.8: A hypothesis for a general framework for e-business applications.

be used to extract valuable information from these sources: (a) data mining techniques to induce behavioural patterns and, as a consequence, user profiles or usage patterns, e.g., community or association rules; (b) information extraction techniques to inspect data contained in the chat logs, in order to retrieve other information on possible interests; (c) collaborative filtering techniques and others that can be plugged into the framework.

XML Content Manager It represents and manages data in XML format. XML technologies play an important role in modern architectures, where the portability and the integration with different data sources are key factors for successful integrated environments. Furthermore, the communication between the different modules in the framework is achieved by the use of web services, since a homogeneous representation for data and communication messages is required.

IR Suite This component exploits the different knowledge sources (inferred from the data mining suite, retrieved from previous interactions, dependent on the specific domain, heuristics, and so on) to retrieve the right information at the right time when coping with unexpected or ambiguous situations.

7.5 Related Work

In recent years, several systems have been designed to offer personalised services and to deliver user-tailored content to web site customers. In this context, various learning approaches have been applied to discover user preferences and to construct user profiles. In [122], the authors use text categorisation in their LIBRA system. It makes content-based book recommendations by applying a naive Bayesian text classifier to the product descriptions supplied by Amazon.com. The system builds a profile made of a simple list of key words for each book category preferred by a user. Conversely, profiles inferred in COGITO contain the book categories preferred by a user. A recent prototype of the Profile Extractor enriches the information concerning user-preferred book categories with a list of related key words extracted from the BOL book descriptions by a naive Bayesian text classifier.

In [102], the authors present a system able to provide personalised recommendations for some types of product that a consumer may purchase frequently, such as books, CDs or DVD films. They use an agent-based methodology in which each agent is responsible for a specific sub-task, including information gathering, customer modelling, information managing and performance evaluation. Specifically, the kernel of the system is a learning agent that uses an evolutionary method to model the preferences of a customer for DVD film recommendations. The model is stored in the customer profile used to recognise whether a customer is interested in a specific item or not. The examples used to train this agent are the feature vectors (the key words associated with a film) of the products more recently collected during the browsing history of a user on a movie site. This learning strategy focuses on the capacity to adapt to the customer's changes of interests. In the profiling component of the COGITO system, the learning mechanism uses transactional data to infer long-term preferences (the preferred product categories); it does not adopt a binary decision strategy that categorises the products into the classes of customer-likes and customer-dislikes.

Data mining methods are used by the 1:1Pro system [4]. It uses information learned from a customer's transactional history to construct accurate, comprehensive individual profiles. One part of the profile contains facts about a customer, and the other part contains rules describing his or her behaviour. As in the COGITO system, the behavioural part of the profile is derived from transactional data, representing the purchasing and browsing activities of each user. Using rules to describe customer behaviour has the advantage of being an intuitive and descriptive way to represent the needs of a customer. Furthermore, the rules generated from a huge number of transactions tend to be statistically reliable.

Amongst the systems that use natural language to interact with users, NLA (Natural Language Assistant) is a web-based dialogue system that helps users find relevant products in e-commerce sites. The prototype presented in [33] is hosted by an IBM web site where users can search for PCs according to their wishes and needs concerning features such as CPU, total amount of memory or price. NLA combines classical rule-based AI technologies with statistical parsing techniques, based on decision trees induction to generate the queries that should fulfill users' requests. The decision tree contains a model of a conversation induced by training examples that is used to generate SQL queries transparently. Conversely, the agent of the COGITO system refines the NL queries submitted by the user, expanding them with the knowledge contained in his or her personal profile, in order to filter and rank the results according to the user's needs and preferences.

7.6 Conclusions

In this chapter, we have presented project COGITO, that integrates agents and personalisation for the development of a modern architecture for e-commerce. The COGITO architecture has been designed taking into account the requirements analysis made for a real dot com company. The architecture combines agent technology with intelligent modules for information retrieval and personalisation that are based on the extraction of dynamic user profiles and usage patterns. The adoption of XML as the *lingua franca* for information representation and exchange leaves the architecture open to the integration of third-party (legacy) systems such as e-commerce platforms, back-ends and ERP systems.

Using the COGITO architecture as a baseline, we generalised the fundamental modules identified, in order to define a framework for developing e-business applications. If we implement the main modules using web services, the integration does not have special requirements or platforms. What the web did for the interaction between programmes and users, web services are doing for the interaction between programmes and programmes. Web services allow applications to be integrated more quickly, easily and less expensively than ever before. Integration occurs at a higher level and is based on messages that focus on service semantics instead of network protocol semantics. These characteristics are ideal for connecting business functions across the web, both between and within companies. Web services provide a unifying programming model so that application integration inside and outside the enterprise can be done with a common approach, leveraging a common infrastructure.

Acknowledgements

The authors wish to thank Lynn Rudd for her help to correct the manuscript. The COGITO project is funded by the European Commission under contract IST-1999-13347. The consortium is led by FhG-IPSI and comprises the following partners: Logica pdv Unternehmensberatung GmbH (Hamburg, Germany), BOL Medien GmbH (Rheda-Wiedenbrück, Germany), the System Analysis Department at Risø National Laboratory (Roskilde, Denmark), the LACAM Laboratory at the University of Bari (Bari, Italy), and Sword ICT S.r.l. (Bari, Italy).

About the authors

Giovanni Semeraro   Fabio Abbattista   Marco Degemmis

Oriana Licchelli   Pasquale Lops   Fabio Zambetta

Giovanni Semeraro received the Laurea degree with honors in Computer Science from the University of Bari, Italy, in 1988. In 1991, he joined the University of Bari, where he was a Lecturer with the Department of Computer Science until 1998, when he became a Reader. He leads the research units involved in the IST project COGITO (E-Commerce with Guiding Agents based on Personalised Interaction Tools) and the European Network of Excellence on Digital Libraries DELOS. He is also participating in the IST projects COLLATE (Collaboratory for Annotation, Indexing and Retrieval of Digitised Historical Archive Material) and FAIRSNET (On-line Solutions for Trade Fairs). His research interests focus on the logical and algebraic foundations of machine learning, multi-strategy learning, theory revision, decision tree pruning, discovery of causal relations, and real-world applications of machine learning (user modelling, document processing, map interpretation, intelligent user interfaces), with specific interests towards integration into Internet architectures for digital libraries and electronic commerce. He is the author of over 100 papers published in international journals, books and conference proceedings; he is also the author of a book on formal language theory. He is a member of the IEEE Computer Society, ACM, AI*IA, AICA and GRIN.

Fabio Abbattista is a Lecturer at the Department of Computer Science of the University of Bari, Italy. Since 1992, he is involved in the study of evolutionary intelligent systems; his main research interests concern the modelling of emotions and the development of emotional 3D agents.

Marco Degemmis received the Laurea degree with honors in Computer Science from the University of Bari, Italy, in 1999. He is currently preparing his Ph.D. degree in Computer Science under the supervision of Prof. Semeraro. The topic of his thesis concerns the applications of machine learning techniques to improve information access. After graduation, he researched on using metadata to represent the semantic content of documents within the ESPRIT project P29159 CONCERTO (CONCEptual indexing, querying and ReTrieval Of digital documents) during April 1999–November 2000. His current research interests include knowledge discovery in text, automatic text processing, Internet agents and the Semantic Web. He is a member of the Italian Association for Artificial Intelligence (AI*IA).

Oriana Licchelli received her Laurea degree in Computer Science with honors from the University of Bari, Italy, in March 2001. From July 2000–February 2002, she participated in project COGITO (IST-1999-13347, E-Commerce with Guiding agents based on personalized Interaction Tools). Since November 2001, she is a Ph.D. Student under the guidance of Prof. Semeraro. Her research interests focus on data mining and user profiling applied to e-commerce and e-learning. Currently, she is working on the analysis and application of machine learning techniques to the student evaluation phase carried out by e-learning systems.

Pasquale Lops received his Laurea degree with honors in Computer Science from the University of Bari, in 1997. He is currently preparing his Ph.D. degree in Computer Science, under the supervision of Prof. Semeraro. After graduation, he researched on using machine learning techniques to develop a prototype of an adaptive user interface for digital libraries (project CORINTO). He joined the team working on project COGITO (IST-1999-13347) during 2000–2001, and he applied data mining techniques to infer user profiles from transactional data. His research interests focus on machine learning and automatic knowledge acquisition, in particular for the integration of different learning paradigms. He is a member of the Italian Association for Artificial Intelligence (AI*IA).

Fabio Zambetta is currently a Ph.D. student at the Department of Computer Science Department of the University of Bari, Italy.

His research interests focus on intelligent web agents, 3D character animation and virtual reality systems. His Ph.D. research focus on both the methods and the implementation techniques needed to create intelligent web agents with 3D bodies or faces as a front-end.

Chapter 8

Discovering Relationships for Effective Target Marketing

Kok-L. Ong, Wee-K. Ng, and Ee-P. Lim

8.1 Introduction

In recent years, the explosion of the web and the global ubiquity of e-commerce have brought about major changes to the paradigm of doing business. In a modern organisation, data about customers can be collected at different touch-points such as point-of-sales terminals, web server logs, or mobile phones. More importantly, these advanced data acquisition technologies have allowed an organisation to collect information about their customers down to micro-level details, e.g., web logs. With technologies such as .NET Passport, .NET My Services, and software agents [57, 68] that record detailed user profiles, companies can know more about their customers than before.

An important motivation to collect data about customers is to obtain business intelligence. In the early era of the information economy, data were stored for reporting and statistical purposes, chiefly. In today's knowledge-based economy, data is used to identify business intelligence that provides the competitive advantage [88] needed for survival. Gone were the days when managers sieved through data to find answers to their management questions. Instead, automated techniques called data mining [35] is what underpins the discovery of business intelligence. One popular, important class of business intelligence is target marketing [5, 51]. By running data mining algorithms on customer transactions, data mining can uncover important associations about what products are often purchased together. This intelligence can then be used for product recommendations [100] and product bundling [5].

In the above scenario, target marketing is done by using data mining techniques that depend on analysing past transaction records. In other words, the input to the data mining algorithm is a set of training examples, and the goal is to find patterns that are likely to be repeated in future. Therefore, a business such as `Amazon.com` can identify what books tend to be purchased together as customers buy books on-line, i.e., they record each transaction. This knowledge is then used to make suggestions to other customers. Clearly, existing data mining techniques work well for transaction-based businesses such as a bookstore or a supermarket. However, in cases in which there is not a history of transactions or a changing business landscape exists, classic data mining becomes inadequate as we lack such data for analysis. Such businesses include consultancy, subscription-based services, multi-level marketing, and insurance, for instance.

Given that these businesses also have on-line presence, and therefore data from multiple touch-points, we embarked on a project called CrystalBall whose aim is to investigate this aspect of target marketing. We wanted to know if data mining can help enhance their ability to reach out to potential customers if transactional data is not present. One approach is to apply data mining on customer profiles, which are non-transactional in nature. Our observation shows that there are two types of customers, namely: active and passive. An active customer contributes to the business goals of an organisation, e.g., making a purchase or engaging a service. On the contrary, a passive customer exists in the database of the organisation but has yet become an active customer. An example of passive customers are those that register for trial products, but do not make a purchase thereafter.

Therefore, a passive customer is a potential customer. Since we have data about active and passive customers, we wanted to find how they were related in the context of various non-transactional businesses. One answer is relationships. Given an organisation's customer database, there are many relationships amongst them. This may include relationships like families, friends, and colleagues, similar interests, or living in the same geographical region. More importantly, the use of relationships is sometimes more effective than other business approaches. In fact, knowing how one customer relates to another is a competitive advantage.

To illustrate our point better, consider the following real-life example taken from a consultancy firm . (Due to the nature of their clients, we are not allowed to disclose their name, but this should not affect the appreciation of our discussion.) Clients engage its services to solve management-related problems such as managing losses or market share expansion. To reach out to new customers, the firm addresses potential clients on an ad-hoc basis, but this has been ineffective. This is because clients are unwilling to acknowledge that a problem exists within their organisation, or have reservations about the services provided by the firm. This is when relationships contribute to a competitive advantage. Looking into their existing pool of active customers, the firm identifies a client that has a relationship with the target. The active customer who is related to the potential customer is more likely to acknowledge a problem if he or she knows about it, and can act as the "bridge" to recommend the firm or help arrange a meeting to the potential client. As a result, this improved the chances of the firm in providing services. In other words, by capitalising on the influence capability of the active customer on the passive party, the firm gains a competitive advantage over their competitors.

In the context described above, our contributions are as follows.

We propose a way to determine, extract and warehouse relationships from existing databases. This process is made easy to use by means of a wizard-based interface, and does not require technical know-how.

The analysis of relationships does not fall within conventional data mining algorithms. Instead, we introduce a novel algorithm to mine important relationships.

The results of data mining need to be summarised and presented in a way suitable for the business goals. We developed a complete GUI application to provide the necessary interaction for the end user.

To achieve these goals in the practical business world, we can no longer work within a laboratory setting. Instead, we have to consider target environments, business setups and requirements, as well as end users. This chapter discuss the development of CrystalBall to solve a real-world business problem. It is organised as follows: In Section 8.2, we deal with warehousing relationships from a database with information about clients; in Section 8.3, we present an algorithm for discovering important relationships; in Section 8.4, we report on how to visualise the web of relationships discovered by our algorithm; in Section 8.5, we discuss our .NET-based implementation; in Section 8.6, we compare our proposal with other authors' work; finally, in Section 8.7, we report on our conclusions and future research directions.

8.2 Warehousing Relationships

Prior to data mining, we need to have data. In this case, the data are relationships between people. For instance, "Joe and John are friends" represents a relationship; similarly, "Susan and Peter live in California" is another relationship. The question, therefore, is where to find such relationships? Do they exist within the context of an organisation?

From our experience with the firm, relationships are never explicitly stored in the database. Given a customer profile, his or her relationships are often implicit. This means that mining relationships first entails an identification process. This is the job of the domain expert. Given a number of databases, tables and fields, the domain analyst needs to determine relationships that are potentially useful in the context of the business and the goal of such analysis. In our consultancy example, this means identifying potential relationships that can help influence a passive customer to use their services.

Technically, a relationship can be easily identified. For instance, a record about Joe working for IBM forms a relationship with every other who works for the same company. Therefore, if Joe and John are colleagues, then two records should exist in the table stating "Joe works for IBM" and "John works for IBM". These two fields in the table therefore contribute to a relationship. The technical reader shall immediately realise that this can be easily warehoused for mining by issuing an SQL statement. Although the domain analyst would have a competent level of computer literacy, it is nevertheless a daunting task to formulate SQL statements when performing such an analysis.

The result is the incorporation of the Relationship Wizard as shown in Fig. 8.1. The wizard uses two key technologies to abstract the technical aspects behind warehousing relationships. First, it discovers databases, tables and fields automatically by issuing SQL statements on behalf of the users. It then presents the information graphically so that the user can identify relationships by selecting different fields in the tables. The selection forms relationship templates used by the wizard to construct SQL statements that warehouse the data from different sources to form a relationship database.

In Fig. 8.1, we also see how a relationship template is constructed. Available tables are shown on the left panel. By selecting a table, the fields are shown on the right of the dialog. Putting the mouse over a selected field pops a tool-tip containing additional information. There is another drop-down combo associated with each field. When a field is selected, the drop-down combo on the right gets enabled and allows the user to choose between "Person" and "Relationship". When a field is marked with "Person" and another is marked with "Relationship", the "Create template" button becomes enabled. If clicked, the relationship template based on these fields is created and listed at the base of the dialog box.

The final screen of the wizard saves the templates created and proceeds to warehouse

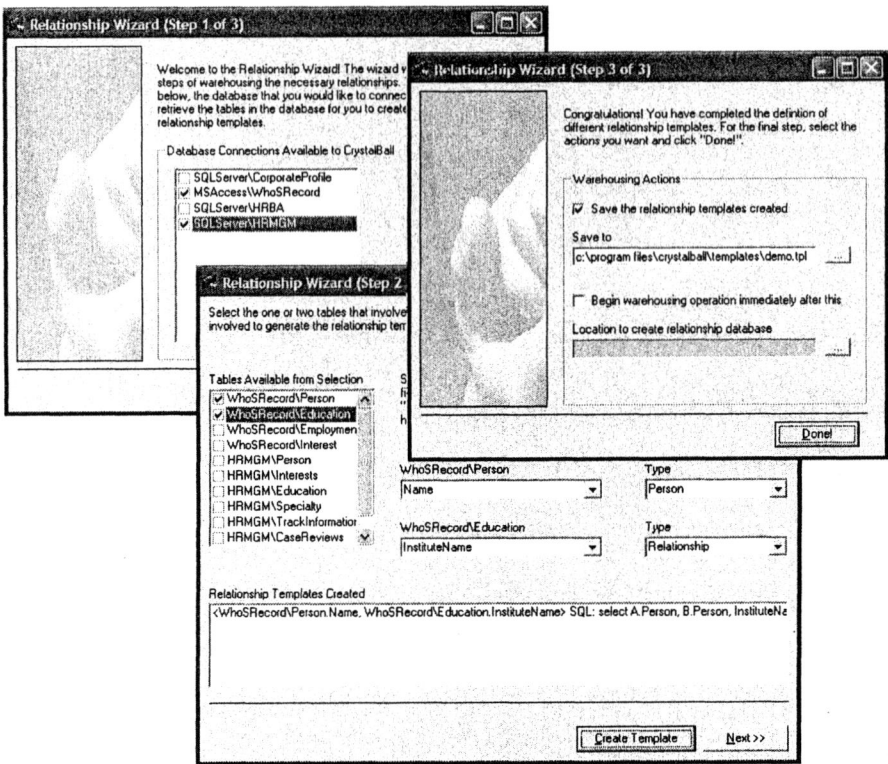

Figure 8.1: The Relationship Wizard.

the relationships using the series of SQL statements generated from the templates. Once the warehousing completes, the analyst may next stick with the data mining task, which is described in the following section.

8.3 Discovering Important Relationships

We begin with a discussion of the problem formulation, followed by the idea behind discovering important relationships. Based on these ideas, we then introduce our algorithm for mining relationship graphs [124].

8.3.1 Problem formulation

Let $C = \{c_1, c_2, \ldots, c_i\}$ be the set of all passive and active customers in an organisation, and $R = \{r_1, r_2, \ldots, r_j\}$ the set of all possible relationships that exist between two customers. A tuple t in the relationship database D is of the form $\langle c_\alpha, c_\beta, r \rangle$ where $c_\alpha, c_\beta \in C$ and $r \in R$; it defines the existence of a relationship r between customers c_α and c_β. A relationship graph (G) is a set of tuples $\{t_1, t_2, \ldots, t_k\} \subset D$ that represents a set of relationship paths from active customer c_a to a set of passive customers $\{c_{p_1}, c_{p_2}, \ldots, c_{p_j}\}$. A relationship path is a set of tuples $P = \{t_x, t_y, \ldots, t_z\} \subset G$ where $t_1.\alpha = c_a \vee t_1.\beta = c_a$ and $t_k.\alpha = c_{p_i} \vee t_k.\beta = c_{p_i}$

such that $\forall t_x \in P \setminus \{t_1, t_k\} \cdot \exists t_y \in G \cdot t_x.\beta = t_y.\alpha$.

For the sake of simplicity, all relationships are undirected. Even with this simplification, a huge number of potential relationships can be obtained from an organisation warehouse. For instance, a domain expert may choose to relate two entities by their addresses, interests, working organisations, professions, geographic regions, or expertise, and this generates a huge number of tuples. To limit the number of relationship paths in G, only the strongest ones in the organisation's goals are considered for a given c_a. The minimum strength (δ) is the score that a relationship path must achieve in order to be selected. This is a quantitative value that acts as a measure on the likely effectiveness of a relationship path, according to the domain expert's opinion. This is computed by a user defined function $\mathcal{S}(\{t_0, t_1, \ldots, t_k\})$ where the strength is determined by the evaluation of the relationships $t_0.r_0$, $t_1.r_1$, ..., $t_k.r_k$. The motivation behind $\mathcal{S}$ is to model complex interactions between different relationships that cannot be represented by the direct assignment of weights used in typical graph exploration algorithms, e.g., shortest path [160].

We also define the distance to determine the radius of graph G with c_a as the centriod. Intuitively, as the distance gets larger, the effectiveness of the relationship weakens. Therefore, it may not be cost-effective to mine beyond a certain distance. Formally, the distance (π) is the maximum allowable distance for a relationship path from an active customer to a passive one. Together with the notion of strength, we obtain the size (φ) of a relationship graph. The size is thus the maximum number of allowable relationship paths that satisfy δ and are within π. Therefore, φ represents the top strongest relationship paths.

8.3.2 Discussion

In a relationship database, each tuple defines two people that are related. Within the database, the association of two people is not constrained by their customer type. That is, they may both be active or passive, or only one of them.

Fig. 8.2 shows a snapshot of CrystalBall at work. The left panel shows a summary of the customer under consideration; the panel below allows to control the type of relationships to be displayed; the toolbar shows a set of commonly used functions. Beneath the toolbar, there is a tool that allows us to search for a particular customer. The right half of the screen shows a graphical render of the relationship graph obtained from mining the relationship database. The dark coloured node represents the customer under consideration.

Essentially, the relationship database is a huge relationship graph; that is, if a person represents a node and a relationship an edge, we can graphically represent the relationship database as a graph [160]. Such a graph is huge and unsuitable for analysis. Thus, the goal of data mining is to find the sub-graph containing the customer that satisfies the constraints of data mining. These constraints are used as a quantitative measure to determine a sub-graph that is considered useful according to the analyst's opinion. As discussed earlier, these constraints include the minimum strength (δ), distance (π) and size (φ). In a large relationship database, many relationship paths may satisfy the criteria of strength and distance. Often than not, only a small number of paths are useful. Specifying the size limits the number of relationship paths and therefore simplifies the result rendered to the analyst.

The key to the entire algorithm is the definition of a relationship score. The relationship score determines the strength of a path and, in turn, has an effect on the subsequent data mining decisions. A relationship score can be defined by an equation, and for each relationship, a real value indicating its importance. An important relationship has a higher positive real value, and thus contributes with high score to indicate the strength of the relationship

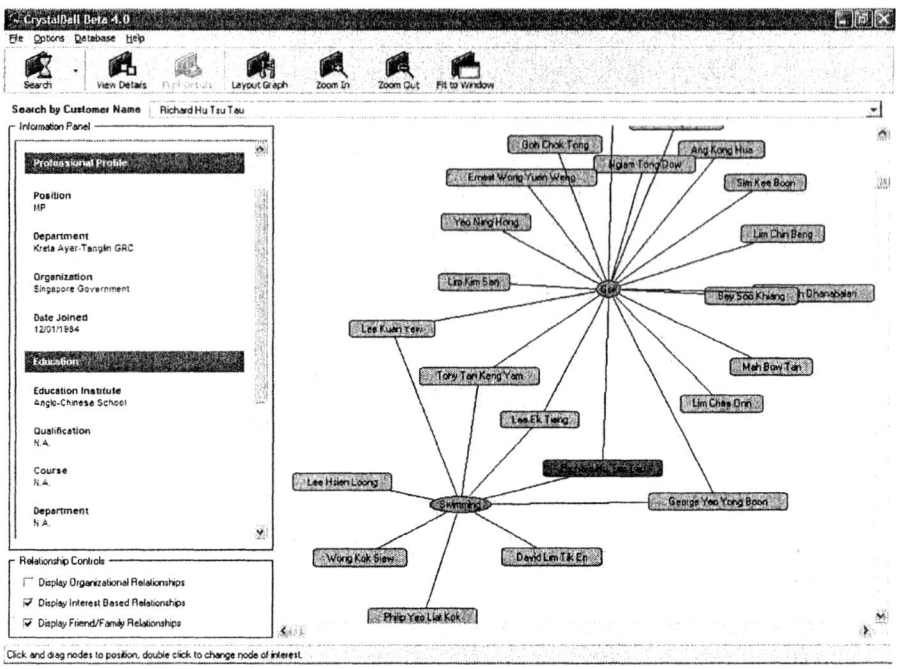

Figure 8.2: The main screen of CrystalBall.

path. For instance, we may define the scoring function as follows:

$$f_{R_k}(T) = \begin{cases} v_k & \text{if } \exists t \in T \cdot t.r \in R_k \\ 0 & \text{otherwise} \end{cases} \quad (8.1)$$

where v_k is a real value that is assigned to each group of relationships (R_k); it is considered to be of the same level of importance. Then, a possible score for any relationship may be defined as follows:

$$\mathcal{S}(T) = C + f_{R_1}(T) + f_{R_2}(T) - f_{R_3}(T)\frac{1}{f_{R_4}(T)} + \ldots + f_{R_j}(T) \quad (8.2)$$

where $\mathcal{S}$ is the scoring function, T is the relationship path, f_{R_j} is a function that returns a value for a relationship R_j if it exists in T. The equation above is just one example. It is entirely up to the analyst to define the equation to derive the final score for a given relationship path. The algorithm uses it to determine a given relationship strength and performs data mining accordingly.

The definition of the scoring function also plays an important optimisation role in the performance of the data mining engine. Data mining is known to be computationally intensive. Thus, traditional data mining has been a one-shot affair. However, analysis is often an iterative and exploratory process. Thus, to make data mining applications useful, they must be able to interact with the analyst. In the development of the data mining core, we modified the base algorithm to include optimisation based on the general scoring function pattern in the consultancy case. This heuristic helps eliminate the exhaustive search of the problem space and finds strong relationship paths quickly. As a result, the response time is within seconds. This means that the cost to re-mine with different parameters and potential customers is reduced, thus achieving exploratory mining.

8.3.3 Algorithm

Below, we show our algorithm for mining a single relationship graph given an active customer (C_a). It comprises two steps, namely: (a) tuples that are involved in the current computation are identified and selected into the corresponding ordered lists; (b) scan the lists to construct the top φ strongest path for a given active customer.

[Algorithm for mining a relationship graph]
```
01   procedure MineGraph
02   begin
03       let B = { b_0, b_1, ..., b_{π-1} } and G = ∅ and B_c = { c_a }
04       let b_0 = ArrangeTuple({ t ∈ D | t.α = c_a ∨ t.β = c_a }, B_c)
05       foreach t ∈ b_0 do t.δ = S({t}); Sort b_0 using δ in descending order
06       for (k = 1; k < π; k++) begin
07           let B_c = B_c ∪ { t.β | t ∈ b_{k-1} }
08           let b_k = ArrangeTuple(
                        { t ∈ D − {b_0, b_1, ..., b_{k-1}} | t.α ∈ B_c ∨ t.β ∈ B_c }, B_c)
09           foreach t ∈ b_k do t.δ = S({t}); Sort b_k using δ in descending order
10       endfor
11       b_k = b_k − { t ∈ b_k | t.α is active customer ∧ t.β is active customer }
12       foreach tuple t ∈ b_0 do
13           let T = { t } and t_c = t
14           for (k = 1; k < π; k++) begin
15               if ( FindTuple(t_c, b_k) = ∅) then exit for-loop else T = T ∪ { t_c }
16           endfor
17           if (S(T) ≥ δ ∧ |T| ≤ π) then
18               G = G ∪ { T }; φ = φ − 1
19               if (φ = 0) then end return solution G
20           endif
21       endfor
22   end

23   procedure ArrangeTuple(list of tuples T, B_c)
24   begin
25       foreach tuple t ∈ T do
26           if (t.α ∉ B_c) then Swap contents of t.α and t.β
27       endfor
28       return T
39   end

30   procedure FindTuple(tuple t_c, ordered list b_k)
31   begin
32       foreach tuple t ∈ b_k do
33           if (t.α = t_c.β) then return t' | t'.α = t.β ∧ t'.β = t.α
34           if (t.α = t_c.α) then return t
35       endfor
36       return ∅
```

37 **end**

The algorithm first creates π ordered list (line 3) denoted by $b_0, b_1, \ldots, b_{\pi-1}$; each one holds tuples selected from D. Starting with b_0, we select all tuples in the relationship database D that contain the active customer denoted as c_a. Instead of the lexicographical ordering in the database, we order the tuples so that the first customer, i.e., $t.\alpha$, is c_a; we use function *ArrangeTuple* in line 4 to do so.

We then compute the strength using S and then sort, in descending order, the strength of their relationship (line 5). This generates the relationship graph with distance 1. The loop from line 6 to 10 and line 11 construct the remaining list up to the distance specified by π. Notice that the construction of the kth list depends on the results of the $(k-1)^{th}$ list. This is equivalent to a breadth-first search of the tuples in D to construct the super-graph with c_a as centroid up to the distance of π. In line 7, we identify the selection criteria for the next list and store it in B_c. We then select tuples (line 8) containing a customer in B_c. Line 11 prunes tuples containing all active customers. Such tuples are unnecessary by definition and should be removed to reduce memory consumption and speed up computation.

The second half of the algorithm finds the subgraph of c_a that satisfies φ and δ. Since all tuples in b_0 contain c_a, all tuples in this group must be considered regardless of the relationship strength. For each tuple in b_0 (line 12), we construct the path up to the maximum distance possible by finding matching tuples to form a relationship path. In the algorithm, T holds the set of tuples that forms a relationship path (line 13) and t_c is the tuple under consideration. Function *FindTuple* attempts to find a corresponding tuple that joins to the current tuple (t_c) and thus extends the distance of the current path by 1 in the next list b_k (lines 14-16). Once the path is obtained, we measure its strength (line 17). If it satisfies δ, it is added to the solution G and φ is decreased (line 18-19).

This procedure is repeated until the set of tuples is exhausted or the top φ solution is discovered. The algorithm then terminates and return solution G in line 19.

In most cases, approximately φ tuples of b_0 need to be scanned if φ is smaller than the number of strong relationships. For the remaining lists, an average of $\varphi \log_2(|b_k|)$ tuples are scanned if a binary search is used. This reduction is based on a simple heuristic that allows the relationship graph to be discovered quickly. Specifically, tuples in the list are sorted by their relationship strength. For a given path P, we observe that if $\mathcal{S}(P) \geq \delta$, then adding the next tuple t_c, regardless of its strength, is likely to be stronger than both T and t_c. Thus, sorting each list amounts to a higher probability of finding strong paths without traversing every tuple in the lists.

In the best case (assuming a binary search), only $\frac{1}{h}(\varphi + \log_2(|b|(\pi - 1))$ tuples need to be scanned, where h is the probability of finding a matching tuple such that the length of the current relationship path is extended by 1 and b is the average number of tuples in each ordered list.

Compare this to the trivial approach in which $b_0 b_1 \ldots b_{\pi-1}$ (i.e., $|b|^{\pi}$) tuples are scanned and its relationship strength computed to find the top φ list. Clearly, the use of such heuristics is desirable when the relationship database and the number of active customers to discover in each run are large.

8.4 Visualising the Web of Relationships

Fig. 8.2 shows a snapshot of the main screen of CrystalBall. Since the application is to be used by non-technical business analysts, our design goal is user friendliness. One way

Discovering Relationships for Effective Target Marketing 169

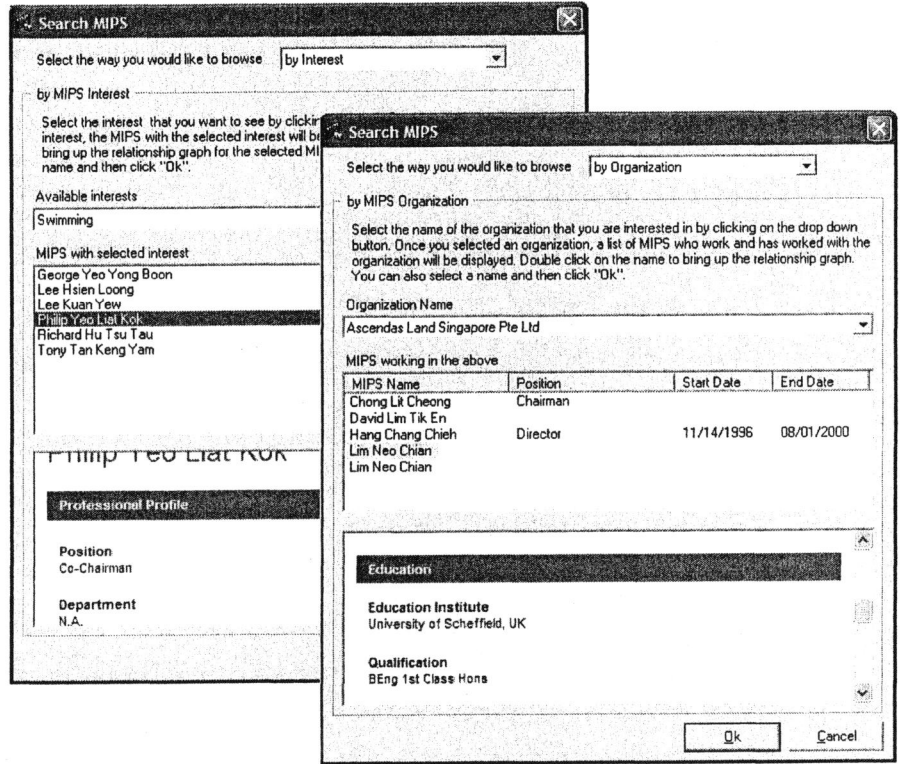

Figure 8.3: Dialogs to search for potential customers.

to make the interface simple is to reduce the number of interactions between the user and the application. As such, we decided to assume the availability of the entire screen space, i.e., maximised window. This assumption is acceptable for our users with Windows 2000, as the task bar provides an elegant way to switch applications if needed. Based on this assumption, we have carefully divided the screen space into several sections.

Advanced and infrequent features are kept in the pull down menus organised by their categories. Beneath the pull down menu, there is an Internet-Explorer-like toolbar where frequently used functions are made available. These buttons are made larger to facilitate the access using a mouse. For our test environment, the most frequently used search option is the name of the customer under consideration. Therefore, we made the search available on the screen without the need to open another dialog box. To facilitate tasks, we populated the search box with customers found in the relationship database. As the user types in the input area, relative matches are shown and the user can simply hit enter at any point to initiate the analysis.

Alternative aids to finding relationship graphs of interest are placed in the toolbar and their dialog boxes shown in Fig. 8.3. This dialogs group the potential customers (known as MIPS in the context of the consultancy example) according to their interest or organisation. This helps the analyst determine the customer to analyse without the need to know his or her name exactly, a common situation. A summary view of the customer is also shown at the bottom of the dialog box to aid selection. There are two ways to select a customer, namely: (a) view the customers by their organisation; (b) group customers according to their interests. In either case, the search alternatives assist the analyst to look up the customer under consideration if he or she is not sure of the primary search key.

A typical analysis scenario is as follows: The analyst finds out some issues that are in line with the goal of his or her company. In the consultancy example, this may be some organisation issues that the consultancy firm can solve by providing their services. Given that he or she does not know who should address, he or she looks up the people related to the organisation. In Fig. 8.3, we see that as the analyst inspects the name of each customer, a summary of the data available is provided. Once a customer is selected as the person to address, the system begins mining the relationship graph from the relationship database using current data mining parameters.

The relationship graph is then displayed on the right half of the screen. The summary of the target customer is shown on the left panel. Beneath the summary panel, there is the widget that allows to select the type of relationships to be displayed. In this case, they are classified into three major classes. Checking off a relationship removes a class of relationships within the relationship graph, and facilitates the analysis of the insights by means of multiple views and details. From the graph, the analyst may then observe that the potential customer has a relationship with an existing customer of the firm. Double clicking on the active customer, the relationship graph of this active customer is retrieved. He or she can then generate a detailed report of the active customer as shown in the Fig. 8.4. The information presented in this report results from a series of SQL queries in which the person under consideration is the key. The results are returned in XML and then formatted using XSLT to generate an HTML page. The HTML pages are then rendered using Internet Explorer. This allows the analyst to observe that the active customer has a good relationship with the firm. He or she can then decide to address the active customer to help arrange a meeting, and offers to charge the current assignment of the active customer at a discount in return.

Instead of displaying the data mining results in its raw form, we present them graphically as shown in Fig. 8.2. This is to take advantage of modern hardware to enhance the presentation of results using visual spaces and colours to distinguish between different components of the data mining results. In addition, a pictorial view also packs more information on a single screen, which is more effective to communicate the insights obtained to the analyst.

8.5 Implementation and Deployment

Although the algorithm we presented in Section 8.3.3 is the kernel of CrystalBall, it represents only 20% of the application. To move it out of the lab into the hands of the end users, the GUI and deployment of the final application contributes the remaining 80%, and involves a wide range of technologies.

During the construction of the Relationship Wizard, a mechanism to identify available data sources within the organisation is needed. Such data sources may be stored on different databases across different physical locations. To provide uniform access at the implementation level, we used Microsoft's Database Access Components (MDAC) [168] to reach a variety of data sources. Furthermore, databases, tables, and their respective fields are discovered automatically by the wizard by means of SQL statements. Relationships are also extracted by translating each relationship template into a sequence of SQL statements.

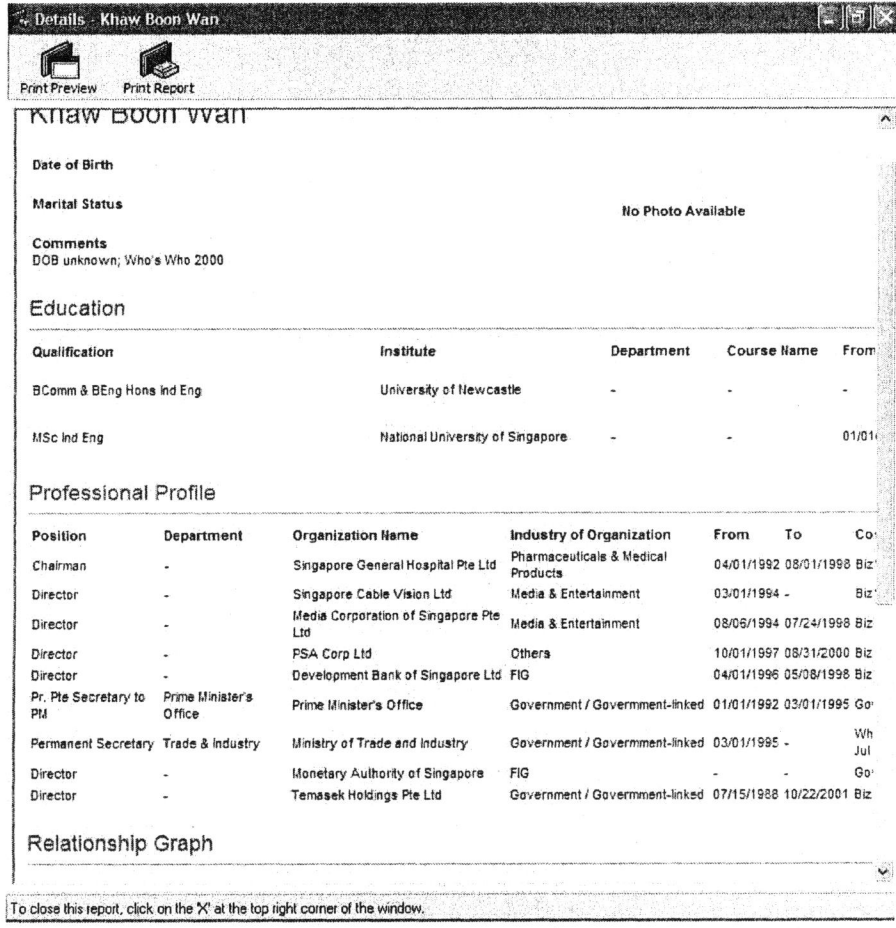

Figure 8.4: A detailed report of an active customer.

The visualisation of results comes in two forms. Primarily, the relationship graph is a pictorial representation of the data mining results. We use a commercial OCX component called AddFlow [163] to render the graphics; we parse the XML output of the data mining engine and then perform the appropriate API calls to AddFlow. This is done using the built-in XML parser in the .NET platform. The other visualisation is the combination of additional queries with the relationship graph to generate reports about interesting customers in our user evaluations. The SQL results are also formatted in XML and rendered using XSLT [28]. This generates an HTML document that is displayed using the AxwebBrowser class in the AxSHDocVw name space; this also provides print previews and printing capabilities without writing code. We then use VB .NET as the glue to prototype the interface quickly.

The data mining engine was first developed using C++. It had to be integrated with the GUI developed in VB .NET. An attractive option in .NET is its multiple language support under a common runtime system. Therefore, there is no need to rewrite the code.

Instead, we created a COM+ wrapper and exposed the necessary data mining interfaces. This reduced programming time because we did not need code what was already built and tested. We also improved robustness due to the component-based approach. In particular, the browser component exposed by Internet Explorer helps eliminate the complex task of building the report screen. This, in turn, reduces costs as this component is readily available for free on most Windows machines.

Finally, the deployment of the application requires the creation of application installers. Within the .NET environment, this is straightforward. We simply need to deploy the .NET framework on each target machine, and copy the executable and its configuration file to the designated directory. Rather than the usual .ini files or attempts to write to the Windows registry, the configuration file is also an XML file. Being a text document, we are able to modify it easily, and our applications can easily retrieve the related configuration settings. Settings such as colour, font size, visualisation characteristics, location of the database files, or the available relationship priorities are stored in this file.

8.6 Related Work

To the best of our knowledge, the discovery of relationship graphs using data mining techniques is a novel proposal. The closest technique is called association analysis [5] or association rule mining. Unlike our approach, association analysis focus on finding rules between items, which can correspond, conceptually, to the customers in our relationship graph, and the associations amongst items, which can correspond to our relationships. The differences lie in both the type of results produced and the type of data been processed.

In association analysis, transactional data is used to find interesting associations [161]. An interesting association is measured by a quantitative value called support which is the statistical significance of the items appearing in the database. If the items appear sufficiently often, then these items are considered to have some association. This association represents some relationship between the two items but is not explicitly represented by the algorithm. Therefore, the task here is to enumerate all possible combinations of items, and check that each enumeration fulfills the support. If so, the association is considered interesting and rules may be generated from it.

In the case of mining relationship graphs, relationships are explicit in the results, and the process of evaluating their interestingness does not depend on how often they appear in the database. Rather, it depends on some constraints, i.e., strength, distance or size; the task is to explore the giant relationship graph to retrieve a set of paths that satisfies the constraints. Here, the approach is to analyse customer profiles which are not transactional in nature. Despite the type of data used and the methodology, both proposals share a common goal because they aim at looking for insights into the data to help enhance businesses.

The analysis of non-transactional data is relatively new in the domain of data mining. Besides our work, in [135], the authors have also proposed mining knowledge-sharing sites to help achieve effective viral marketing. The idea, similar to ours, is to take advantage of the network of influence to attempt to change the buying behaviour of a user. Instead of relationship graphs, the results of data mining are probabilistic models that help determine the best viral marketing plan so as to maximise the effect of a marketing campaign.

8.7 Conclusions

CrystalBall represents a custom-made data mining solution for a new class of business intelligence in which there is no transactional information. In such a situation, traditional data mining methods do not perform well. Therefore, we proposed the mining of relationship graphs from customer profiles. In our experience with user evaluations, getting the technology is only the first step on the road to success. To realise the benefits completely, data mining needs to go beyond the algorithm and data. The process of extracting, transforming, and loading, is as important as the presentation of the results and the analysis and fusion of insights with existing information; they determine the success of the technology.

So far, developing our application requires HTML, XML, XSLT, graph rendering, databases and Internet protocols. Developing them from scratch would be a daunting, costly task. Therefore, development platforms with built-in support for these technologies became an important criteria in our selection. Eventually, we narrowed down to Java and the .NET framework, which have these pre-built components well integrated and organised. The choice towards .NET [98] was primarily motivated by the following issues:

- Java Swing classes lack the speed demanded to render the graphical elements required by our application, and tuning its performance incurs in additional development costs.

- Java lacks multi-language support, which is an elegant solution to avoiding rewriting our data mining engine. Furthermore, .NET allows rapid prototyping of the GUI using VB .NET whilst writing the performance-critical data mining algorithm in C++.

- The cost of acquiring the components is also comparatively lower in .NET. In the case of our project, the cost of an industrial-strength web browser component in Java is out of our budget. As a result, it makes sense to turn towards the web browser component exposed by Internet Explorer.

Finally, the choice towards .NET is also motivated by the future work that we plan to do. Next, we briefly discuss it and outline how .NET can help us.

First, the biodata data on the left panel of Fig. 8.2 is often useful when the firm's consultants meet a potential client unexpectedly. Being able to quickly obtain a short piece of biodata would help the consultant interact more effectively. Therefore, the ability to retrieve such information using mobile devices such as phones and personal digital assistants is desired. With .NET, this is possible by means of the Mobile Internet Toolkit, which contains mobile controls that integrate with ASP .NET to deliver web-like experiences on mobile devices.

Another future direction is to expose the server-side queries using web services. Due to security concerns for customer data, the back-end database cannot be replicated on individual notebooks that consultants carry to different customer sites. The solution is to install a thin client that makes a connection back to the database using web services technology. Unlike other protocols, a web service uses the HTTP port, which is commonly available at customers' sites; this makes it possible to have access to a foreign site whilst enjoying a richer graphical experience on the web browser. Since our existing queries are already encapsulated as individual function calls, the web service is a proxy between the user and the application server. In other words, it is a wrapper that marshalls the data between the user and the application server.

Finally, we intend to improve the algorithm to take temporal associations between two people into account. This is due to the observation that a relationship may be temporary, and does not hold after a certain time frame. Such relationships may be important within the valid time frame, but would be uninteresting subsequently. As a result, we need to maintain the validity of the relationship graphs along the time. To mine the data for all customers involved would be computationally expensive. Therefore, an incremental version of the algorithm would also be very useful.

To summarise, data mining to support business solution has never been more relevant and important. With the web and digital acquisition technologies acting as a sink for data and the availability of new technology for analysis, competitive advantage through the understanding of customer relationships is becoming a reality. The application presented in this chapter demonstrates it in a real business context.

Acknowledgements

We would like to thank Mr. Wai-Hoong Leung, business analyst of the firm who initiated this project, and the editors of this book, who helped us improve the quality of the manuscript.

About the authors

Kok-Leong Ong   Wee-Keong Ng   Ee-Peng Lim

Kok-Leong Ong got his B.Sc. (Hons) degree in computer engineering from the Nanyang Technological University in 2000. He is currently pursuing a Ph.D. in computer engineering in the same university. His research interests include data mining, the World Wide Web and software agents.

Wee-Keong Ng got his M.Sc. and Ph.D. degrees from the University of Michigan at Ann Arbor in 1994 and 1996, respectively. He is an Associate Professor at the School of Computer Engineering at the Nanyang Technological University. He works and publishes in the areas of web warehousing, information extraction, electronic commerce and data mining. He has organised and chaired international workshops, including tutorials, and has actively served in the programme committees of numerous international conferences. He is a member of the ACM and the IEEE Computer Society.

Ee-Peng Lim is an Associate Professor at the School of Computer Engineering at the Nanyang Technological University. His research interests are web warehousing, database integration, and digital libraries. He is currently the director of the Centre for Advanced Information Systems (CAIS), a research centre that focus on web computing and database research. He is also the guest editor of the special issue on mobile commerce of the Journal of Database Management. His research has been published in a number of international journals including IEEE Transactions on Knowledge and Data Engineering, ACM Transactions on Information Systems, Decision Support Systems, and Distributed and Parallel Databases. He is a member of the ACM and a senior member of the IEEE.

Part V
Recommended Bibliography

Bibliography

[1] F. Abbattista, M. Degemmis, O. Licchelli, P. Lops, G. Semeraro, and F. Zambetta. Improving the usability of an e-commerce web site through personalization. In F. Ricci and B. Smyth, editors, *Proceedings of the Workshop on Recommendation and Personalization in Electronic Commerce, International Conference on Adaptative Hypermedia and Adaptative Web Based Systems*, pages 20–29, 2002.

[2] F. Abbattista, A. Paradiso, G. Semeraro, and F. Zambetta. An agent that learns to support users of a web site. In R. Roy, M. Koeppen, S. Ovaska, T. Furuhashi, and F. Hoffman, editors, *Soft Computing in Industry. Recent Applications*, pages 489–496. Springer–Verlag, 2001.

[3] C. Adamson and M. Venerable. *Data Warehousing Design Solutions*. John Wiley & Sons, 1998.

[4] G. Adomavicius and A. Tuzhilin. Using data mining methods to build customer profiles. *IEEE Computer*, 34(2):74–82, 2001.

[5] R. Agrawal and R. Srikant. Fast algorithm for mining association rules. In *Proceedings of International Conference on Very Large Databases*, pages 487–499. Morgan Kaufmann, 1994.

[6] D. Aha, D. Kibler, and M. Albert. Instance-based learning algorithms. *Machine Learning*, 6(1):37–66, 1991.

[7] S. Aissi, P. Malu, and K. Srinivasan. E-business process modeling: the next big step. *IEEE Computer*, 35(5):55–62, 2002.

[8] S. Alagic. The ODMG object model: Does it make sense? In *Proceedings of the Conference on Object-Oriented Programming, Systems, Languages, and Applications*, pages 253–270. ACM Press, 1997.

[9] A. Albano, D.G. Antognoni, and G. Ghelli. View operations on objects with roles for a statically typed database language. *IEEE Transactions on Knowledge and Data Engineering*, 12(4):548–567, 2000.

[10] A. Albano, R. Bergamini, G. Ghelli, and R. Orsini. An object data model with roles. In *Proceedings of the International Conference on Very Large Databases*, pages 39–51. Morgan Kaufmann Publishers, 1993.

[11] A. Albano, G. Ghelli, and R. Orsini. Fibonacci: A programming language for object databases. *Very Large Databases Journal*, 4(3):403–444, 1995.

[12] D. Alur, J. Crupi, and D. Malks. *Core J2EE Patterns: Best Practices and Design Strategies*. Prentice–Hall, 2001.

[13] S. Angelov and P. Grefen. An approach to the construction of flexible B2B e-contracting processes. Technical Report CTIT 02-40, Department of Computer Science, Universiteit Twente, 2002.

[14] K. Apshankar, D. Sadhwani, G. Samtani, B. Siddiqui, M. Clark, P. Fletcher, J. Hanson, R. Irani, M. Waterhouse, and L. Zhang. *Web Services Business Strategies and Architectures*. Expert Press, 2002.

[15] Electronic Commerce Code Management Association. *UNSPSC. Universal Standard Products and Services Classification*. Electronic Commerce Code Management Association, 1999.

[16] C. Bachman and M. Daya. The role concept in data models. In *Proceedings of the Very Large Databases Conference*, pages 464–476. Morgan Kaufmann Publishers, 1977.

[17] G. Ball, D. Ling, D. Kurlander, J. Miller, D. Pugh, T. Skelly, A. Stankosky, D. Thiel, M. Dantzich, and T. Wax. Lifelike computer characters: the Persona project at Microsoft Research. In J.M. Bradshaw, editor, *Software Agents*, pages 191–222. AAAI/MIT Press, 1997.

[18] P. Barros, A.H.M ter Hofstede, and C. Szyperski. Retrofitting workflows for B2B component assembly. In *Proceedings of the IEEE International Computer Software and Applications Conference*, pages 123–128, 2001.

[19] D. Bäumer, D. Riehle, W. Siberski, and M. Wulf. Role object. In N. Harrison, B. Foote, and H. Rohnert, editors, *Pattern Language of Program Design 4*, pages 15–32. Addison–Wesley, 2000.

[20] E. Bertino and G. Guerrini. Objects with multiple most specific classes. In *Proceedings of the European Conference on Object-Oriented Programming*, volume 952 of *Lecture Notes in Computer Science*, pages 102–126. Springer–Verlag, 1995.

[21] P. Bhoj, S. Shingal, and S. Chutani. SLA management in federated environments. *Computer Networks*, 35:5–24, 2001.

[22] B. Bhushan, M. Tschichholz, E. Leray, and W. Donnelly. Federated accounting: service charging and billing in a B2B environment. In *Proceedings of the International Symposium on Integrated Network Management*, pages 107–121, 2001.

[23] M. Bichler. *The Future of e-Markets. Multidimentional Market Mechanisms*. Cambridge University Press, 2001.

[24] D. Billsus and M. Pazzani. Learning probabilistic user models. In A. Jameson C. Paris and C. Tasso, editors, *Proceedings of the Workshop on Machine Learning for User Models, International Conference on User Modeling*. Springer–Verlag, 1997.

[25] M. Blaschka, C. Sapia, and G. Hofling. On schema evolution in multidimensional databases. In *Proceedings of the Data Warehousing and Knowledge Discovery Conference*, pages 153–164, 1999.

[26] M. Böhlen. Temporal database system implementations. *SIGMOD Record*, 24(4):53–602, 1995.

[27] F. Bordeleau. *Behavior Integration Patterns*. PhD thesis, School of Computer Science, Carleton University, 2001.

[28] F. Boumphrey, T. Jenkins, J. Graf, S. Mohr, C. McQueen, P. Houle, A. Kingsley-Hughes, K. Kingsley-Hughes, O. Renzo, J. Duckett, P. Jones, and D. Hollander. *XML Applications*. Wrox Press Inc., 1998.

[29] K. Braithwaite. Choosing CASE tools. *Database Management Systems*, 4(1):44–51, 1991.

[30] C. Bussler. B2B integration technology architecture. In *Proceedings of the IEEE International Workshop on Advanced Issues of E-Commerce and Web-based Information Systems*, pages 137–142. IEEE Press, 2002.

[31] J. Cao, T. Fong, H. Li, and X. Wang. E-union: Concept and framework of open B2B e-trading marketplaces. In *Proceedings of the International Parallel and Distributed Processing Symposium*, pages 218–225. IEEE Press, 2002.

[32] R.G.G. Cattel and D.K. Barry. *Object Data Management Group: The Object Database Standard ODMG, Release 3.0*. Morgan Kaufmann Publishers, 2000.

[33] J. Chai, V. Horvath, N. Nicolov, M. Stys, N. Kambhatla, W. Zadrozny, and P. Melville. Natural language assistant. A dialog system for on-line product recommendation. *Artificial Intelligence Magazine*, 23(2):63–75, 2002.

[34] P. Chamoni and S. Stock. Temporal structures in data warehousing. In *Proceedings of the Data Warehousing and Knowledge Discovery Conference*, pages 353–358, 1999.

[35] M.S. Chen, J. Han, and P.S. Yu. Data mining: An overview from a database perspective. *IEEE Transactions on Knowledge and Data Engineering*, 8(6):866–883, 1996.

[36] A. Christopher, S. Ishikawa, and M. Silverstein. *A Pattern Language: Towns, Buildings, Construction*. Oxford University Press, 1979.

[37] J. Chung and L. Zhang. Beyond e-marketplace and next generation e-business: Grid, autonomic computing and web services. In *Proceedings of the International Conference on Electronic Commerce. Invited Keynote Paper*, 2002.

[38] S.M. Clamen. Schema evolution and integration. *Distributed and Parallel Databases: An International Journal*, 2(1):101–126, 1994.

[39] E. Codd, S. Codd, and C. Smalley. Providing OLAP to User-Analysts: An IT mandate. Technical report, Hyperion Solutions Corporation, 1993. Available at http://www.hyperion.com.

[40] J. Cole, J. Derrick, Z. Milosevic, and K. Raymond. Policies in an enterprise specification. In *Proceedings of the International Workshop on Policies for Distributed Systems and Networks*, volume 1995 of *Lecture Notes on Computer Science*, pages 1–17. Springer-Verlag, 2001.

[41] D. Connolly, F. van Harmelen, I. Harrocks, D. McGuinness, P.F. Patel-Schneider, and L.A. Stein. Annotated DAML+OIL ontology markup.

[42] World Wide Web Consortium. RDF model and syntax specification. Available at http://www.w3.org/TR/1999/REC-rdf-syntax-19990222.

[43] F. Curbera, M. Duftler, R. Khalaf, W. Nagy, N. Mukhi, and S. Weerawarana. Unraveling the web services web an introduction to SOAP, WSDL, and UDDI. *IEEE Internet Computing*, 6(2):86–93, 2002.

[44] F. Curbera, Y. Goland, J. Klein, F. Leymann, D. Roller, S. Thatte, and S. Weerawarana. Business process execution language for web services. Available at http://www-106.ibm.com/developerworks/webservices/library/ws-bpel.

[45] B. Czejdo, R. Elmasri, M. Rusinkiewicz, and D. Embley. A graphical data manipulation language for an extended entity-relationship model. *IEEE Computer*, 23(3):26–36, 1990.

[46] B. Czejdo, M. Rusinkiewicz, V. Reddy, and D. Embley. A visual query language for an ER data model. In *Proceedings of the IEEE Workshop on Visual Languages*. IEEE Press, 1989.

[47] T. Dahlén. Integration tier patterns for the J2EE platform. Available at http://java.sun.com/javaone/javaone2001/pdfs/2399.pdf.

[48] A. Dan, D. Dias, R. Kearney, T. Lau, T. Nguyen, F. Parr, M. Sachs, and H. Shaikh. Business-to-business integration with tpaML and a B2B protocol framework. *IBM Systems Journal*, 40(1):68–90, February 2001.

[49] DCMI. Dublin core metadata initiative. Available at http://dublincore.org.

[50] E.W. Dijkstra. *Discipline of Programming*. Prentice–Hall, 1976.

[51] S. Dua, E. Cho, and S.S. Iyengar. Discovery of web frequent patterns and user characteristics from web access logs – A framework for dynamic web personalization. In *Proceedings of the International Conference on Application Specific Systems and Software Engineering Technology*, pages 3–8. IEEE Computer Society, 2000.

[52] J. Eder and C. Koncilia. Changes of dimension data in temporal data warehouses. In *Proceedings of the Data Warehousing and Knowledge Discovery Conference*, volume 2114 of *Lecture Notes in Computer Science*, pages 284–293. Springer–Verlag, 2001.

[53] J. Eder, C. Koncilia, and T. Morzy. A model for a temporal data warehouse. In *Proceedings of the International Workshop on Open Enterprise Solutions: Systems, Experiences, and Organizations*, pages 48–54, 2001.

[54] J. Eder, C. Koncilia, and T. Morzy. The COMET metamodel for temporal data warehouses. In *Proceedings of the International Conference on Advanced Information Systems Engineering*, volume 2348 of *Lecture Notes in Computer Science*, pages 83–99. Springer–Verlag, 2002.

[55] M. Burnett et al. *Visual Object-Oriented Languages*. Manning Publisher Corp., 1995.

[56] O. Etzion, S. Jajodia, and S. Sripada, editors. *A consensus Glossary of Temporal Database Concepts*, pages 367–405. Lecture Notes in Computer Science. Springer–Verlag, 1998.

[57] O. Etzioni and D.S. Weld. Intelligent agents on the Internet: Fact, fiction and forecast. *IEEE Expert*, 10(4):44–49, 1995.

[58] S. Field, C. Facciorusso, Y. Hoffner, A. Schade, and M. Stolze. Design criteria for a virtual marketplace (ViMP). In C. Nikolaou and C. Stephandis, editors, *Proceedings of the Second European Conference on Research and Advanced Technology for Digital Libraries*, number 1513 in Lecture Notes in Computer Science. Springer–Verlag, 1998.

[59] D.H. Fishman, D. Beech, H.P. Cate, E.C. Chow, T. Connors, J.W. Davis, N. Derrett, C.G. Hoch, W. Kent, P. Lyngbaek, B. Mahbod, M.A. Neimat, T.A. Ryan, and M.C. Shan. Iris: An object-oriented DBMS. *ACM Transactions on Office Information Systems*, 5(1):48–69, 1987.

[60] Apache Software Foundation. Axis user's guide. Available at http://xml.apache.org/axis.

[61] Apache Software Foundation. Tomcat user's guide. Available at http://jakarta.apache.org/tomcat/tomcat-5.0-doc.

[62] M. Fowler. Dealing with roles. Technical Report WUCS-97-34, Department of Computer Science, Washington University, 1989.

[63] E. Franconi, F. Grandi, and F. Mandreoli. Schema evolution and versioning: A logical and computational characterisation. In *Proceedings of the International Workshop on Foundations of Models and Languages for Data and Objects*, volume 2065 of *Lecture Notes in Computer Science*, pages 85–99. Springer–Verlag, 2001.

[64] E. Frank and I.H. Witten. Generating accurate rule sets without global optimization. In *Proceedings of the International Conference on Machine Learning*, pages 144–151. Morgan Kaufmann Publishers, 1998.

[65] R.P. Gabriel. *Patterns of Software: Tales from the Software Community*. Oxford University Press, 1998.

[66] E. Gamma, R. Helm, R. Johnson, and J. Vlissides. *Design Patterns: Elements of Reusable Object-Oriented Software*. Addison–Wesley, 1995.

[67] H. García-Molina, J. Ullman, and J. Widom. *Database System Implementation*. Prentice–Hall, 2000.

[68] M.R. Genesereth and S.P. Ketchpel. Software agents. *Communications of the ACM*, 37(72):48–53, 1994.

[69] M. Gisler. *Vertragsrechtliche Aspekte Elektronischer Märkte. Nach Schweizerischem Obligationenrecht*. PhD thesis, Universität St. Gallen, 1999.

[70] M. Gisler, K. Stanoevska-Slabeva, and M. Greunz. Legal aspects of electronic contracts. In H. Ludwig, Y. Hoffner, C. Bussler, and M. Bichler, editors, *Proceedings of the International Conference on Advanced Information Systems Engineering. Workshop on Infrastructures for Dynamic Business-to-Business Outsourcing*, June 2000.

[71] I. Goralwalla, A. Tansel, and M. Özsu. Experimenting with temporal relational databases. In *Proceedings of the International Conference on Information and Knowledge Management*, pages 296–303. ACM Press, 1995.

[72] G. Gottlob, M. Schrefl, and B. Rock. Extending object-oriented systems with roles. *ACM Transactions on Information Systems*, 14(3):268–296, 1996.

[73] S. Graham, S. Simeonov, T. Boubez, D. Davis, Glen Daniels, Y. Nakamura, and R. Neyama. *Building Web Services with Java*. SAMS Publishing, 2002.

[74] H. Gregersen and C. Jensen. Temporal entity-relationship models. A survey. *IEEE Transactions on Knowledge and Data Engineering*, 11(3):464–497, 1999.

[75] M. Greunz, B. Schopp, and K. Stanoevska-Slabeva. Supporting market transactions through XML contracting container. In *Proceeding of the Americas Conference on Information Systems*. Association for Information Systems, 2000.

[76] Object Management Group. OMG CORBA/IIOP specifications. Available at http://www.omg.org/technology/documents/corba_spec_catalog.htm.

[77] Object Management Group. Unified modeling language specification (UML 1.4). Available at http://www.omg.org.

[78] H. Günzel. *Darstellung von Veränderungen im multidimensionalen Datenmodell*. PhD thesis, Friedrich-Alexander-Universität Erlangen-Nürnberg, 2001.

[79] S. Ha and S. Park. Matching buyers and suppliers: An intelligent dynamic-exchange model. *IEEE Intelligent Systems*, 16(4):28–40, 2001.

[80] W. Harrison and H. Ossher. Subject-oriented programming (a critique of pure objects). *ACM SIGPLAN Notices*, 28(10):411–428, 1993.

[81] D.J. Hatley. CASE tool evaluation: A real-time example. In *Proceedings of CASE Conference*, pages 28–32, 1988.

[82] Y. Hoffner, S. Field, P. Grefen, and H. Ludwig. Contract-driven creation and operation of virtual enterprises. *Computer Networks*, 37(2):111–136, 2001.

[83] B. Hüsemann, J. Lechtenbörger, and G. Vossen. Conceptual data warehouse design. In *Proceedings of the International Workshop on Design and Management of Data Warehouses*, pages 1–11, 2000.

[84] R. Iannella. Open digital rights language (ODRL). Available at http://odrl.net.

[85] Optimization Methods in Object Query Languages. J. Płodzień. PhD thesis, Institute of Computer Science, Polish Academy of Sciences, 2000.

[86] A. Jodłowski, P. Habela, J. Płodzień, and K. Subieta. Objects and roles in the stack-based approach. In *Proceedings of the Database and Expert Systems Applications Conference*, volume 2453 of *Lecture Notes in Computer Science*, pages 514–523. Springer–Verlag, 2002.

[87] M. Juric, R. Nagappan, R. Leander, and S.J. Basha. *Professional J2EE EAI*. Wrox Press Inc, 2001.

[88] L. Kahaner. *Competitive Intelligence: From Black Ops to Boardrooms – How businesses gather, analyze, and use information to succeed in the global marketplace.* Simon and Schuster, 1996.

[89] G. Kappel, S. Rausch-Schott, and W. Retschitzegger. A framework for workflow management systems based on objects, rules and roles. *ACM Computing Surveys*, 32(1):1–27, 2000.

[90] A. Keller and H. Ludwig. The WSLA framework: Specifying and monitoring service level agreements for web services. Technical Report RC 22456, IBM T.J. Watson Research Center, 2002.

[91] G. Kiczales, J. Lamping, A. Mendhekar, C. Maeda, C. Lopes, J. Loingtier, and J. Irwin. Aspect-oriented programming. In *Proceedings of the European Conference on Object-Oriented Programming*, volume 1241 of *Lecture Notes in Computer Science*, pages 220–242. Springer–Verlag, 1997.

[92] A. Kobsa. Tailoring privacy to users' needs. In *Proceedings of the International Conference on User Modelling*, volume 2109 of *Lecture Notes in Artificial Intelligence*, pages 303–313. Springer–Verlag, 2001.

[93] M. Koetsier, P. Grefen, and J. Vonk. Contracts for cross-organizational workflow management. In *Proceedings of the International Conference on Electronic Commerce and Web Technologies*, number 1875 in Lecture Notes in Computer Science, pages 110–121. Springer–Verlag, 2000.

[94] B.B. Kristensen. Object-oriented modeling with roles. In *Proceedings of the International Conference on Object-Oriented Information Systems*, pages 57–71. Springer–Verlag, 1996.

[95] B.B. Kristensen and K. Østerbye. Roles: Conceptual abstraction theory and practical language issues. *Theory and Practice of Object Systems*, 2(3):143–160, 1996.

[96] A. Kurz. *Data Warehousing. Enabling Technology.* MITP-Verlag, 1st edition, 1999.

[97] M. L'Abbate and U. Thiel. Intelligent product information search in e-commerce: Retrieval strategies for virtual shop assistants. In B. Stanford-Smith and E. Chiozza, editors, *E-work and E-commerce*, pages 347–353. IOS Press, 2001.

[98] H. Lam and T. Thai. *.NET Framework Essential*. O'Reilly & Associates Inc., 2002.

[99] P. Langley. Machine learning for adaptive user interfaces. In *Proceedings of the German Annual Conference on Artificial Intelligence*, number 1303 in Lecture Notes in Artificial Intelligence, pages 53–62. Springer–Verlag, 1997.

[100] R.D. Lawarence, G.S. Almasi, V. Kotlyar, M.S. Viveros, and S.S. Duri. Personalization of supermarket product recommendations – Applications of data mining to e-commerce. *International Journal on Data Mining and Knowledge Discovery*, pages 433–442, 2001.

[101] R.M. Lee. Distributed electronic trade scenarios: Representation, design, prototyping. Technical Report RP 1998.09.01, Erasmus University Research Institute for Decision and Information Systems, 2000.

[102] W.-P. Lee, C.-H. Liu, and C.-C. Lu. Intelligent agent-based systems for personalized recommendations in internet commerce. *Expert Systems with Applications*, 22(4):275–284, 2002.

[103] A. Levy. Obtaining complete data from incomplete databases. In *Proceedings of the International Conference on Very Large Databases*, pages 402–412. Morgan Kaufmann Publishers, 1996.

[104] R. Levy, J. Nagarajarao, G. Pacifici, M. Spreitzer, A. Tantawi, and A.Youssef. Performance management for cluster based web services. In *Proceedings of the International Symposium on Integrated Network Management*. IEEE Press, 2003.

[105] C. Li and X. Wang. A data model for supporting on-line analytical processing. In *Proceedings of the International Conference on Information and Knowledge Management*, pages 81–88. ACM Press, 1996.

[106] Q. Li and F.H. Lochovsky. ADOME: An advanced object modeling environment. *IEEE Transactions on Knowledge and Data Engineering*, 10(2):255–276, 1998.

[107] Q. Li and R.K. Wong. Multifaceted object modeling with roles: A comprehensive approach. *Information Sciences*, 117(3):243–266, 1999.

[108] C. Liu, S. Chang, and P. Chrysanthis. Database schema evolution using EVER diagrams. In *Proceedings of the workshop on advanced visual interfaces*, pages 123–132. ACM Press, 1994.

[109] H. Ludwig and Y. Hoffner. CRAFT: A framework for integration facilitation in cross-organisational distributed systems. In *Proceedings of the EUROMICRO Workshop on Parallel and Distributed Processing*, pages 317–326. IEEE Press, 2001.

[110] H. Ludwig and Y. Hoffner. The role of contract and component semantics in dynamic e-contract enactment configuration. In *Proceedings of the IFIP Workshop on Data Semantics*, pages 26–40. The Hong Kong Polytechnic University, 2001.

[111] H. Ludwig, A. Keller, A. Dan, and R. King. A service level agreement language for dynamic electronic services. In *Proceedings of the IEEE International Workshop on Advanced Issues of E-Commerce and Web-Based Information Systems*, pages 25–32. IEEE Press, 2002.

[112] International Business Machines. E-business on demand is the next utility. Available at http://www-1.ibm.com/services/ondemand.

[113] International Business Machines. IBM patterns for e-business. Available at http://www-106.ibm.com/developerworks/patterns.

[114] International Business Machines. IBM web services tool kit. Available at http://www.alphaworks.ibm.com/tech/webservicestoolkit.

[115] International Business Machines. Web services solution. Available at http://www-3.ibm.com/software/solutions/webservices.

[116] M.T. Maybury and W. Wahlster, editors. *Readings in intelligent user interfaces*. Morgan Kaufmann Publishers, 1998.

[117] J. Melton, A.R. Simon, and J. Gray. *SQL:1999. Understanding Relational Language Components*. Morgan Kaufmann Publishers, 2001.

[118] M. Merz, F. Griffel, T. Tu, S. Müller-Wilken, H. Weinreich, M. Boger, and W. Lamersdorf. Supporting electronic commerce transactions with contracting services. *International Journal of Cooperative Information Systems*, 7(4):249–274, 1998.

[119] K. Messa and B. Czejdo. Generating database applications in Smalltalk from an extended entity-relationship model. In *Proceedings of the Energy-sources Technology Conference*, pages 227–236, 1994.

[120] K. Messa and B. Czejdo. Visual software development using an object-relationship model. In *Proceedings of the ACM Southeast Regional Conference*, pages 142–149. ACM Press, 1999.

[121] M. Minock, M. Rusinkiewicz, and B. Perry. The identification of missing information resources by using the query difference operator. In *Proceedings of the International Conference on Cooperative Information Systems*, 1999.

[122] R.J. Mooney and L. Roy. Content-based book recommending using learning for text categorization. In *Proceedings of the ACM Conference on Digital Libraries*, pages 195–204. ACM Press, 2000.

[123] B. Moore, E. Ellesson, J. Strassner, and A. Westerinen. Policy core information model version 1 specification. Technical Report RFC 3060, The Internet Engineering Task Force, 2001.

[124] K.-L. Ong, W.-K. Ng, and E.-P. Lim. Mining relationship graphs for effective business objectives. In *Proceedings of the Pacific-Asia Conference on Knowledge Discovery and Data Mining*, pages 561–566. Springer–Verlag, 2002.

[125] UDDI Organisation. UDDI api specification. Available at http://www.uddi.org.

[126] M. Orkin and R. Drogin. *Vital Statistics*. McGraw Hill, 1990.

[127] G. Paliouras, C. Papatheodorou, V. Karakaletsis, C. Spyropoulos, and V. Malaveta. Learning user communities for improving the service of information providers. In *Proceedings of the Conference on Research and Advanced Technology for Digital Libraries*, volume 1513 of *Lecture Notes in Computer Science*, pages 367–384. Springer–Verlag, 1998.

[128] M. Papazoglou. Roles: A methodology for representing multifaced objects. In *Proceedings of the Database and Expert Systems Applications Conference*, pages 7–12, 1991.

[129] N. Pendse. The OLAP report: Database explosion. Available at http://www.olapreport.com.

[130] N. Pendse. The OLAP report: Market share analysis. Available at http://www.olapreport.com.

[131] B. Pernici. Objects with roles. In *Proceedings of the Conference on Office Information Systems*, pages 205–215. ACM, 1990.

[132] J. Płodzień and A. Kraken. Object query optimization through detecting independent subqueries. *Information Sciences*, 25(8):467–490, 2000.

[133] J.R. Quinlan. *C4.5: Programs for Machine Learning*. Morgan Kaufmann Publishers, 1993.

[134] J. Richardson and P. Schwarz. Aspects: extending objects to support multiple, independent roles. In *Proceedings of the Symposium on Principles of Database Systems*, pages 298–307. ACM Press, 1991.

[135] M. Richardson and P. Domingos. Mining knowledge sharing sites for viral marketing. In *Proceedings of the Conference on Knowledge Discovery and Data Mining*, pages 61–70. ACM Press, 2002.

[136] D. Riehle and T. Gross. Role model based framework design and integration. In *Proceedings of the Conference on Object-Oriented Programming, Systems, Languages, and Applications*, pages 117–133. ACM Press, 1998.

[137] K.M. Ripin and L.R. Sayles. *Insider Strategies for Outsourcing Information Systems: Building Productive Partnerships, Avoiding Seductive Traps*. Oxford University Press, 1999.

[138] A. Runge, B. Schopp, and K. Stanoevska-Slabeva. The management of business transactions through electronic contracts. In A. Camelli, A. Min Tjoa, and R.R. Wagner, editors, *Proceedings of the International Conference on Database and Expert Systems Applications*, pages 824–831. Springer, 1999.

[139] SAP America and SAP AG. Data modelling with BW. ASAP for BW accelerator. Available at http://www.sap.com.

[140] N. Sarda. Structuring business metadata in data warehouse systems for effective business support. Technical Report cs.DB/0110020, Department of Computer Science and Engineering, Indian Institute of technology, 2001. Available at http://arXiv.org.

[141] M. Sayal, F. Casati, U. Dayal, and M. Shan. Integrating workflow management systems with B2B interaction standards. In *Proceedings of the International Conference on Data Engineering*, pages 287–296, 2002.

[142] R. Schmelzer, T. Vandersypen, J. Bloomberg, M. Siddalingaiah, S. Hunting, M. Qualls, C. Darby, D. Houlding, and D Kennedy. *XML and Web Services Unleashed*. SAMS Publishing, 2002.

[143] B. Schneier. The case for outsourcing security. *IEEE Security and Privacy*, 1(1):20–21, 2002.

[144] M. Schrefl and E.J. Neuhold. Object class definition by generalization using upward inheritance. In *Proceedings of the International Conference on Data Engineering*, pages 4–13. IEEE Press, 1988.

[145] K. Schulz and M.E. Orlowska. Architectural issues for cross-organisational B2B interactions. In *Proceedings of the International Conference on Distributed Computing Systems Workshop*, pages 79–87. IEEE Press, 2001.

[146] E. Sciore. Object specialization. *ACM Transactions on Information Systems*, 7(1):103–122, 1989.

[147] G. Semeraro, S. Ferilli, N. Fanizzi, and F. Abbattista. Learning interaction models in a digital library service. In *Proceedings of the International Conference on User Modelling*, volume 2109 of *Lecture Notes in Artificial Intelligence*, pages 44–53. Springer–Verlag, 2001.

[148] M.W.A. Steen and J. Derrick. ODP Enterprise Viewpoint Specification. *Computer Standards and Interfaces*, 22:165–189, September 2000.

[149] L. Stein and S. Zdonik. Clovers: The dynamic behavior of type and instances. Technical Report CS-89-42, Department of Computer Science, Brown University, 1989.

[150] L.A. Stein. Delegation is inheritance. In *Proceedings of the Conference on Object-Oriented Programming, Systems, Languages, and Applications*, pages 138–146. ACM Press, 1987.

[151] M. Stolze. Soft navigation in product catalogs. In *Proceedings of the European Conference on Research and Advanced Technology for Digital Libraries*, number 1513 in Lecture Notes in Computer Science, pages 385–396. Springer-Verlag, 1998.

[152] M. Stolze and M. Ströbel. Utility-based decision tree optimization: A framework for adaptive interviewing. In *Proceedings of the International Conference on User Modeling*, pages 105–116, 2001.

[153] M. Ströbel. Communication design for electronic negotiations. *Computer Networks*, 39:661–680, 2002.

[154] M. Ströbel. *A Design and Implementation Framework for Multi-Attribute Negotiation Intermediation in Electronic Markets*. PhD thesis, Universität St. Gallen, 2002.

[155] K. Subieta. LOQIS: The object-oriented database programming system. In *Proceedings of the International East/West Database Workshop*, volume 504 of *Lecture Notes in Computer Science*, pages 403–421. Springer–Verlag, 1990.

[156] K. Subieta, Y. Kambayashi, and J. Leszczyłowski. Procedures in object-oriented query languages. In *Proceedings of the International Conference on Very Large Databases*, pages 182–193. Morgan Kaufmann Publishers, 1995.

[157] K. Subieta, F. Matthes, J.W. Schmidt, A. Rudloff, and I. Wetzel. Viewers: A dataworld analogue of procedure calls. In *Proceedings of the International Conference on Very Large Databases*, pages 269–277. Morgan Kaufmann Publishers, 1993.

[158] K. Subieta and J. Płodzień. Object views and query modification. In J. Barzdins and A. Caplinskas, editors, *Databases and Information Systems*, pages 3–14. Kluwer Academic Publishers, 2001.

[159] A. Sutcliffe and N. Lammont. The planet method for designing relationships in B2B e-commerce. In *Proceedings of the 33rd Hawaii International Conference on Systems Sciences*, pages 2291–2300. IEEE Press, 2002.

[160] M.N.S. Swamy and K. Thulasiraman. *Graphs, Networks and Algorithms*. John Wiley & Sons, 1981.

[161] P.-N. Tan, V. Kumar, and J. Srivastava. Selecting the right interestingness measure for association patterns. In *Proceedings of the Conference on Knowledge Discovery and Data Mining*, page ACM Press. 32–41, 2002.

[162] C. Tasso and P. Omero. *Personalization of web content: e-commerce, i-access, e-government*. Franco Angeli, 2002. (in Italian).

[163] Lassalle Technologies. Addflow OCX component for Windows. Available at http://www.lassalle.com.

[164] U. Thiel, A. Everts, B. Lutes, and K. Tzeras. A logic-based approach to search in digital libraries. In P. Fankhauser and M. Ockenfeld, editors, *Integrated Publication and Information Systems. 10 Years of Research and Development*, pages 169–186. GMD Forschungszentrum Informationstechnik, 1998.

[165] International Telecommunications Union. ITUT recommendation X.911: Open distributed processing reference model. Available at http://www.itu.int/itudoc/itu-t/com7/contr/contr5/221.htm.

[166] A. Vaisman. *Updates, View Maintenance and Time Management in Multidimensional Databases*. PhD thesis, Universidad de Buenos Aires, 2001.

[167] P. Vassiliadis and T. Sellis. A survey of logical models for OLAP databases. *ACM SIGMOD Record*, 28(4):64–69, 1999.

[168] W.B. Vaughn and P. Blackburn. *ADO.NET Examples and Best Practices for C# Programmers*. Apress L.P., 2002.

[169] H. Weigand and L. Xu. Contracts in e-commerce. In *Proceedings of the IFIP Workshop on Data Semantics*, pages 11–25. The Hong Kong Polytechnic University, 2001.

[170] R. Wieringa and W.D. Jonge. The identification of objects and roles. Object identifiers revisited. Technical Report IR-267, Faculty of Mathematics and Computer Science, Vrije Universiteit Amsterdam, 1991.

[171] I.H. Witten and E. Frank. *Data Mining: Practical Machine Learning Tools and Techniques with Java Implementations*. Morgan Kaufmann Publishers, 2000.

[172] R.K. Wong. Heterogeneous and multifaceted multimedia objects in DOOR/MM: A role-based approach with views. *Journal of Parallel and Distributed Computing*, 56(3):251–271, 1999.

[173] R.K. Wong and Q. Li. Manufacturing systems modeling with roles. a comprehensive approach. In *Proceedings of the IFIP Working Conference on Database Semantics*, pages 461–478. Chapman and Hall, 1995.

[174] M. Wu and A. Buchmann. Research issues in data warehousing. In *Proceedings of the Datenbanksysteme in Büro, Technik und Wissenschaft*, Informatik Aktuell, pages 61–82. Springer-Verlag, 1997.

[175] J. Yang. *Temporal Data Warehousing*. PhD thesis, Stanford University, 2001.

[176] A. Yee. Making enterprise application integration work in the real world. Available at http://eai.ebizq.net/enterprise_integration/yee_3.html.

[177] A. Yee. Order out of chaos: Understanding B2B integration patterns. Available at http://b2b.ebizq.net/ebiz_integration/yee_1.html.

[178] L. Zhang, H. Chang, and T. Chao. Web services relationships binding for dynamic e-business integration. In *Proceedings of the International Conference on Internet Computing*, pages 561–567, 2002.

[179] L. Zhang, H. Li, H. Chang, and T. Chao. XML-based advanced UDDI search mechanism for B2B integration. In *IEEE International Workshop on Advanced Issues of E-Commerce and Web-based Information Systems*, pages 9–16, 2002.

INDEX

A

acceptance, xviii, 3, 8, 13, 15, 49, 143
Adapter Pattern (GoF), 121
administration tool, 93
algorithm, viii, 167
Apache eXtensible Interaction System (AXIS), 6, 11
application programming interfaces (APIs), 33, 55, 120, 121, 125, 126
Aspect-Oriented Programming (AOP), 53, 64
aspects of objects and heterogeneous collections, 63
asynchronous one-to-many communication, 119
asynchronous one-to-one communication, 119
atomic objects, 58
authentication, 34, 37
authorisation, viii, 34, 35, 37, 43, 132
automation, xvi, 3, 5, 14, 20-22, 42, 129, 130

B

base collection, 106, 107
base sections, 59
Bayesian text classifier, 157
binding, vi, 3, 14, 15, 31, 43, 57, 59-61, 63, 66, 70, 191
broker, 29, 36, 50-52, 118, 119
brokering house, 50
Business Explorer for Web Services, 33
business objects, 73
business partners, 8, 25, 26
Business Process Execution Language (BPEL) for web Services, 17
business relationship, 3-5
businessEntity, 14
businessService, 14
buyers, xvii, 21, 26, 42, 184

C

cell values, 80, 85, 86, 94
chronons, 78
Closed Process Automator Pattern, 129
COGITO project, 142, 145, 147
Cognos, 73, 93
COMET, vi, x, 77, 89-93, 96, 97, 182
commodity goods, 3
company, xv, xvi, xviii, 3, 13, 31, 36, 40, 50-52, 61, 90, 97, 115, 116, 129, 131, 135, 136, 145, 157, 163, 170
complex objects, 58
Compliance Monitor (CM), 12, 17, 18, 22
conceptual modelling, xvii, 49, 52, 55, 62
connection and control centre (CCC), 28, 34, 35
Consensus Glossary of Temporal Database Concepts, 80
Container Managed Persistence (CMP), 133, 135
contract service, 11, 12
contracting process, ix, xvi, 3-5, 7-11, 13, 17, 20, 22
contractors, 25
conversational agent, 155
CORBA integration wrapper, 133
COSMOS system, 15
counteroffers, 8, 10
Create, Retrieve, Update, Delete (CRUD), 55
CrossFlow contract language, 17
CrystalBall, x, 162, 163, 165, 166, 168, 170, 173
customer relationship management (CRM), 13, 28, 29, 73
customer satisfaction, 141
customer, v, x, xvi, xviii, 3-17, 20, 21, 28, 29, 31, 45, 73, 104, 105, 132-134, 142-145, 147-149, 153, 154, 157, 161-165, 167-174, 179
CustomerInformationWrapper, 133

D

Data Access Object (DAO), 116, 132, 133
data mapping pattern, vii, x, 116, 127, 128, 132, 133
data mapping, vii, x, xviii, 116, 117, 127, 128, 130, 132, 133, 136
data sources, vii, xvi-xviii, 57, 73, 101, 103, 106, 112, 113, 148, 156, 170
deferred synchronous one-to-one communication, 119
directories, 10, 33
discovery engine, v, 28, 30-33, 39
document, 6, 7, 11, 14, 16, 20, 50, 159, 171, 172
domain-independent concepts, 21
dynamic inheritance, 63

E

ecommerce, xviii, 27, 41, 45, 137, 141-143, 145, 157-159, 161, 179, 185, 189, 190
eHub, ix, xvii, 26, 28-30, 32, 35-38, 41
electronic contract, 4, 5
electronic representation, 4
Emarketplaces, 41
enterprise application integration (EAI), xviii, 115-117, 137, 184, 191
environment stack (ES), ix, 57-61
EProcurement services, 29
eprocurement, 27
European Union (EU), xix, 15, 142
Extended FactConstellation Schemas, 90
eXtensible Markup Language (XML), xv, xvii, 25, 28, 29, 32, 36, 42, 46, 54-57, 70, 117, 137, 142, 145, 146, 148, 149, 154, 156, 158, 170-173, 181, 184, 188
eXtensible Markup Language (XML), 146
external name, 57

F

façade, 116, 124, 126
firewall, 25
flexibility, xvi, 3, 7, 20-22, 150
fulfillment system, ix, 4-8, 10, 13-15, 18, 20-22
fun, 142, 144

G

generic dimensionality, 90
global ubiquity, 161

H

horizontal business services, 26, 27, 29
human resources applications, 27
Hyperion Solutions, 73, 181

I

ICONS project, 54
identifiers, 53, 57, 58, 60, 61, 63, 64, 66, 85, 190
identity, 49, 53, 55, 63, 70
implementation, xv, xvii, 3, 5, 9-11, 13, 18, 19, 21, 22, 44, 49, 50, 52, 57, 62, 66, 67, 69, 80, 86, 89, 93, 97, 124, 147, 149, 150, 152, 155, 160, 163
incomplete attribute, 112
independent parties, 3
information networks, 25
infrastructure services, 26, 27, 32, 118
inheritance link objects, 58
instances, 78
Instant Messaging Personalities (IMP), 144
instantiation, 58
integration broker pattern, vii, x, 117-121
integration broker, vii, x, xviii, 117-122, 126, 136
integration mediator pattern, vii, x, 116, 122, 123
integration mediator, vii, x, xviii, 116, 117, 122, 123, 126, 128, 130, 133, 134, 136
integration wrapper, vii, x, xviii, 116, 120, 121, 124, 126, 128, 132, 133, 136
interactive data processing, 141
internal identifier, 57
Internet browser, 131
investment advisor, 50
IR Suite, 156
Iris system, 52

J

Java, 33, 34, 53, 67, 94, 106, 132, 134-137, 173, 184, 190
joins, 62, 101, 113, 168

K

KEPEX Trading Network, 26, 36, 38

L

learning server, 149
legal regulation, 50

Index

Library of Objectoriented Database Abstractions (LODA), 106
link objects, 58
Linux, 10, 14
LODA system, 102, 113
loyalty, 141, 145

M

man-machine dialogue, 141
map data, 76, 84, 85
matrices, 86-89, 92
Metadata support, 64
Microsoft, 73, 144, 170, 180
Microsoft's Database Access Components (MDAC), 170
MicroStrategy, 73
mobile phones, 131, 161
multidimensional view, 74, 75, 77
multilevel model, 26
multiperiod comparisons, 90
multiple inheritance, 62
multiple interfaces, 53, 67
multipleaspect inheritance, 62

N

name-value tuples, 16
non-contiguous structure versions, 87
nontransparent interfaces, 143

O

Object Access Protocol, 25
object migration, 63
object-roles, 49
offer(s), x, 3-11, 13-15, 17, 21, 22, 25, 28, 32, 41, 54, 55, 62, 89, 93, 96, 97, 118, 125, 141, 143, 145, 153, 156, 170
on-line analytical processing (OLAP), 73-75, 77, 90, 93, 96, 97, 181, 186, 187, 190
on-line directory service, 4
on-line marketplaces, 10
on-line transaction processing (OLTP), xv, xvi, 73, 75
Open Digital Rights Language (ODRL), 17, 22, 184
Open Distributed Processing (ODP), 17, 189
operator, 60, 101, 107, 109-111, 131, 187
Oracle, xix, 73, 93, 94
organisation basic data, 52
organisation role, 51
organisational unit, 50
outsourcing of information systems, 25
overriding, 63

P

performing selections, 101
person basic data, 52
person role, 51
person, ix, 20, 49-52, 61, 165, 170
personalisation suite, 155
PO Listing, 32
privacy, 142, 144, 188
private exchanges, 41
Process Automator Pattern, viii, x, 128-130, 133, 134, 136
Process Automator, viii, x, xviii, 116, 128-130, 133, 134, 136
process controller, 128
Process Coordination Framework (PCF), 42
Profile Extractor, x, 145-150, 157
Profile Rules Extractor, 147, 148
projections, vii, 101, 102, 104, 109, 112, 113
Proportional Aggregation, 90
provider list, 15
provider, v, xvi, 3, 4, 6-16, 20, 21, 29, 36, 38, 39
purchase order (PO), v, vi, ix, 26, 29, 30, 32, 35-40, 43, 44

Q

query language, vi, 60
query, x, xv-xvii, 15, 34, 50, 53-61, 70, 76, 84, 92, 93, 97, 101-113, 146, 154, 155, 182, 187-189

R

reduction of costs, 5
referential consistency, 63
rejection messages, 8
Remote Procedure Call protocol (RPC), 29
repeating inheritance, 62
Resource Description Framework, 16
Rodan Portal, 54, 56
root objects, 58, 69

S

Schemas, 78, 90
SeCo project, 7
SeCo, 7, 15, 21
Secure Contract Container, 15

Secured Infrastructure, 34
service level agreements (SLA), 7, 30, 42, 137, 180
service outsourcing manager, v, 26-31, 35, 42
service providers, vi, xvii, 6, 10, 12, 15, 21, 26-28, 31, 38, 39, 41, 43
service requirement, 12-14
services market, xvi, 3
share, 18, 20, 26, 35, 36, 42, 50, 61, 79, 90, 116, 117, 129, 162, 172, 187
SilkRoad project, 21
Simple Object Access Protocol (SOAP), 6, 25, 28, 29, 30, 36, 42, 43, 147, 182
simplicity, 142
sine qua non prerequisite, 53
speed, 142, 144
Stack-Based Approach (SBA), vi, 50, 55, 57-59, 61
stock instrument, 50
stock order, 50
stock session, 50
stock transaction, 50
subject role, 51, 52
substitutability principle, 58, 59, 63
substitutability, 63
subtyping, 63
Sun's Java and Microsoft's COM, 53
suppliers, xvii, 13, 26, 42, 141, 184
synchronous one-to-one communication, 119
system behaviour, 144
system management services, 26, 27

T

temporal data warehouse, 76-79, 82, 83, 93, 94, 182
temporal data warehousing, 89, 191
temporal properties, 63
text-to-speech (TTS), 144
Tomcat servlet engine, 7
trading partners, 26, 28
transaction models, 41
transformer, 94
typing, 63

U

Unified Modeling Language (UML), ix, x, 49-52, 62, 69, 89, 91, 102, 106, 113, 184
Universal Description, Discovery, and Integration engine, (UDDI), ix, xvii, 14, 21, 25, 26, 29, 31-34, 36, 39-41, 43, 182, 187, 191
Universal Standard Products and Services Classification scheme (UNSPSC), 14, 21, 180

V

value-added services, 26
variants, 62
vertical industry applications, 26, 27
Virtual Component Pattern, vii, x, 124-126, 133, 134
Virtual Component, vii, x, 116, 117, 122, 124-126, 130, 132-134, 136
virtual dialoguing agents, viii, 143

W

warehouse data, 88
Web Service Level Agreement language (WSLA), 11, 12, 17-20, 22, 185
Web Services Agreement Level, 17
Web Services Definition Language (WSDL), 6, 15, 16, 22, 25, 29, 182
Web Services Flow Language (WSFL), 25
Web Services Inspection Language (WSIL), 25
Web Services Invocation Framework (WSIF), 29
Web Site, 155
WebSphere, 7
What You See Is What You Get (WYSIWYG), 141
Windows 2000 server, 11
WSTK Utility Services solution, 6, 11, 19, 21, 22